14030

720.28

D0717450

A

This book is to be returned on or before
the last date stamped below.

9

24 NOV 1998 A

McGRAW-HILL TECHNICAL EDUCATION SERIES

Norman C. Harris, Series Editor

Architectural Drawing and Planning • Goodban and Hayslett

Introductory Applied Physics, 2d ed. • Harris and Hemmerling

Experiments in Applied Physics • Harris

Pulse and Switching Circuits • Ketchum and Alvarez

Introduction to Microwave Theory and Measurements • Lance

Specifications Writing for Architects and Engineers • Watson

(Other volumes in preparation.)

WILLIAM T. GOODBAN

JACK J. HAYSLETT

Member of The American Institute of Architects

Architectural
Drawing
&
Planning

McGRAW-HILL BOOK COMPANY

New York · Toronto · London

ARCHITECTURAL DRAWING AND PLANNING

23749

Preface

This text presents the basic subject matter, order of development, and drafting techniques of architectural drawing. The goal is to develop drafting, not design ability; however, material on simple planning procedures is included to make the overall development of a set of drawings clear. The material is limited to residential and light-commercial construction.

In order to make the book adaptable to more teachers and their teaching methods, the subject matter has been divided into 26 short chapters arranged in a logical order of procedure. Each chapter is limited to a group of related aspects of planning or to a single working drawing. This makes it possible for an instructor to proceed by either the *project method* or the *unit method* merely by choosing the desired order of assignment of chapters. If the instructor wishes to teach the rudiments of functional design, the first seven chapters may be stressed; if drafting techniques only are to be considered, the last 19 chapters should be emphasized.

In any case, because of the many related factors involved in a set of drawings, the student must refer often to chapters other than the one being studied. In addition, references are cited which contain material of great importance to him. Because a draftsman must understand construction and construction materials as well as drafting techniques, the authors recommend that the student visit construction sites, building-supply houses, and drafting rooms for information not easily available in books. Finally, the book will be of more value when used in a classroom, with a teacher to interpret and supplement the text and to guide and criticize the student in his work.

Because architectural drafting is highly specialized and the book is intended to be used at the technical institute or junior college level, it is assumed that the student who uses the book will have first completed a basic course in drafting. This seems to be a reasonable prerequisite in view of the fact that all technically trained students are required to take a course in beginning drafting.

Following are the principles which governed the writing of the book and our reasons for adopting them:

1. There is no conscious regional bias in design or construction expressed. Therefore, all instruction concerning weather, types of construction, building codes, etc., is in general terms. This naturally places more responsibility for research on the student, and research is a necessary part of good design.
2. Each student should have an adult "client" and should make use of the checklist provided. This creates a realistic situation for the student and assures him the opportunity of getting well-organized information on which to base his drawings. At this stage, the student has more enthusiasm than ability; consequently he can learn much from his client, who probably knows more about many aspects of building than the student. Admittedly, a beginning draftsman may never have the opportunity to deal directly with a client, but the situation while learning provides good motivation.
3. Emphasis is placed on planning, preliminary drawings, and drafting procedures. Much leeway is allowed at all stages of drawing to provide for individual instructors and local practices. The entire procedure in the development of a complete set of architectural drawings must be understood by the student. Without this knowledge, drafting rules and procedures become mere rote learning, isolated from the problems of functional design and actual construction problems.
4. The relationships between drawings are emphasized to reinforce the fact that the student is working on a *set* of drawings in which each drawing shows various aspects of the same structure. This is necessary because the average student is seldom aware of obvious conflicts in his drawings.
5. *Architectural design* as defined in this book refers to the functional planning of space and structure, not to architectural styles, periods, or appearance. The principal reason for this em-

phasis is that simplicity and function alone in a structure often constitute good design. In addition, such factors as the student's background, local practices, the great scope of the subject, and the principal objectives of the book argue against the addition of a section on architectural styles. Decisions in this area must be based upon the student's or instructor's judgment.

6. The section on planning is divided into two parts, residential and light-commercial, because of the wide differences in functions between the two. Each of these sections can be used equally well with the remainder of the book, which deals with factors common to both types of occupancy and to the many types of structures.

7. In order to tie the text to the illustrations and to demonstrate the step-by-step method of the book, two sets of drawings, from sketch to working drawings, have been developed. One is a complete set of drawings for a small residence, and the other is a partial set for a light-commercial building. Each of the working drawings is drawn to the usual architectural scale and reduced to page size. Extracts from each of the various drawings are shown full scale to illustrate explanatory material from the text. Where possible, freehand drawings, approximately to scale, illustrate typical details or principles of construction. Because of the wide variation in practice in various parts of the country, these drawings are not completely dimensioned. They are drawn freehand to emphasize the use of sketching in architectural practice.

Our aim of writing a nationally usable book accounts for the liberal use of "generally," "usually," "commonly," "local practice," "see local building codes," and "etc." While this places the responsibility for defining the meanings of these terms on the teacher, it also gives him the opportunity to acquaint the student with local regulations and practices.

We feel that any student using the book should have access to the following references or their equivalent:

1. Ramsey and Sleeper, "Architectural Graphic Standards," or "Time-Saver Standards"
2. A local building code
3. Sweet's File, or a personal collection of manufacturers' literature

We wish to thank our wives for their encouragement and help in preparing and proofreading the manuscript. For their technical help and criticism we thank R. E. Billing, T. R. Kennedy, A. C. Metcalf, A.I.A., J. E. Moring, A.I.A., and M. L. Triplett.

William T. Goodban AND *Jack J. Hayslett*

Note to the User

"Architectural Drawing and Planning" is a basic text to be supplemented by additional references and classroom instruction. Depending upon his background and methods, each instructor will use the book in a slightly different manner. Even if you plan to study the book outside of school, we feel that you can gain a good understanding of architectural-drafting methods and standards from it. Many of the references cited are available in most libraries, and others in print are equally good. In place of the teacher, we offer some advice for using the book which will help it serve you better.

First read the Contents and Preface, skim through the text, and look at the illustrations to get an idea of what is in store for you. This is a good first step with any text. When you're ready to start drawing, start at the beginning of the book with pencil and paper in hand. Sketch as you read; it will clear up many important points. When you encounter references to subjects which are more fully covered later in the book, mark your place and skip ahead to the chapters indicated. Before starting any drawing, study the vocabulary and symbols which apply; you will go faster this way. When working on any particular drawing, first make freehand sketches of what you intend to do. This will eliminate much erasing and redrawing. Use the Review Questions and Study Suggestions at the ends of the chapters. They should extend your knowledge and help you apply the material you have studied.

Contents

Preface   v

Note to the User   vi

Chapter 1

Basic Skills and Terminology   1

Chapter 2

Lettering   11

Chapter 3

Residential Planning   14

Chapter 4

Planning Light-commercial Buildings   19

Chapter 5

Mechanical Steps in Planning   24

Chapter 6

Orientation   35

Chapter 7

Landscaping   43

Chapter 8

Regional Differences in Design and Construction   46

Chapter 9

Presentation Drawings   48

Chapter 10

Working Drawings   52

Chapter 11

Relationships among Drawings   63

Chapter 12

Floor Plan   66

Chapter 13

Door, Window, and Room-finish Schedules   75

Chapter 14

Structural Sections   83

Chapter 15

Stair and Fireplace Details   99

Chapter 16

Exterior Elevations   109

Chapter 17

Foundation Plan   115

Chapter 18

Roof and Floor Framing Plans   124

Chapter 19

Electrical Plan   128

Chapter 20

Heating, Ventilating, and Air-conditioning Plan   135

Chapter 21

Plumbing Plan   142

Chapter 22

Plot and Landscaping Plans   151

Chapter 23

Interior Elevations   159

Chapter 24

Door and Window Details   164

Chapter 25

Miscellaneous Details   170

Chapter 26

Specifications   177

Appendix   179

Bibliography   227

Answers to Review Questions   229

Index   231

Chapter

1

Basic Skills and Terminology

Requirements

The student approaching the study of architectural drafting needs a certain background of knowledge and skills. He must know simple research procedures and orthographic projection. He must have some artistic ability. These elements are basic. Moreover, he should become adept at freehand sketching and perspective.

Materials

Freehand sketching is the best means of capturing and developing ideas in the planning stage of an architectural project. The principles are simple, and only a few basic tools and materials are needed. In fact, cheap paper, a soft pencil, and an eraser are enough equipment for the beginner.

An inexpensive paper is suitable for practice sketching. Some students like unlined binder paper; all the sheets are the same size, and it is easy to organize and keep track of information in a binder. It is best to use fairly transparent paper; the best parts of previous sketches can be traced and improved upon without the need of tedious measuring. Architects and draftsmen use large rolls of cheap transparent paper and tear it off as needed. Use a soft 2B to 6B pencil. A soft pencil encourages freedom of line, and the marks are easy to erase. Use a big soft eraser; the first idea is usually not the best one.

Methods

Good freehand sketching looks freehand. Do not try to duplicate mechanical drawing in sketches. At the start, too much precision in drawing wastes time. More accurate measurement and more careful drawing can be used after a general scheme has been decided upon. A few suggestions follow:

1. Use a free arm motion with the pencil, not a cramped finger stroke.
2. Do not try to make all corners and line intersections precise; let them cross occasionally.
3. Sketchy, multiple lines are sometimes more effective than a single line.
4. Make the sketches fairly large; small drawings are hard to read. As a guide, no more than two rough floor plans should be drawn on one side of a sheet of $8\frac{1}{2}$ by 11-in. binder paper.
5. Be careful of proportions, but do not worry about actual measurements. If the drawing is in proportion, size is unimportant at this stage.
6. Label everything! A week-old drawing without notes will mean very little, even to the person who drew it.
7. Avoid small detail in rough sketches. The overall effect is most important, particularly in pictorial drawings. Use plan views of trees, shrubs, furniture, automobiles, etc., on floor plans and plot plans to give an effect of scale (Fig. 1-1).
8. Use simplified human figures, trees, shrubs, automobiles, etc., on elevations and pictorial drawings to give scale, depth, and a natural effect (Fig. 1-2).
9. Try to copy the sketching style of some professional delineator. Few students can develop a distinctive style in a short time (see Bibliography).

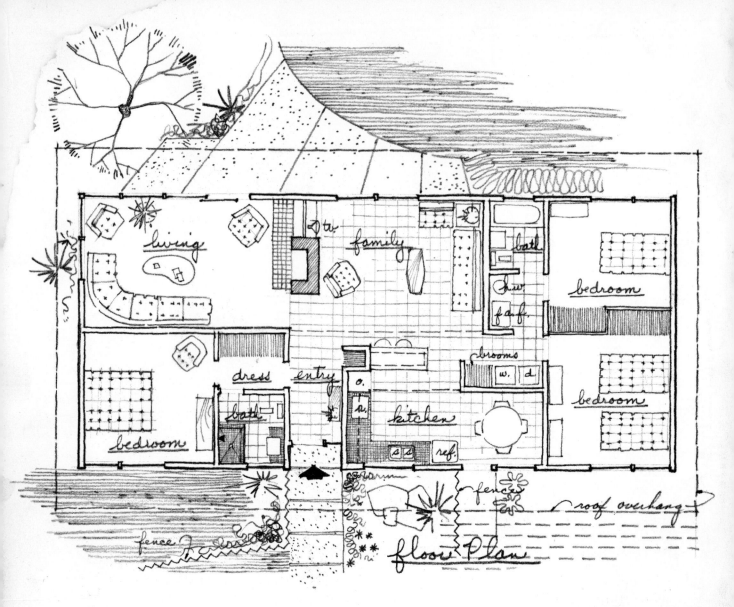

Fig. 1-1. Use of trees, shrubs, and furniture to give scale to a preliminary floor plan.

10. Learn the standard symbols required for each type of drawing before starting on it.
11. Avoid paints, colored pencils, and crayons at first. They are unsatisfactory unless you have a good background in their use.
12. Practice sketching in any spare time you have.

"Practice makes perfect" may sound trite, but it is true.

When more accuracy in a sketch is required, two easy means of achieving it are available. First, the use of a grid placed behind transparent sketch paper

Fig. 1-2. Use of trees, cars, and people to lend realism and scale to a preliminary elevation.

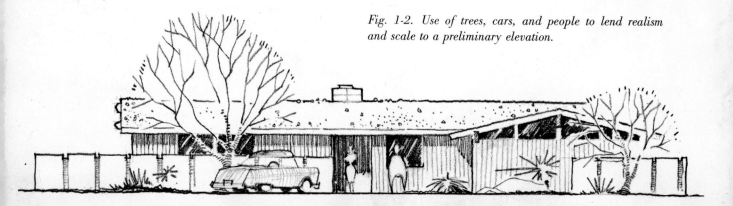

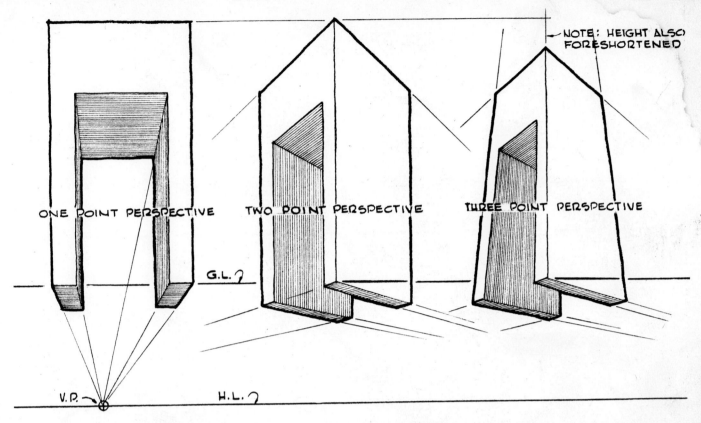

ONE POINT PERSPECTIVE   TWO POINT PERSPECTIVE   THREE POINT PERSPECTIVE

NOTE: HEIGHT ALSO FORESHORTENED

G.L.

V.P.   H.L.

Fig. 1-3. *Appearance of an object drawn in one-, two-, and three-point perspective.*

provides accurate guides. Second, prints can be made on blue-lined grid tracing paper, and the grid lines will not show. This tracing paper is especially useful for working out floor plans at scale size. The grids are made for orthographic and pictorial drawings.

Approximate Perspective

A working knowledge of approximate-perspective drawing is necessary in order to show what a pro-

posed building might look like when finished. As most textbooks on drafting contain a section on mechanical perspective, which is easily learned, only approximate, or "eyeball," perspective will be treated here. Approximate perspective is accurate enough for preliminary studies even when done by an amateur, and in the hands of an expert it may be used for presentation drawings. The best way to

Fig. 1-4. *Definitions of terms as used in approximate perspective drawing.*

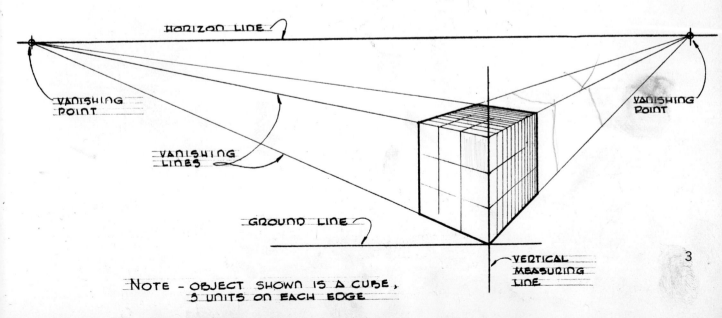

HORIZON LINE

VANISHING POINT

VANISHING LINES

GROUND LINE

VANISHING POINT

VERTICAL MEASURING LINE

NOTE - OBJECT SHOWN IS A CUBE, 5 UNITS ON EACH EDGE

3

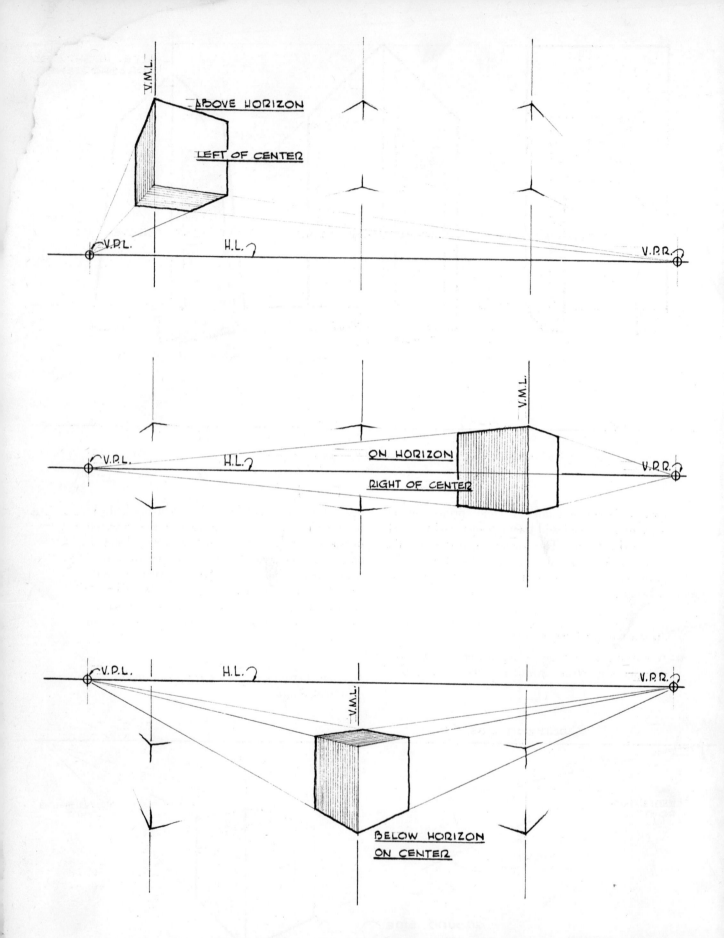

Fig. 1-5. Appearance of a cube viewed from three different angles.

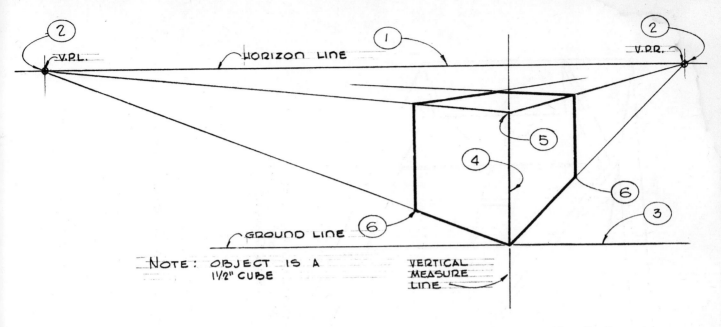

Fig. 1-6. *Procedure in drawing a perspective block. (Circled numbers agree with outline in text.)*

learn is to read the following text and look at the illustrations with a pencil and paper in hand and to follow the instructions by sketching while reading.

Two-point perspective is most often used. One- and three-point perspectives will not be described (Fig. 1-3). The method of drawing two-point per-

(continued on page 8)

Fig. 1-7. *Method of dividing perspective spaces by the use of diagonals.*

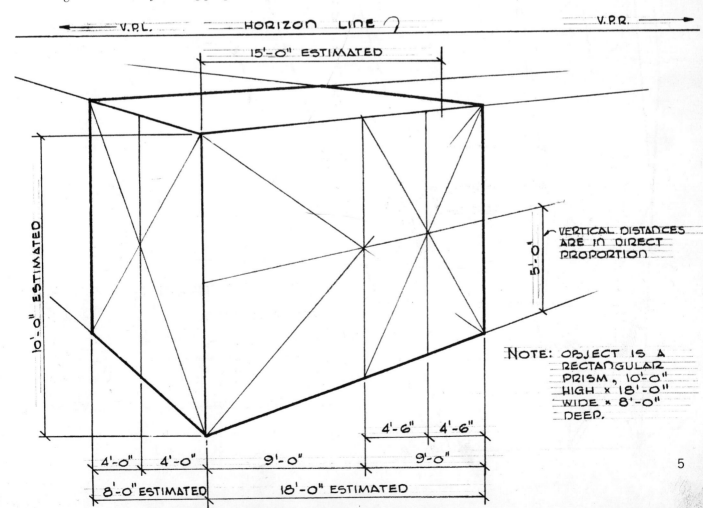

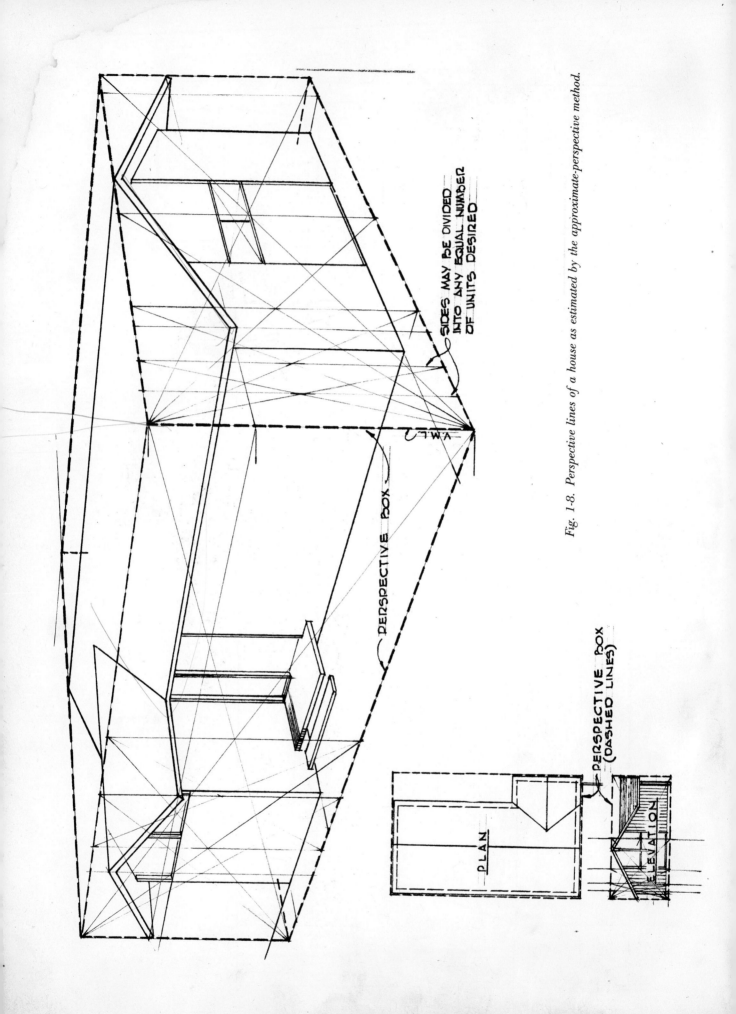

SIDES MAY BE DIVIDED
INTO ANY EQUAL NUMBER
OF UNITS DESIRED

V.M.L.

PERSPECTIVE BOX

PERSPECTIVE BOX
(DASHED LINES)

PLAN

ELEVATION

Fig. 1-8. Perspective lines of a house as estimated by the approximate-perspective method.

Fig. 1-9. Finished sketch derived from Fig. 1-8.

7

spective as described here is not the only method, but many draftsmen feel that it is the simplest. The finished drawings will be very similar to those drawn by other methods.

DEFINITIONS

Definitions of perspective terms (Fig. 1-4):

1. *Horizon:* The eye level of the person viewing the drawing. Place it below the ground line for a worm's-eye view; place it above for a bird's-eye view; place it near the ground line for a normal view.
2. *Ground line:* The bottom of the object being drawn. Place it below the horizon for a bird's-eye view; place it near the horizon for a normal view; place it above for a worm's-eye view.
3. *Vanishing points:* The points on the horizon where parallel horizontal lines converge. Place them far apart for a distant perspective; place them close together for a closer view.
4. *Vertical measuring line:* The part of the object closest to the person viewing the object. It is also the line on which heights are measured. Place it to the left to see more of the right side of the object, to the right to see more of the left side. Vertical distances may be measured or estimated by a uniform scale.
5. *Vanishing lines:* Horizontal lines of the object which converge on the vanishing points. The nearest foot (starting at the vertical measuring line) is longer than the next foot behind it, and so on. When the vanishing points are far apart, the distances diminish slowly as they approach the vanishing points; when they are close together, distances diminish rapidly (Fig. 1-5).

PROCEDURE

A bird's-eye view is easiest when you are learning to draw a perspective. The procedure follows (Fig. 1-6):

1. Establish the horizon line as desired. A straightedge may be used for drawing long lines.
2. Mark the vanishing points.
3. Establish the ground line of the object.
4. Establish the vertical measuring line.
5. Lay off on the vertical measuring line the estimated total height of the object.
6. Lay off on the vanishing lines the estimated total width and depth of the object. Remember that if the vertical measuring line is off-center to the

right, a given distance on the right of the object will be apparently shorter than the same distance on the left and vice versa. In any case, a given distance in a horizontal direction will always appear smaller than the same distance on the vertical measuring line. To estimate horizontal distances in either direction, lay off the estimated total length of that side between the vanishing lines. Draw lines from opposite corners of this four-sided figure. The intersection will always be in the perspective center of the area. Draw a vertical line through the intersection. This process may be repeated as often as desired, and the space will always be divided in half. These points may then be used as a basis for estimating any desired distance (Fig. 1-7).

7. Steps 5 and 6 will form a box exactly large enough to contain the whole object. From this point on, "cut out" the shape of the object, using the methods in step 6 for estimating distance. Cut out only large masses; estimate most detail by eye. After a little practice it will be easy to estimate practically every dimension (Fig. 1-8).
8. When the shape of the object, in this case a house, is finished, erase unnecessary lines, sketch in trees, shrubbery, people, etc., and strengthen the essential lines (Fig. 1-9). Letter in desired notes and title to finish sketch.

SHORTCUTS

Two simple methods which will speed up the construction of perspective sketches follow. First is the *rubber-band perspective board.* Simply drive a short nail in at each vanishing point on the drawing board and tie a piece of strong rubber band between them. To draw a vanishing line, pull the band tight; it will act as a quite rigid straightedge. Pull it in the other direction for a line to the opposite vanishing point. All other instructions regarding perspective drawing should be followed. Second, *perspective grid forms,* based on several distances and angles of view, are available. These grids, when used properly, enable one to produce mechanically correct drawings.

To Increase Effect of Depth

Some visual devices which will strengthen the feeling of perspective are (Fig. 1-10):

1. The use of overlapping planes, such as fences and trees. Any object or plane, regardless of size, which overlaps another object or plane is naturally the closest to the viewer.

(A) THE USE OF OVER-LAPPING PLANES

(B) THE USE OF RELATIVE SIZES OF FAMILIAR OBJECTS

(C) THE USE OF DETAIL TO INDICATE DEPTH

COMBINATION OF METHODS A-B-C TO INCREASE THE PERSPECTIVE DEPTH AND INDICATE RELATIVE SCALE

Fig. 1-10. Devices used to create a feeling of depth in a drawing.

2. The use of objects of known size, such as people, at varying distances from the observer. A person near the observer appears larger than one farther away.
3. The use of aerial perspective. Objects near the observer are drawn in more detail than those farther away.

Once a student has the basic tools—the ability to sketch and make perspectives—he is ready to start the actual planning of a residence or commercial building. At the start remember that the first attempt at planning will be slow, since all the factors in planning must be learned one at a time. The second project attempted will go much faster, because the student learns to anticipate more of the problems. An architect has the advantage over the student of knowing all the factors at the start, and he is able to avoid many conflicts.

REVIEW QUESTIONS

1. Which pencil is best for sketching, 4H or 4B?
2. Idea sketches are casual and not precise. Give two good reasons.
3. Which is more important in a sketch, proportion or measurement?
4. Name the terms used in approximate perspective drawing, and define them in your own words.
5. In a sketch, show the order of sketching in perspective.
6. Name three methods of strengthening the feeling of perspective in a drawing.

STUDY SUGGESTIONS

1. Make several perspective sketches of simple objects; label the principal construction lines. Try several angles and distances from the observer. Try normal, bird's-eye, and worm's-eye positions.
2. Practice rendering trees, people, automobiles, etc., on your perspective drawings.
3. Mount a photograph of a building on a large sheet of paper and, using a straightedge, extend pairs of lines in each plane until they intersect at the vanishing points. Various drawings will demonstrate one-, two-, or three-point perspective.

Chapter

2

Lettering

Use of Lettering

Much of the information found in a set of architectural working drawings is in verbal form. It would be practically impossible to build a house from pictures alone. It would be even more difficult to build it from a purely verbal description. Drawings, notes, dimensions, specifications—all of these are needed in a complete set of working drawings. It is important that the quality of the lettering equal the quality of the drawings.

Requirements

The first requirement of good lettering is that it be legible. This means that the shapes of the letters must be uniform, easily recognized, of proper size, and dark enough to print every time. The second requirement is that it be well proportioned and in good taste. Architectural lettering usually differs from machine lettering in that more differences in letter shapes are permitted from one office to another. The artistic effect of the lettering is important to most architects. Though ordinary Gothic lettering is frequently used, only specifically architectural lettering styles will be discussed here (Fig. 2-1).

In all cases, legibility is considered far more important than artistic effect. Therefore, do not try to invent an architectural alphabet; very few people have this ability. It is best for the student to copy a style that has been proved through use.

Methods

The ability to letter well comes from practice. Some helpful rules follow:

1. Experiment to find the pencil that works best. It may be a different grade from the one used for linework.
2. Always use guidelines.
3. Try for accuracy at the start; develop speed later.
4. Practice whenever possible.

Even though the draftsman may always use the same lettering case, he should know several others. There are two types of letters, uppercase, or capital, and lowercase. The shapes of individual letters may vary in upper and lowercase, and they may be vertical or slant. Special lettering types are used for presentation drawings, large titles, and displays; experiment with these also.

Lettering Guides

There are several types of lettering devices using guides or templates (Fig. 2-2). By using such an aid, it is possible to have absolute uniformity in lettering. These devices have certain advantages and disadvantages compared with freehand lettering. They afford uniformity of shape in letters, even with a drawing on which several people have worked, but they are slower and make the lettering look mechanical. They are particularly useful, though, for titles, record strips, and display lettering.

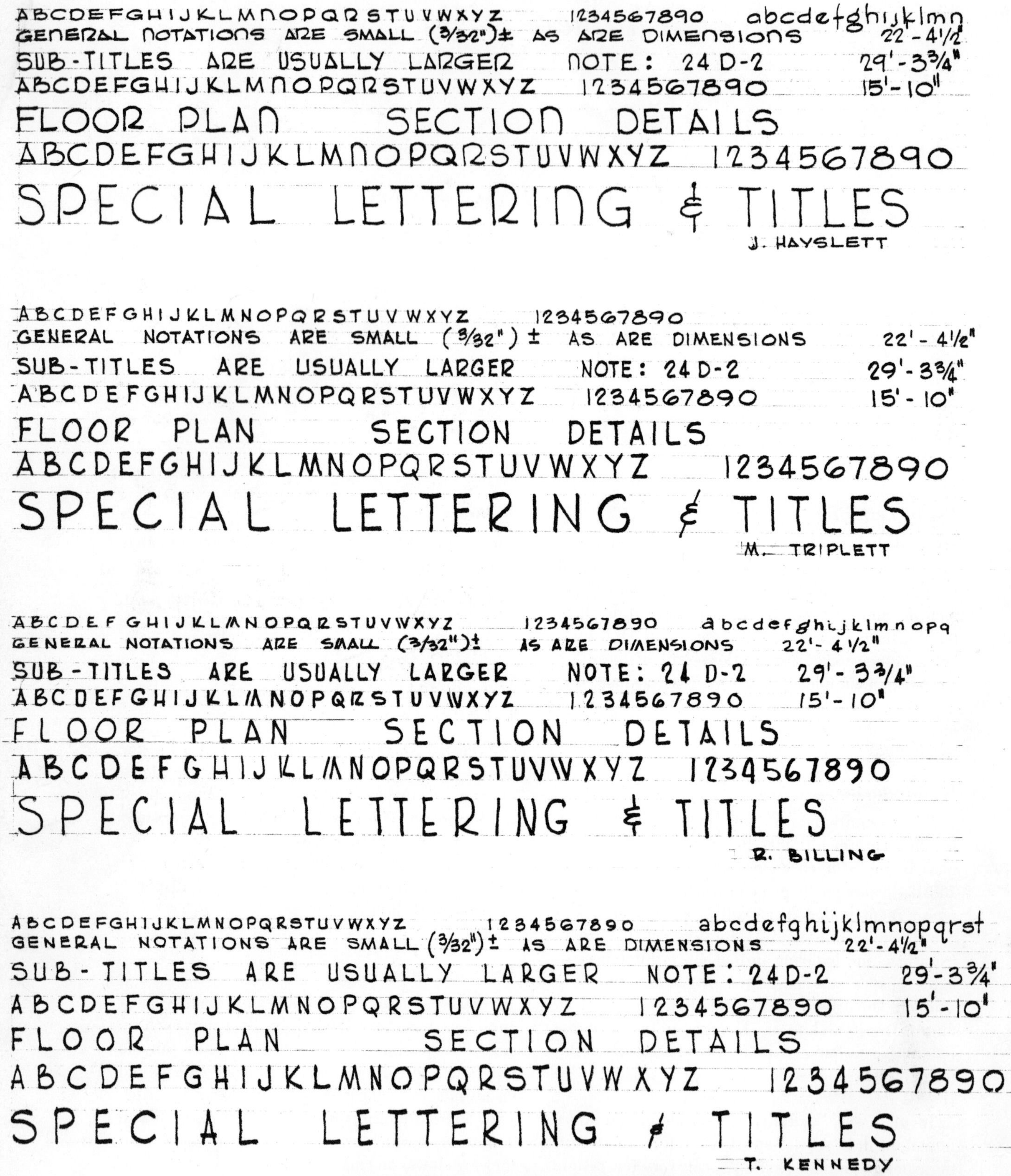

ABCDEFGHIJKLMNOPQRSTUVWXYZ   1234567890   abcdefghijklmn
GENERAL NOTATIONS ARE SMALL (3/32")± AS ARE DIMENSIONS   22'-4½'
SUB-TITLES ARE USUALLY LARGER   NOTE: 24 D-2   29'-3¾"
ABCDEFGHIJKLMNOPQRSTUVWXYZ   1234567890   15'-10"
FLOOR PLAN   SECTION   DETAILS
ABCDEFGHIJKLMNOPQRSTUVWXYZ   1234567890
SPECIAL LETTERING & TITLES
J. HAYSLETT

ABCDEFGHIJKLMNOPQRSTUVWXYZ   1234567890
GENERAL NOTATIONS ARE SMALL (3/32") ± AS ARE DIMENSIONS   22'-4½"
SUB-TITLES ARE USUALLY LARGER   NOTE: 24 D-2   29'-3¾"
ABCDEFGHIJKLMNOPQRSTUVWXYZ   1234567890   15'-10"
FLOOR PLAN   SECTION   DETAILS
ABCDEFGHIJKLMNOPQRSTUVWXYZ   1234567890
SPECIAL LETTERING & TITLES
M. TRIPLETT

ABCDEFGHIJKLMNOPQRSTUVWXYZ   1234567890   abcdefghijklmnopq
GENERAL NOTATIONS ARE SMALL (3/32")± AS ARE DIMENSIONS   22'-4½"
SUB-TITLES ARE USUALLY LARGER   NOTE: 24 D-2   29'-3¾"
ABCDEFGHIJKLMNOPQRSTUVWXYZ   1234567890   15'-10"
FLOOR PLAN   SECTION   DETAILS
ABCDEFGHIJKLMNOPQRSTUVWXYZ   1234567890
SPECIAL LETTERING & TITLES
R. BILLING

ABCDEFGHIJKLMNOPQRSTUVWXYZ   1234567890   abcdefghijklmnopqrst
GENERAL NOTATIONS ARE SMALL (3/32")± AS ARE DIMENSIONS   22'-4½"
SUB-TITLES ARE USUALLY LARGER   NOTE: 24D-2   29'-3¾"
ABCDEFGHIJKLMNOPQRSTUVWXYZ   1234567890   15'-10"
FLOOR PLAN   SECTION   DETAILS
ABCDEFGHIJKLMNOPQRSTUVWXYZ   1234567890
SPECIAL LETTERING & TITLES
T. KENNEDY

Fig. 2-1. *Examples of lettering by practicing architects and draftsmen.*

ABCIJK78!   ABCDaabc90¢

ABCDabcde3456   ABCD abc4567

ABCaab 678   ABCD bc 90

ABCDE abcde 7890¢   ABCDE bcd890¢

ABCD abcd 7890   ABCDE abcd456¢

ABCD abcde 456¢   ABC ab 90

ABC abcd 890   ABCab 45¢

Fig. 2-2. Examples of lettering produced by the use of lettering guides.

REVIEW QUESTIONS

1. List the desirable qualities of good architectural lettering in the order of their importance.
2. Does the type of pencil have much effect on the quality of your lettering?

STUDY SUGGESTIONS

1. Study working drawings from several architectural offices and evaluate the effect of the lettering on the total drawing.
2. Practice lettering whenever you have spare time.

Chapter

3

Residential Planning

Speculative Building

Most residences built for a large building development are designed to suit an "average" family. The main trouble is that there is no such thing as an average family. Families differ in size, distribution of sexes, interests, desires, habits, income, and so on. The sites for residences vary in size, climate, relation to other buildings, trees and shrubbery, zoning restrictions, cost, etc. It is possible to design a house to be built for a mass market that will, in many ways, suit many people and many sites. However, people who live in this house will have to make a number of adjustments and get along without many things they desire. To design a house for a particular family, it is first necessary to investigate the client and his family, as well as the building site.

The Client and the Site

The client and the site together determine the house. Do not try to design a house for someone until all the information regarding the site has been assembled. A house that works well when faced north might be unsatisfactory when faced west.

The student should plan a house for someone he knows, not for himself. This will create a more realistic problem. Architects plan many more houses for others than they plan for themselves. The largest part of the problem in architectural planning lies in executing the half-formed plans of other people. They usually know approximately what they want, but not how to develop, refine, or express their ideas. For the student, relatives and neighbors are all good prospective clients. Another good project might be to design a new house that will suit the needs of a family better than the house they now live in.

Research

A checklist is provided in A-1, on which the client can indicate what he desires in his house. Use it. It will help to avoid changes, extra visits to the client, and unnecessary work. It will also force the client to organize his thoughts, and, in the end, he will likely be happier with the job.

A student will not be required to do as much research on his client or consider as many problems as an architect would. The factors mentioned here are generally felt to be most important; however, any others encountered should also be considered.

THE CLIENT

The client's needs and desires must be the starting point in planning, as the house will be for him. Some of the factors involved are simple and need no explanation, while others are more complex and will be discussed.

Some obvious points are:

1. The size of the family determines the size of the house.
2. The distribution by age and sex determines the number of bedrooms.
3. The number of automobiles determines the size of the garage or carport.
4. The amount of money available for building will affect the quality and size of the entire project. (Cost estimating is a field in itself; the student should consider costs in general terms only.)

More complex factors to be considered:

1. Social habits. Some families live very formally and have no use for a family, rumpus, or game room. Others will need such a special-purpose room to suit their informal way of life. Durable, easily cleaned walls and floors are necessary if the family likes to entertain and give parties often. An open plan, in which the living and working areas flow together, lends itself to informal entertaining. A more rigid plan, in which these areas are closed off from each other, works better for formal living. Extra bedrooms and baths will be needed if the family often entertains overnight guests.

2. Furniture and appliances already owned by the family. Standard-size furniture will not cause much trouble, but oversize pieces can create problems. Be sure they will fit into the house.

3. Special interests and hobbies. Books, collections, and hobbies all require space. Often, special storage or rooms must be added for them. For instance, hobbies like woodworking and photography require special rooms; stamp collecting generally does not.

4. The client's ideas. His ideas for the number of bathrooms, architectural style, colors, etc., should be worked into the house as far as possible. If they cannot be used, show him why not.

HUMAN SCALE

Houses are built for people. Therefore, all parts of a house should be built to the scale of the owners and the things they use. A 5-ft ceiling, a 5-ft-square bedroom, a 5-ft-high table—all of these are obviously ridiculous and would not work; however, other errors are not so easy to see. For instance, a 30-in.-high built-in food bar is just right, while 24 in. would be too low to use with the average chair. Before starting, check the Appendix for the sizes of furniture, appliances, standard working heights, etc.

THE THREE BASIC AREAS

The first step in the development of the floor plan is to determine the approximate floor-area requirements of the client, and separate them into the three basic areas of a house: sleeping area, living area, and working area. The requirements for these areas can be taken from the client's checklist. The sleeping area includes the bedrooms, den, bath, storage, and halls in that part of the house. The living area includes the living room, family room, and dining room. The working area includes the kitchen, utility room, pantry, and possibly bath. Where rooms serve two purposes, such as working and living, be sure to keep the areas close together. Room for the furnace or air-conditioning unit must be provided in the area in which it is to be placed. The sleeping, living, and working areas are represented by "balloons" in the first sketches (see Chap. 5, "Mechanical Steps in Planning").

There are many general arrangements of the rooms in a house which will satisfy different people. Try to plan for efficient use of space and ease of traffic flow. A particular client may want changes made from the most efficient arrangement and may resist all logical argument. Remember, it is part of the designer's job to satisfy the client.

TRAFFIC

The problem of traffic flow should be considered first—that is, the most-used areas of the house should be kept fairly close together to avoid unnecessary steps (Fig. 3-1). As the housewife is in the house much more than the rest of the family and is responsible for its upkeep, it stands to reason that "traffic" refers mainly to her traffic.

SPECIFIC ROOMS

The basic requirements of the main rooms of the house, starting in a logical order from the front door, are listed here:

1. *Entry.* An entry is a great convenience. Though not required in all houses, the use of an entry is generally considered preferable to the alternative of having the front door open directly into the living area. The entry should, when possible, provide access to the living, working, and sleeping areas of the house. It has no required size or shape as long as it works. It may be completely walled or set off by room dividers, or it may be an extension of the living, family, or dining room.

2. *Living room.* The living room should be fairly close to the front door but should not be a passageway to other parts of the house. It should be near the kitchen or dining room for ease of entertaining and hospitality. Isolate it from the bedrooms for quiet and privacy in the bedrooms. An average size for a living room is 300 sq ft.

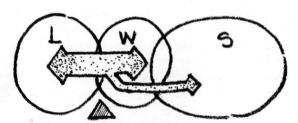

INADVISABLE, TRAFFIC LANES
TOO LONG, LACK OF PRIVACY.

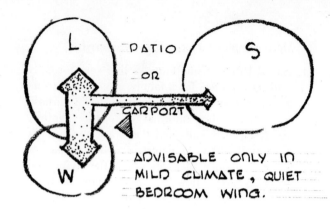

ADVISABLE ONLY IN
MILD CLIMATE, QUIET
BEDROOM WING.

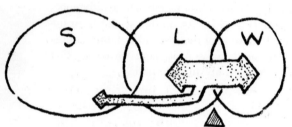

RAMBLING, INADVISABLE IN
VERY COLD, WINDY CLIMATE.

ENTRANCE
SYMBOL

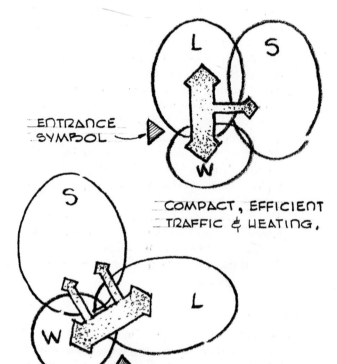

COMPACT, EFFICIENT
TRAFFIC & HEATING.

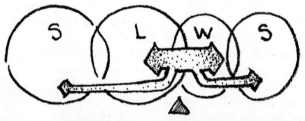

RAMBLING, VARIATION OF ABOVE.

"ELL" OR "TEE" SHAPED, EFFICIENT
TRAFFIC, PROTECTED PATIO.

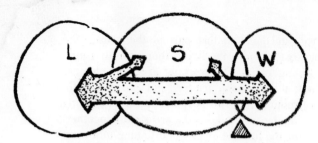

VARIATION OF ABOVE, SEPARATE
APARTMENT FOR MASTER BEDROOM,
MOTHER-IN-LAW OR RENTAL UNIT.

GENERAL NOTES:

1. S = SLEEPING, L = LIVING, W = WORKING AREA.
2. WIDTH OF ARROWS INDICATE AMOUNT OF TRAFFIC.
3. ANY SCHEME MAY BE VARIED BY PLACING ANY OF
   THE AREAS ON ANOTHER LEVEL.

Fig. 3-1. Simplified residential traffic-flow diagrams.

3. *Kitchen.* This is the most important room in the house from the standpoint of the housewife, since she spends a great deal of her time here. It should be near the front door for admitting front-door visitors, adjacent to the utility room for washing, storage, etc., and near the back door for facilitating traffic to the service yard and garage. An average size for a kitchen is 120 sq ft.

4. *Dining room.* A dining room is not always needed when a dinette, family room, or similar room is included in the plan. But when it is required, it should be adjacent to the kitchen and close to the living room for serving and hospitality. An average size for a dining room is 120 sq ft.

5. *Family room, all-purpose room, den, rumpus room, etc.* Many contemporary homes have such rooms. Some of them are used mainly for dining and may be extensions of the kitchen. Others are entirely separate and are used for television viewing, hobbies, entertaining, and sometimes sleeping. In any case a room of this type should be near the kitchen and patio or terrace. Depending upon its main use, it could be near the living room or the sleeping area of the house. An average size for an all-purpose room is 240 sq ft.

6. *Utility room.* It should be adjacent to the kitchen and back door and should provide easy access to the service yard and garage. An average size for a utility room is 60 sq ft.

7. *Bedrooms.* Bedrooms should be isolated from the noisy areas of the house, adjacent to the bathroom, and preferably arranged around a storage hall with a bathroom. An average size for a bedroom is 130 sq ft.

8. *Bathroom.* At least one bathroom should be in the bedroom wing of the house. If there is more than one bath, the other could be near the back door and utility area, or adjoining the master bedroom. An average size for a bathroom is 50 sq ft.

9. *Halls.* When space and expense must be considered, halls should be kept small. One hall should be in the bedroom wing and have access to the bathroom and linen closets. Do not try to omit halls entirely to save space; they are necessary in an efficiently planned house. The recommended minimum width for a hall is $3\frac{1}{2}$ ft.

10. *Basement.* When a basement is included, it can be placed under any desired part of the house.

The entrance may be either outside or inside. Avoid a basement entrance from the bedroom wing or living room. Place heating and ventilation equipment, water heaters, and water softeners in the basement. A large basement is useful as a rumpus room or storage area. A basement may be any desired size.

11. *Heater room.* When no basement is provided and a central heating and/or cooling plant is called for, the equipment may be put in the garage or in a special heater room. The room should be designed around the particular pieces of equipment desired. An average size for a heater room housing a gas-fired unit is 15 sq ft.

12. *Storage space.* Space must be provided in each of the three main areas of the house for the things that people own. Generally, too much storage is better than too little. In the living area of the house provide a coat closet and space for books, hi-fi equipment, television, games, extra tables and chairs, etc. The linen closets in the sleeping area of the house must be large enough for linens, extra blankets, and bathroom supplies. The closets should be about 18 in. deep. Bedrooms and dens should have adequate wardrobe or closet space for clothing. The largest amount of storage space is needed in the working area. Various types of storage must be allowed for: dry, canned, frozen, and fresh foods; dishes; silverware; food utensils; linens; cleaning equipment; and staple items. For more complete information, check "Time-Saver Standards," or "Architectural Graphic Standards." The designer should remember that storage requirements will vary greatly with clients. Be sure to get the client's ideas about storage.

If the house has more than one level, draw the proper stair sections to check for clearance in stairwells, access to rooms, and space required for stairs and halls. When the relationships between the rooms become definitely established, check the plan for unnecessary "jogs" and setbacks in the wall lines. Unless needed for functional reasons, corners cost money but contribute little to the livability of the house.

Proper orientation of the building to the sun and weather must be considered at all times as the floor plan is developed. Read Chap. 6 before attempting the floor plan. Chapter 5 and other specific chapters must also be used in conjunction with this chapter to furnish needed planning information.

REVIEW QUESTIONS

1. In your own words, explain the importance of having full information regarding the client and the site before starting the preliminary sketches. Use a hypothetical case to prove your points.
2. Do the three basic functions of a house (living, working, sleeping) sometimes overlap in one room of the house? Explain.
3. On the basis of convenience and efficiency, point out the advantages and disadvantages of placing a washing machine and dryer in the utility room, in the bathroom, in the bedroom hall.
4. Discuss the use of a patio, lanai, terrace, or breezeway in your own locality. Would your answers be different if you lived 500 miles north or south? Three thousand feet higher or lower in elevation?
5. What are the main reasons for using or not using basements in your area?
6. Are most of the residences in your area of single or multistory construction? Why?

STUDY SUGGESTIONS

1. Sketch a rough plan of your own house and divide it into the three basic areas. Try to improve the plan from the standpoint of traffic and your own family's needs.
2. Compare the floor plans of two houses from different parts of the country. Try to explain why they best suit their own areas and why they probably would not work as well if built elsewhere.
3. Many texts and magazines contain home planning information and descriptions of new developments in materials and equipment. Study them.

Chapter

4

Planning Light-commercial Buildings

Residential versus Commercial Planning

Many factors affect the design of a light-commercial building. The main difference in planning lies in the many different functions of commercial occupants compared with the relatively limited functions of a resident. Though the average commercial building may be simpler to design than the average residence, the problem of instruction in planning becomes more difficult merely because of the wide range of businesses encountered. Obviously, it would be impractical to attempt a detailed analysis of every type of business likely to be encountered by an architect. Because of this problem, the method here will be to list the important considerations encountered in the design of any commercial building. Use this list only as a guide in any particular problem. For instance, the category "Merchandising Areas" generally does not apply to a storage warehouse. Some projects will demand much more independent research on the part of the designer than others. It is better to start with a fairly simple problem.

General-use Categories

Rules of thumb for relative areas and traffic flow which will apply to all businesses are impossible to state. Determination of these factors is the responsibility of the client or the designer. Following is the list of general-use categories to be considered in the design of a commercial building:

1. Merchandising areas
   a. Sales
   b. Display and advertising
   c. Demonstration
2. Areas provided for the comfort of employees and/or customers
   a. Living
   b. Sanitation, rest rooms, etc.
   c. Rest and recreation
   d. Waiting rooms
3. Working areas
   a. Preparation
   b. Receiving
   c. Shipping
   d. Administration and records areas
   e. Customer services—tellers windows, cash registers, booths, etc.
4. Storage areas
   a. Warehousing, stock rooms
   b. Special storage, lockers, safes, vaults
   c. Refrigerated storage
5. Outdoor areas
   a. Parking and access for automobiles
   b. Transport facilities, spur tracks, etc.
   c. Landscaping
   Note: Any of the other categories may be entirely or in part out of doors. In some cases, such as a horticultural nursery in a hot climate, most of the business is in the open.
6. Provision for future expansion
   a. More land for horizontal expansion
   b. Proper design of footings and walls for vertical expansion
7. Utilities
   a. Lighting and electrical services
   b. Ventilating and air conditioning

c. Plumbing, sewage, water, gas, steam, etc.
8. Miscellaneous
    a. Stairs, elevators, ramps, etc.
    b. Overhead facilities, cranes, tracks, etc.
    c. Provision for mobile equipment

Though these last facilities are difficult to classify elsewhere, they do take up space and volume and in all cases affect the structure as well as the floor plan of the building.

Procedure

To use this list to advantage, it is best to first determine the categories into which all the areas of a project will fall. Determine the floor space required by all areas. Check the sizes of all equipment which will be installed or used in each area. Establish the relationship of each area with all the others, and determine the most efficient traffic pattern between areas (Fig. 4-1). This information, when compiled, will correspond to the client's checklist used in the design of a residence. Use the methods of Chap. 5 from here on.

Sources of Information

It is the student's responsibility at this stage to do some independent research for his client. As with any other job, the quality of the result will depend upon the effort expended. Fortunately, many sources of research material are at hand to aid in

the solution of these problems. Here are a few:

1. The client. He is usually the one who knows most about his type of business. It is necessary to spend much time with him at all stages of planning and development. Record all of his ideas, and try to work them into the building.
2. Existing businesses of similar kind. A lot can be learned, both good and bad, from the client's competitors. Investigate them and consider their plants in the light of the problem.
3. Trade papers. Most businesses subscribe to papers which report on the overall problems and progress of the trade. Though each man is in competition with his neighbor, it is to the advantage of both to keep up with the trade as a whole. The trade paper keeps its subscribers abreast of new trends and developments as well as new products, processes, and equipment of interest to the business man.
4. Architectural magazines. In recent years, most of the important architectural magazines have made it a practice to devote several issues each year to particular types of buildings. Certain issues will feature schools, department stores, service stations, small retail buildings, warehouses, etc. These articles contain many examples of good work in each category and are well illustrated and documented.
5. Books. Any library has references which will be of use in solving many aspects of problems.
6. Time and motion study. This is a particularly

Fig. 4-1. Four overlapping traffic patterns in a small restaurant.

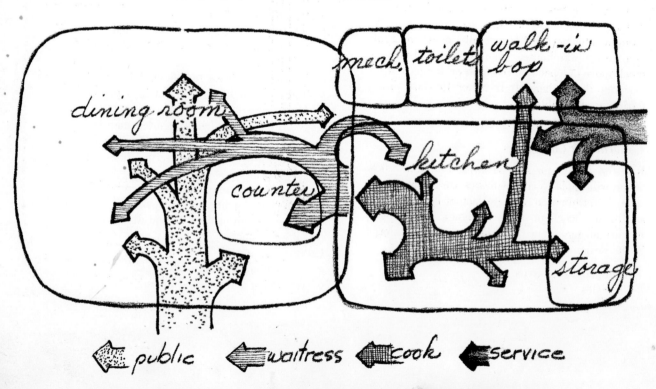

useful subject to the architect. A person aware of the possibilities in this field may be able to do a client a great service. Sometimes the location of a check-out stand at a certain spot may eliminate the need for an extra employee; sometimes the salary of one employee may mean the difference between a profit or a loss in a small business.

The fresh viewpoint of the architect or designer, though not exactly a research source, may be extremely valuable to the client. The client may be so close to his problems that he is unable to see them in proper perspective. In other words, his awareness of small detail may prevent him from seeing the overall problem clearly. It is possible that the designer's ignorance of the client's small troubles may be turned into an asset to the project.

Problems of Commercial Planning

Here are some of the problems which are peculiar to commercial planning and which must be considered carefully:

1. Traffic flow and access to the public. Most commercial occupancies must be more carefully planned than the average residence in order to handle large numbers of people. In a residence, the housewife is the one to be considered; in a retail store, the employees and customers should have plenty of room and access to various areas but should not get in each other's way (Fig. 4-2). Exits must be provided according to code requirements.

2. Large equipment. Many businesses require such equipment as display cases, grease racks, checkout counters, and forklift trucks, and they must go into place or have adequate space in which to operate when the building is finished. Get all the information about required equipment (Fig. 4-3).

3. Site conditions. Often a commercial building may have to be placed in a very restricted spot. For instance, a frontage 20 ft wide in a row of buildings may be the only site available for the business. This will limit the solution of the problem in many ways, e.g., orientation and architectural treatment. When placing the building on an open lot, other problems will be encountered, e.g., parking spaces, access to truck or train services, and space for advertising displays.

4. Orientation. Many factors in orientation are common to both types of occupancy, residential or business, but there are several which are peculiar to business buildings. These factors often affect the storage or display of merchandise. Fabrics, wallpaper, cigars, candies, and rubber goods are damaged by sunlight; sugar, salt, fertilizers, furniture, and paper goods are

Fig. 4-2. Two traffic patterns for a small store.

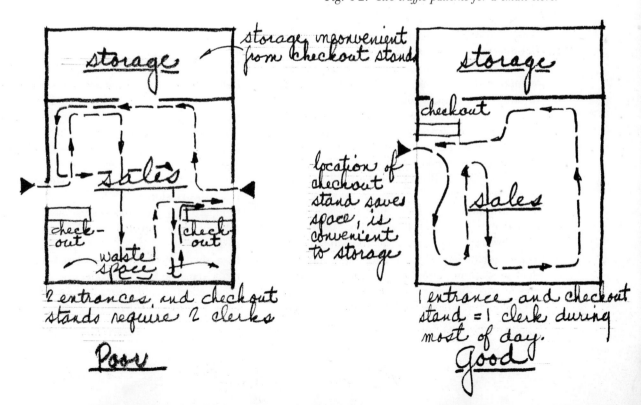

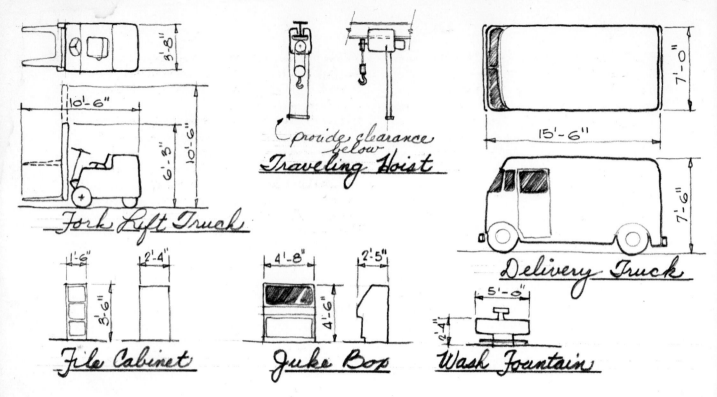

Fig. 4-3. *Space requirements of several common pieces of equipment.*

damaged by water; cameras, fine machinery, and foods are damaged by wind-borne dust. Provide protected display and storage areas for such items.

5. Zoning, building, and architectural-design restrictions. These requirements are generally more detailed and technical than the ones applied to a typical residence. Because of zoning restrictions it may be possible to build a service station on one lot, but not on the one adjacent. Building codes vary from place to place and cover every type of construction work. Architectural restrictions are sometimes very strict. In an area of great historical interest, a certain style of architectural treatment may be required, e.g., Early American or Cape Cod. In many cases the only restriction may be on the heights of awnings and canopies.

6. Surface materials. Because of the hard use that commercial buildings receive, it is more economical from the standpoint of maintenance and depreciation to use high-quality materials. Plastic counter tops, plastic or tile wainscoting, terrazzo or high-quality tile floors, and stainless steel or ceramic-surfaced storefronts are examples of wise choices for a commercial building.

7. Provision for advertising or display. In some businesses, the choice of advertising and display areas is of first importance and will have a tremendous effect upon the success of the venture. Two good examples of this would be a drive-in restaurant and a new-car salesroom.

This chapter should be used in conjunction with Chap. 5.

REVIEW QUESTIONS

1. Define the merchandising areas in a small variety store; an automotive repair garage.
2. Define the areas provided for the comfort of the customer in a doctor's office; a motel.
3. Define the working areas in a small electronics assembly plant; a grocery store.
4. What use areas overlap at the check-out stand in a grocery store?
5. Compare any two businesses on the basis of relative areas devoted to all of the use categories listed.
6. In a small restaurant, what types and lines of traffic must be kept separate?
7. What effect would provision for the use of a large forklift truck have on a small warehouse?

8. Which would demand the more careful orientation to the sun, a warehouse or a candy store?
9. On the basis of your answers to the above questions, can you devise a formula for assigning area requirements, traffic flow, or special provisions for all types of businesses? Why?

STUDY SUGGESTIONS

1. Visit two similar businesses of the same size and try to evaluate their differences in terms of use and traffic flow.
2. Is the grocery store nearest your home laid out as well as it could be? If not, try to sketch your ideas for improvement, and state your reasons for changes.
3. Get a book on time and motion study, and try to apply some of the principles to some small aspect of your drawing project.
4. Study the special issues on Building Types of the *Architectural Record*. The articles are valuable to the student because they explain, in many cases, the controlling factors which have affected the design of the project that is under discussion.

Chapter

5

Mechanical Steps in Planning

Purpose of Preliminaries

When designing a structure for a certain family or business, the first drawings are called preliminary studies. They may be pictorials or three-view drawings or both. The purpose of this type of drawing is to experiment with possible solutions to the problem. These solutions do not usually come to mind in finished form. They develop through knowledge of the client and much research into space requirements, building site, structure, orientation to the weather, and other factors.

Though the floor plan is usually the first drawing started, it is a good idea for the student to read ahead to see how the many factors in planning are interrelated. This chapter deals only with the mechanical processes and procedures of planning; it has nothing to do with planning considerations such as family size, orientation, and structure. This chapter must be used in conjunction with the chapters on residential planning or light-commercial planning regarding floor plans, or the chapters on orientation, structure, elevations, etc., when working out the other preliminaries.

Procedure

When the basic information regarding the client and his needs has been assembled in the checklist, work may start on the preliminary floor plan. This information must be as complete and detailed as possible to avoid backtracking and wasted effort. Now start sketching the preliminary drawings.

FLOOR PLAN

The following method of sketching rough floor plans works very well. Draw the desired area as a "balloon" or oval of the approximate size (Figs. 5-1 and 5-3). Avoid straight lines and exact measurement at the start, but be very careful of proportion. Straight lines and square corners tend to discourage experiment and make it difficult to change existing sketches. On the other hand, balloons flow into and around each other and are easier to manipulate. The relative areas of the balloons can be established from the checklist or client's estimates. Use a light sketchy line that can be easily erased or drawn over. When the shape and organization of the floor plan begin to look right, then start to straighten lines and square the corners (Figs. 5-2 and 5-4). Try more than one solution. Once the plan reaches this stage, have the client choose the scheme he likes best.

Before trying to draw the plan to scale, check the Appendix for the space requirements of certain important items in the building, for instance, fireplace, inside planters, linen closets, showcases, large equipment, halls, and plumbing fixtures. If these are not drawn fairly close to scale on the sketches, trouble will develop later when drawing to exact size.

Take the approved solution and draw a one-line floor plan, at small scale, in which the thickness of walls is not shown (Figs. 5-5 and 5-6). When used as an outside wall or wall break, the single line must represent the outside of the wall; as an inside wall,

(continued on page 27)

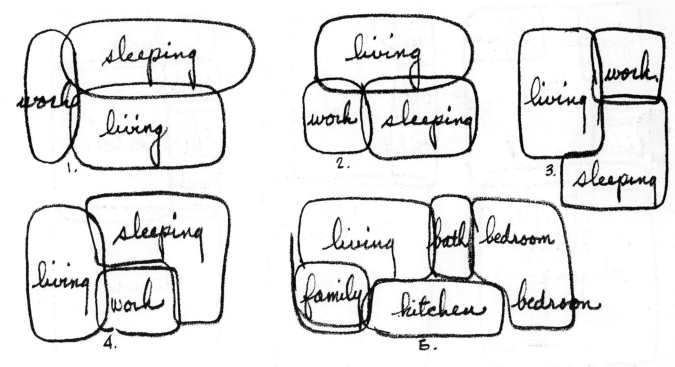

Fig. 5-1. *Five preliminary area studies of a residence.*

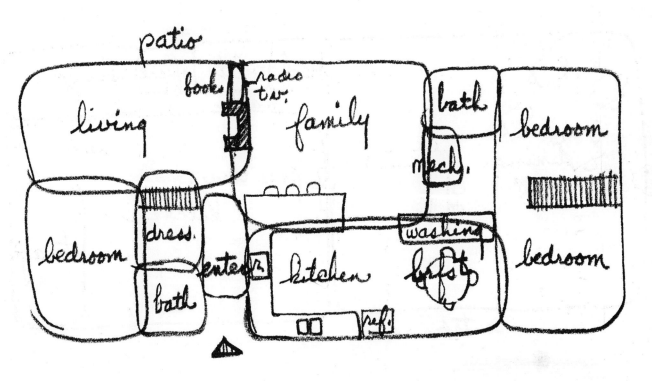

Fig. 5-2. *Further development of scheme No. 5 in Fig. 5-1.*

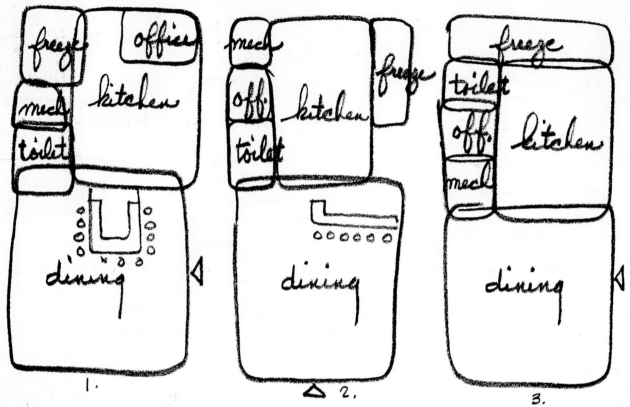

Fig. 5-3. Three preliminary area studies of a restaurant.

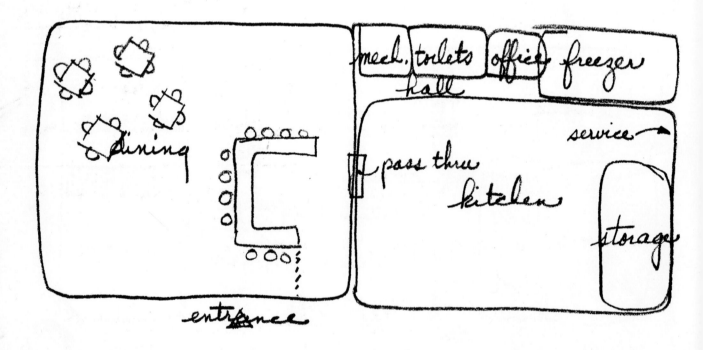

Fig. 5-4. Further development of scheme No. 3 in Fig. 5-3.

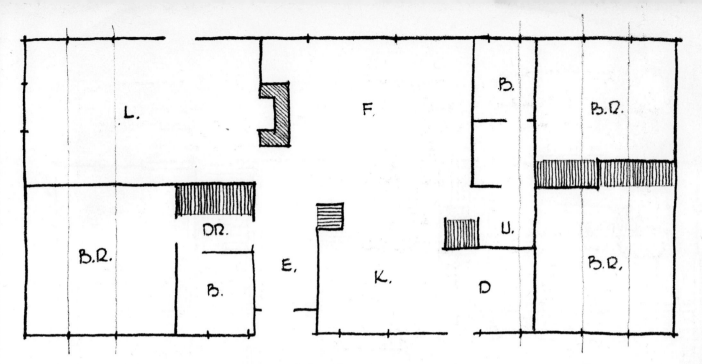

Fig. 5-5. Single-line floor plan developed to scale from Fig. 5-2.

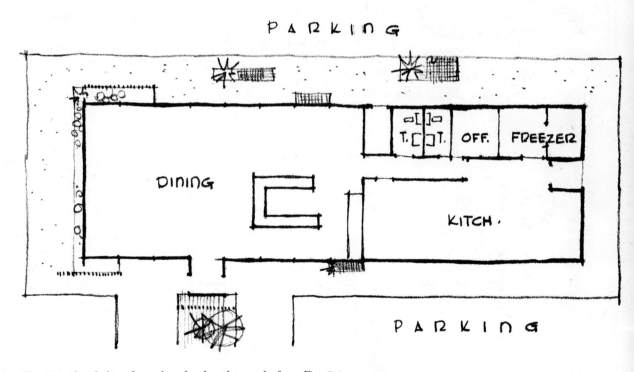

Fig. 5-6. Single-line floor plan developed to scale from Fig. 5-4.

the single line must represent the center line of the wall. This rule should be followed, or the dimensioning when placed later will not be consistent. Finally, trace a plan from this copy showing wall thicknesses. Further refinements of small detail and exact measurement can now be made. The finished floor plan can be drawn from this rough copy after it has been approved by the client. Use $\frac{1}{8}$ or $\frac{1}{4}$ in. to the foot scale for the finished drawing (Figs. 5-7 and 5-8).

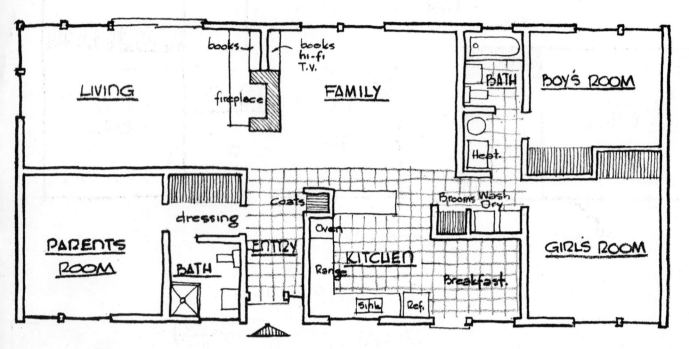

Fig. 5-7. Floor plan, showing wall thickness, traced or copied from Fig. 5-5.

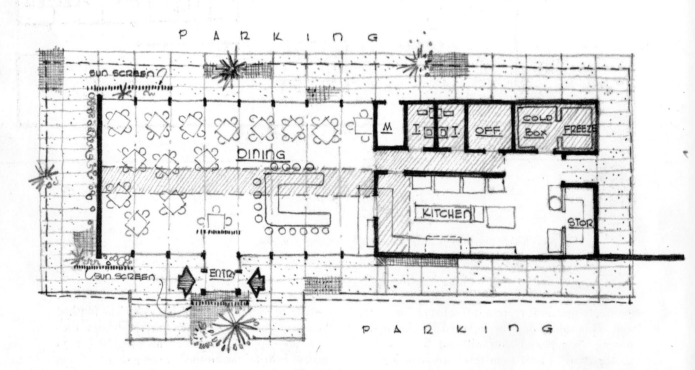

Fig. 5-8. Floor plan, showing wall thickness, traced or copied from Fig. 5-6.

Fig. 5-9. *Preliminary elevation sketch of residence.*

ELEVATIONS AND SECTIONS

At this point some rough sketches of the elevations should be drawn (Figs. 5-9 and 5-10). To do this, it is necessary to decide on the type of structural system to be used.

First, establish the type of floor system. Most people have strong ideas about wood versus concrete floors in a residence. The type of floor construction will affect the overall height of the building above the ground level. Generally, a concrete floor will be 6 to 8 in. above grade, while a wood floor will be 16 to 20 in. above grade. Use these approximate figures in working out your preliminary sketches. Concrete floors, because of economy and durability, are generally used in commercial and industrial structures.

Many types of structural systems are used; some of the more common types are described as follows:

1. Walls. Plate height is usually 8 ft 0 in. for a residence, 8 to 12 ft for a commercial building.

Fig. 5-10. *Preliminary elevation sketch of restaurant.*

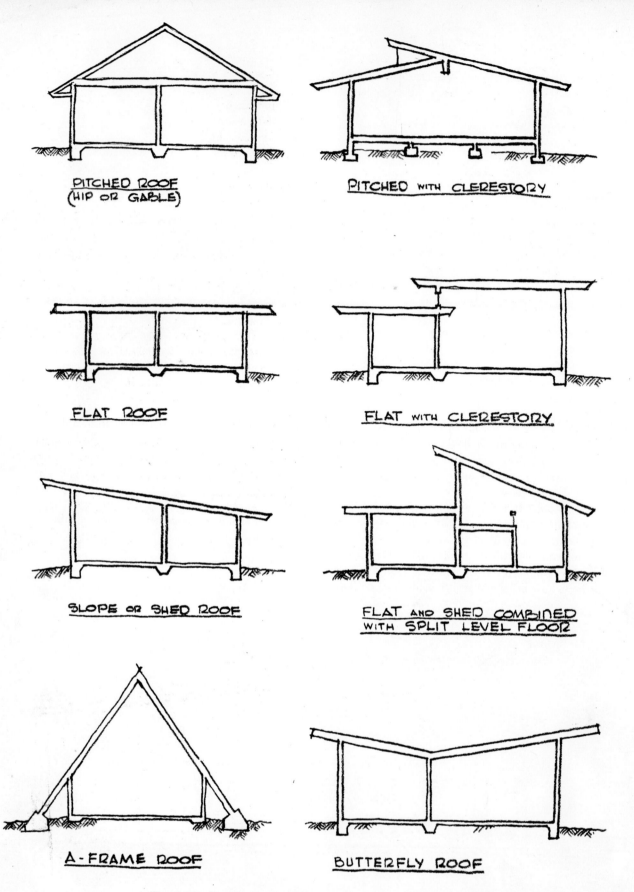

PITCHED ROOF
(HIP OR GABLE)

PITCHED WITH CLERESTORY

FLAT ROOF

FLAT WITH CLERESTORY

SLOPE OR SHED ROOF

FLAT AND SHED COMBINED
WITH SPLIT LEVEL FLOOR

A-FRAME ROOF

BUTTERFLY ROOF

Fig. 5-11. Simple structural shapes suitable for residential or light-commercial buildings.

a. Frame construction: Vertical members of wood or metal covered with any desired material.
b. Masonry construction: Brick, stone, or concrete-block units laid in courses to form a wall.
c. Other types should be investigated, such as modular post and beam construction, either wood or steel, using conventional finished or newly developed prefinished panels.

2. Roof construction.
a. Double-pitched roofs, either gable or hip, are most common in residential construction. The pitch depends upon local conditions and the type of roofing material desired. Clerestory windows may be easily built into a pitched roof.
b. Single-pitched roofs are quite common in residential and commercial construction and are easily designed to use clerestories. Skylights and eggcrate patterns are often used with this type of roof.
c. Flat roofs include pitches under 4 in 12 and may be single- or double-pitched.
d. A-frame roofs are quite spectacular and are widely used in cabins, churches, and certain commercial buildings.
e. Special types of roofs, such as hyperbolic paraboloids and other shell structures, should be left to the experts.

3. Exterior finishes for frame construction.
a. Stucco.

b. Wood sheathing.
c. Plywood, metal, plastics, or other sheet materials.
d. Masonry veneers.
e. Ceramic tile.
f. Wainscoting, using combinations of the above.

4. Windows and doors. Many types are available, and they may be used at the discretion of the designer.

Some simple structural shapes are shown in Fig. 5-11. The cross section is used with the floor plan to establish the size and shape of the elevations (Figs. 5-12 and 5-13). When size and shape are established, it is possible to experiment with window and door arrangements, materials, etc. At this stage of development exact information is not required as long as one has settled on the general appearance of the structure. Further information will be found in Chaps. 14 and 16.

Design

Many different combinations of these structures and materials can be used, and the only "rule" possible is this: Combine them in a way that will suit the client and the conditions of the site. Avoid "period" architecture until more is known about

Fig. 5-12. Sketch of cross sections for residence.

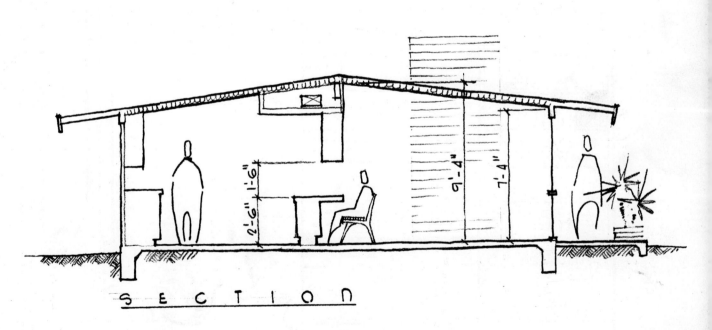

SECTION

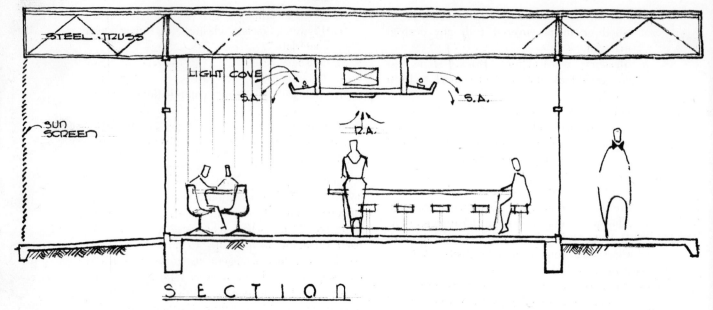

SECTION

Fig. 5-13. *Sketch of cross section for restaurant.*

the periods. The student may discover that many types of period architecture worked well when they were developed but may not be adaptable to present ways of living and construction methods in many areas.

Because of space limitations and the purposes of

the book, it is not practical to take up the subjects of proportion, texture, color, fenestration, and other factors of design. The best advice is to keep the design simple and functional and to be careful of applied decoration. Simplicity with function is often good design.

Fig. 5-14. *Preliminary sketch of fireplace for residence.*

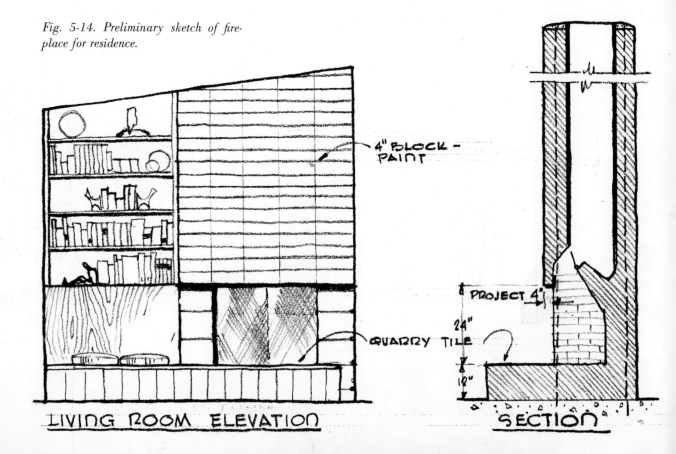

LIVING ROOM ELEVATION

SECTION

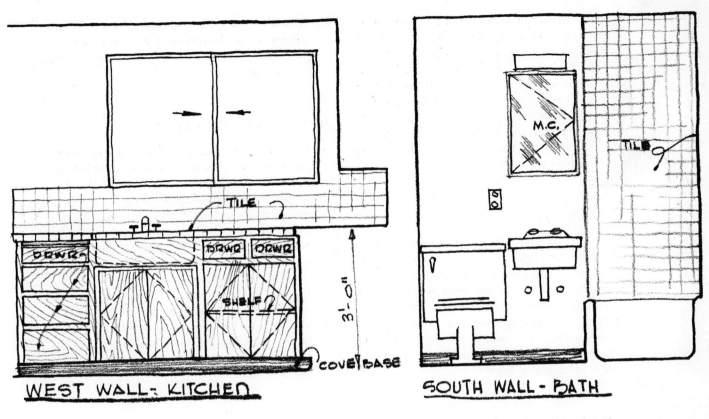

WEST WALL - KITCHEN

SOUTH WALL - BATH

Fig. 5-15. Preliminary sketches of interiors of residence.

Use of Preliminaries

The object of completing a set of preliminary studies is to provide the information required for a complete set of working drawings. At this stage the required drawings are a structural section, at least two elevations, the plot plan, and the floor plan, plus ideas for fireplaces or other masonry work, windows, doors, interior and exterior finishes, major cabinet work, and all features peculiar to the type of building being developed (Figs. 5-14 and 5-15). In most cases these drawings do not have to be completely detailed, but they should clearly indicate the designer's intentions. Finished drawings are based on these preliminaries. When in doubt about how to proceed on a certain drawing, look it up in its proper chapter.

When the preliminary studies are complete, look them over carefully. Check them with such questions in mind as: Does the building fit the site? Is storage space adequate? Is there enough room provided for equipment to be used in the building? Is the orientation correct? When student and instructor agree that the sketches are complete, work can begin on the working drawings.

The final data sheet shown in the Appendix is a useful device for organizing information for a residence (see A-2). The sheet should be clipped to the other sketches and drawings which represent the final form of the project. Keep this packet in a safe place, because all finished working drawings will be based on the information it contains. In addition, good organization at this point will save much drafting time later.

The Next Step

Now that the preliminary drawings have been completed, the student must decide upon the next step: either to start the working drawings or to prepare a presentation drawing. Regardless of experience, it is possible to proceed with the working drawings at once, since this book discusses developing the preliminaries into the various working drawings in logical order and one at a time. From the standpoint of a student draftsman, the question of whether or not to attempt a presentation drawing depends upon his experience and understanding. It would usually be unwise to attempt such a drawing at this point in a first project. The principal reason is that the execution of a presentation drawing demands an understanding of each of the different types of working drawings to be used. Naturally, a beginning student would not have a sufficient background of knowledge for this until the completion of at least one full set of working drawings. It is useful however, from the standpoint of learning, to do the presentation drawing after the working drawings are finished. Granted that this puts the cart before the horse, doing the drawing is still a good experience in drafting.

REVIEW QUESTIONS

1. Is it necessary to refer to other sections of the book at this stage, or is every necessary factor completely described in this chapter?
2. Preliminary studies are extremely accurate, detailed drawings. True or false?
3. When developing a floor plan from a single-line sketch, which room is affected most by the loss of area due to wall thickness, a bathroom or a living room? Why?

4. What are some useful applications of a clerestory window or a skylight in a residence, a warehouse, or a small office? What are some of the disadvantages?

STUDY SUGGESTIONS

1. Break the floor plan of a house or commercial building down into its "use areas" outlined by balloons. Change the overall shape of the plan, or use a differently shaped site, and try to keep the areas in the same relationships. Can this always be done easily?
2. Study the kitchen arrangements shown in a women's magazine. Try to use some of the details on your own project.
3. Discuss the problems of room arrangement, window and door location, and traffic patterns with several housewives. Remember that these factors are considered extremely important by women, whose job it is to decorate and maintain a home.

Chapter

6

Orientation

Definition and Purpose

Though a floor plan may now work well from the standpoint of interior circulation, it must still be related to its surroundings. It is a mistake to assume that a good floor plan will work well on any site. The process of placing a building on the site to take most advantage of the surroundings is called *orientation.* Orientation should always be considered as the floor plan is developed to avoid major changes at a late stage of planning. Orientation will have an effect on every drawing in the set.

Important aspects of the structure which are most affected by the sun and weather are size and location of windows, the extent of the roof overhang, the type of roof, size and type of the heating and cooling plant, insulation, location of outdoor living areas, and landscaping.

Required Information

Before orienting the building, it is necessary to have an accurate drawing of the site showing the north arrow; streets; alleyways; property lines; easements; locations of utilities; locations of existing buildings; and location, type, and size of all trees that might be saved. If the site is hilly, contour lines are needed. It is also necessary to know how far back from the property lines the building must be set. These requirements are determined by local zoning ordinances and deed restrictions. Look them up. Visit the site if possible.

The Sun

One of the most important factors affecting the orientation of a structure is its relation to the sun.

In considering the effect of the sun on the building it is necessary to know both the vertical and horizontal angles of the sun at any time of the year. Charts and tables showing these angles may be found in many references.

The horizontal and vertical angles of the sun vary with the date, time of day, and latitude, or distance from the equator, of the place in question. A few obvious remarks should be made here. The vertical angle of the sun with the ground is steeper in summer than in winter. In the northern hemisphere it is steeper in southern than in northern latitudes at any given time. The horizontal angle of the sun between sunrise and sunset is larger in the summer than in winter. The principal reason that summer is warmer than winter is due to the steeper vertical angle of the sun, plus the longer daylight hours.

When orienting a building to the sun, one should have a plan view of the site and building, tentative cross sections of the structure drawn to scale, and the' sun tables (Fig. 6-1, A-3). Using these data, one may establish three important functional aspects of the structure:

1. The extent of the roof overhang above the largest window areas
2. The location and size of these windows
3. The location of treillage (sun screens) or landscaping to control the sun in relation to the house and outdoor living areas

It is possible to determine the shadow line of the roof or canopy overhang at any time of the day and year. This is best done by graphic means, using orthographic projection in conjunction with the sun tables. It is assumed that any student using this book can do such a construction (Fig. 6-2).

(continued on page 38)

Fig. 6-1. Drawings required to make a study of orientation.

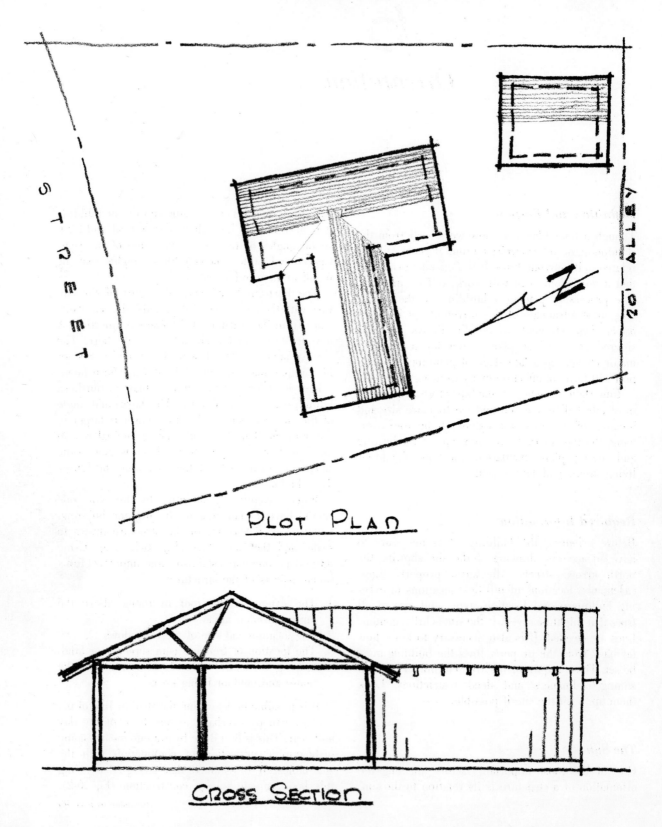

PLOT PLAN

CROSS SECTION

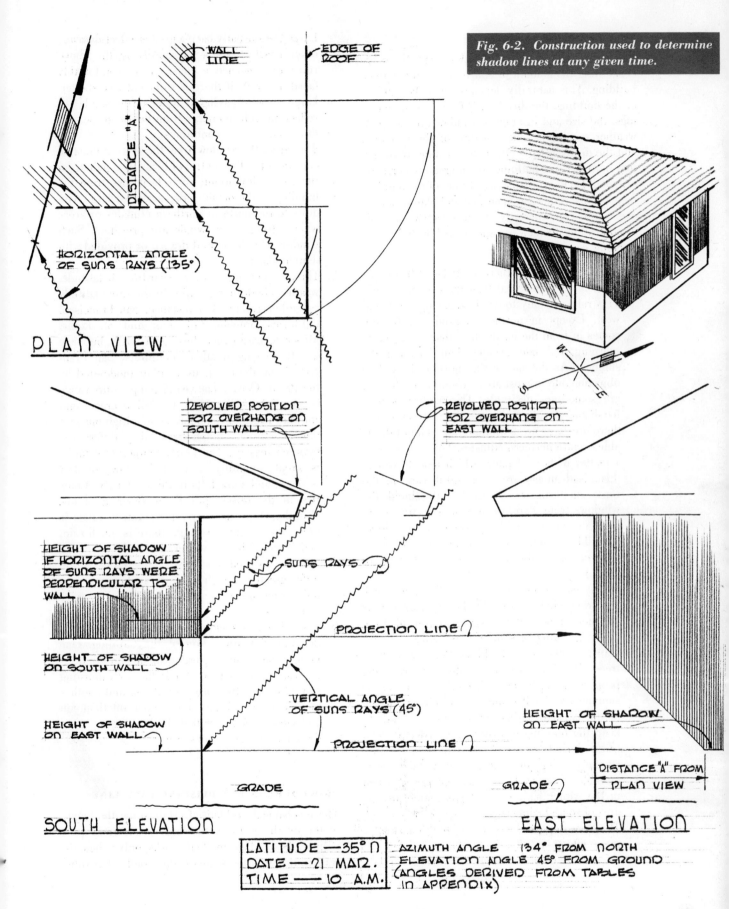

WALL LINE

EDGE OF ROOF

DISTANCE "A"

HORIZONTAL ANGLE OF SUNS RAYS (135°)

PLAN VIEW

W

S

E

REVOLVED POSITION FOR OVERHANG ON SOUTH WALL

REVOLVED POSITION FOR OVERHANG ON EAST WALL

HEIGHT OF SHADOW IF HORIZONTAL ANGLE OF SUNS RAYS WERE PERPENDICULAR TO WALL

SUNS RAYS

HEIGHT OF SHADOW ON SOUTH WALL

PROJECTION LINE

VERTICAL ANGLE OF SUNS RAYS (45°)

HEIGHT OF SHADOW ON EAST WALL

PROJECTION LINE

HEIGHT OF SHADOW ON EAST WALL

DISTANCE "A" FROM PLAN VIEW

GRADE

GRADE

SOUTH ELEVATION

EAST ELEVATION

LATITUDE —35° N
DATE —21 MAR.
TIME —10 A.M.

AZIMUTH ANGLE 134° FROM NORTH
ELEVATION ANGLE 45° FROM GROUND
(ANGLES DERIVED FROM TABLES IN APPENDIX)

37

LOCAL REQUIREMENTS

Unfortunately, no ironclad rules may be made concerning the amount of sun required for a given building. This naturally depends upon the latitude of the building, the direction it faces, its surroundings, the size and location of window area, general weather conditions, the function of the windows, and the desires of the client. It is wrong to assume that most existing buildings in an area are correctly oriented. Do not copy the orientation of the building next door; decide what is needed and plan windows, overhangs, etc., correctly. Some effective methods of controlling the sun are shown in Fig. 6-3.

Some general rules follow:

1. Buildings in far northern latitudes will tolerate more of the sun's heat than those in the south. This refers mainly to windows facing south and west. Except in northern latitudes, little sun comes in from the north other than in the early morning and late evening hours during the summer. As the sun in the morning is seldom objectionable in most areas, windows to the east are sometimes desirable. The western sun is harsh and glaring in the summer in all latitudes, therefore large west windows are seldom desirable even in northern climates. This is, however, a matter of taste. Factors which tend to cancel this disadvantage are a beautiful view to the west, sheltering trees which will shield the windows from glare, or an extensive west overhang or sun screen. West windows are seldom desirable in hot, southern climates. (The word *window*, as used here, refers to large window areas.)

2. In any part of the country, the direction which the large window areas of the building face is the most important factor in sun control. Generally speaking, a southern exposure is better than any other for a building on a plot without trees. By designing the south roof overhang properly, it is possible to keep the sun out in the summer and let it come in at any desired date in the fall and spring. This condition tends to keep the building cool during hot weather and warm during the winter, which makes a substantial saving in heating and cooling costs possible. The amount of heat energy obtained in the winter naturally depends mainly on the area of south-facing windows exposed to the sun.

3. The near surroundings of the building have a great effect on its orientation. A wooded lot offers more choice of orientation than a bare lot.

Large trees usually have a greater effect than any other nearby feature in modifying the above rules. For instance, a house can be comfortably faced due west if there is sufficient tree shelter. Large areas of paving or water to the south will reflect much heat energy from below, so be sure to consider these conditions.

4. The larger the window area, the more it must be considered in the control of heat. Heat gain from the sun is important; so is heat loss from the building to the outside. Be careful of large windows to the north in northern climates or areas where strong north winds are prevalent. Such windows should be well draped or provided with double glazing.

5. Though sun angles vary according to latitude, weather conditions of cities in the same latitude can differ greatly. For instance, San Francisco, California; Pueblo, Colorado; and St. Louis, Missouri, are all very close to lat 38° N, but have widely varying weather conditions. San Francisco is on the coast, its weather moderated by the Pacific Ocean. The yearly temperature range is small, humidity high, rainfall average, and snowfall negligible. Pueblo is on a high plateau; this condition emphasizes the differences between seasons. The yearly temperature range is great, humidity is generally low, rainfall is scant, and snow falls in the winter. St. Louis lies in the Mississippi River Basin at a low altitude. Here the yearly temperature range is great, the humidity is high, there is much rain, and it snows in the winter. It can be seen that houses designed for these three cities would differ greatly, though they are at the same latitude. Remember to provide for local weather conditions.

6. The client's wishes are an important factor in deciding the orientation of the building. One person may want a great deal of sun from all angles; another may want only the early morning sun. One may like many windows, and another may consider privacy more important than sun and view. Remember that the building is being designed for the client's use.

PROCEDURE IN ESTABLISHING EAVE LINE

The mechanical problem of establishing the length of the overhang above the large windows is quite simple. Note: This method works only when the wall in question faces almost due south. Any other

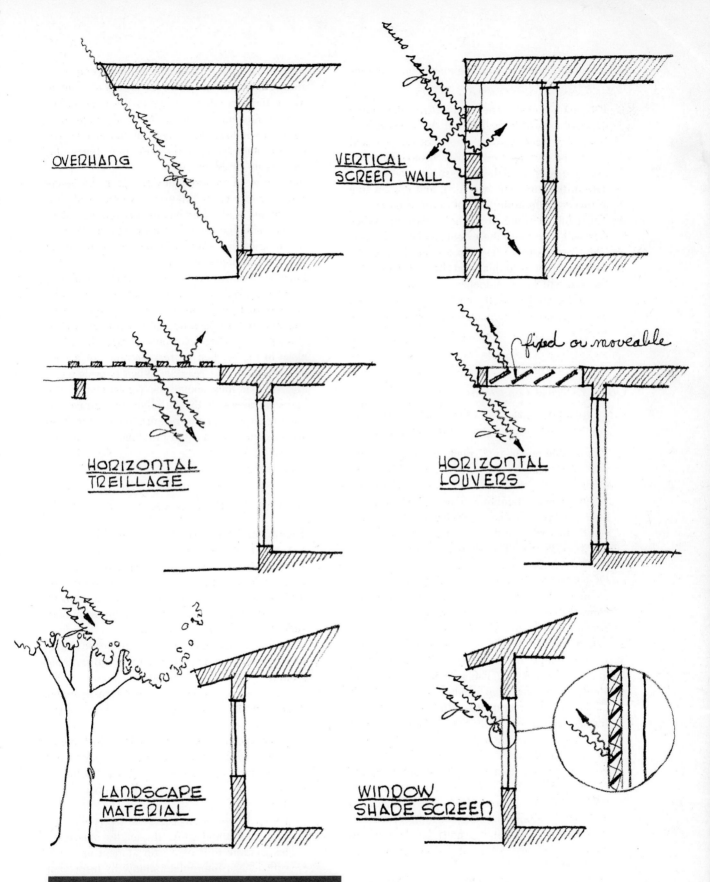

OVERHANG

VERTICAL SCREEN WALL

HORIZONTAL TREILLAGE

HORIZONTAL LOUVERS

fixed or moveable

LANDSCAPE MATERIAL

WINDOW SHADE SCREEN

Fig. 6-3. Devices for controlling solar radiation.

39

exposure will require supplementary constructions (Fig. 6-4).

1. The client and designer should first determine the date on which the sun will be permitted to enter the large windows. This decision is based on all the variables previously listed.
2. Find the vertical angle of the sun on the desired date in the sun table (see A-3), and draw a line at this angle from the bottom of the window.
3. The point at which this line strikes the rafter line will determine the extent of the roof overhang. Establish the fascia board or the edge of the roof structure at this point. In the hot months, the sun will be at a steeper angle and will not reach the window. In the cooler months, the sun will be at a shallower angle and will enter the window.

Other External Conditions

Other conditions that affect orientation and that are not so dependent on sun include the following:

1. The outside temperature range through the year will affect many details of a building. In a cold climate a square building would lose less warmth than a rambling building of the same floor area and thus be more economical to heat. Also, smaller windows would be desirable for the same reason. The alternative to small windows would be double glazing or storm windows. Of course more insulation and better weather stripping are required to keep the structure comfortable. In any climate, good insulation is needed for effective air conditioning.
2. Where prevailing winds blow across an area, houses should be faced so that outside living areas are protected. The side facing the wind should have few large window areas; this prevents excessive heat loss. In extreme cases, houses have been built with the lower half of the windward wall below grade.
3. In an area of heavy rainfall, provide extensive covered areas between buildings and adequate cover over entrances. Gutters and downspouts are needed also. In desert areas, however, gutters are usually eliminated in residential structures.
4. The roof of the building must be designed to support or shed snow if heavy snows are expected.
5. If the site has a desirable view, sometimes a compromise may be made between efficiency and esthetics. For instance, in a hot climate where the site offers a view to the west, either some arrangement should be made to protect the view windows or the view should be ignored. On the other hand, if the view is to the south, there is no problem.
6. One feature of a house that yields great dividends and is closely related to orientation is insulation in roof and walls. Any heating or cooling system needs insulation for efficient operation. Weather stripping of doors and windows is usually done when a building is insulated.
7. Further compromises with thermal efficiency, lot size, traffic, and personal preference must be made so that service areas, access between areas, and automobile parking can be provided. The clothesline, garbage can, and garage should be close to the kitchen or rear entrance of a residence for obvious reasons. When parking areas are needed, they should be convenient to the main entrances of the building, the garage (or loading dock), or both. Be sure to consider these areas when orienting the building.

REVIEW QUESTIONS

1. What natural force has the greatest effect on the orientation of a structure?
2. What are the highest vertical angles of the sun at noon in midsummer and midwinter where you live? What are the horizontal angles at sunrise and sunset in midwinter and midsummer? (Use A-3.)
3. What are the principal reasons, from the standpoint of orientation, for having large trees around a house in your locality?
4. In your locality, what are the advantages and disadvantages of having large windows to the south? To the north?
5. a. What are the horizontal and vertical angles of the sun on May 21 at 4 P.M. in your area?
   b. What are the angles for April 5 at 2 P.M.?
   c. What are the angles for November 21 at 11:30 A.M.?
   (Note: It will be necessary to interpolate for problems b and c. As the angles must only be accurate to 2 or 3° for student use, it is sufficient to interpolate simply by inspection of the chart.)

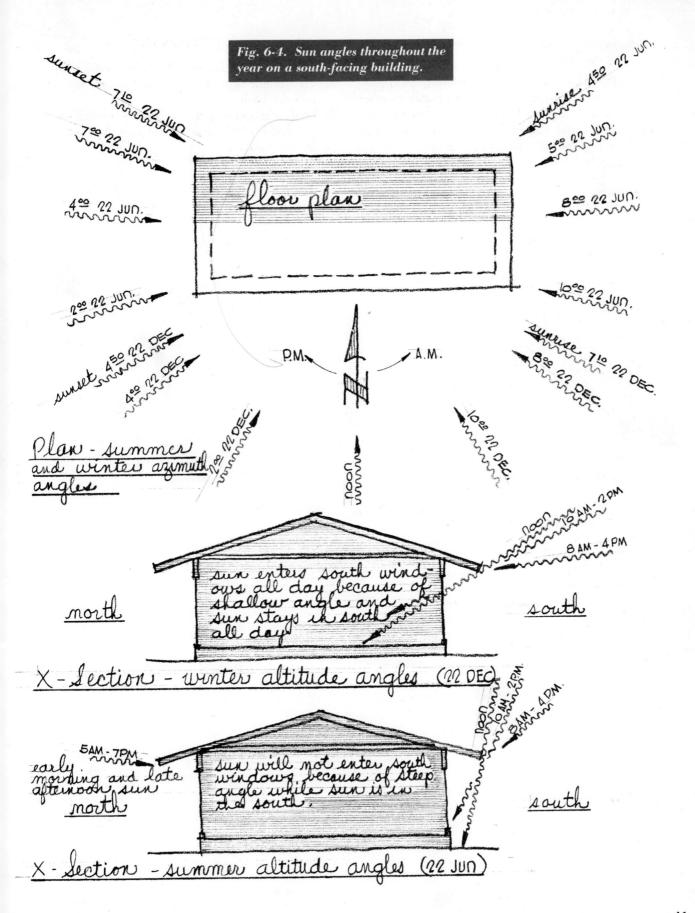

Fig. 6-4. *Sun angles throughout the year on a south-facing building.*

floor plan

sunset 7¹⁶ 22 JUN.
7⁰⁰ 22 JUN.
4⁰⁰ 22 JUN.
2⁰⁰ 22 JUN.
sunset 4⁵⁰ 22 DEC.
4⁰⁰ 22 DEC.

sunrise 4⁵⁰ 22 JUN.
5⁰⁰ 22 JUN.
8⁰⁰ 22 JUN.
10⁰⁰ 22 JUN.
sunrise 7¹⁶ 22 DEC.
8⁰⁰ 22 DEC.
10⁰⁰ 22 DEC.

P.M.   A.M.

noon   noon 10 AM - 2 PM
8 AM - 4 PM

Plan - summer and winter azimuth angles
2⁰⁰ 22 DEC.

north   sun enters south windows all day because of shallow angle and sun stays in south all day   south

X - Section - winter altitude angles (22 DEC)

noon 10 AM - 2 PM
8 AM - 4 PM

5 AM - 7 PM
early morning and late afternoon sun
north   sun will not enter south windows because of steep angle while sun is in the south.   south

X - Section - summer altitude angles (22 JUN)

41

6. In what ways does heavy rainfall affect the design of the building?

7. Pick an area of the country which has a climate greatly different from your own home; all other factors being equal, what changes would climate alone make in your own building project if it were to be built elsewhere?

STUDY SUGGESTIONS

1. Evaluate, on the basis of orientation, some existing building with which you are familiar. Try to improve on it.

2. Study a magazine article or text on orientation, and decide which factors are of most importance in your locality.

Chapter

7

Landscaping

Values of Landscaping

Any building, no matter how well or poorly designed, may be improved by landscaping. The soft lines of trees and shrubs set off the sharp lines of the building, and the presence of growing things moderates the weather around the structure. To prove this, compare the appearance and livability of a brand-new house on a bare plot with its well-established neighbors. Certain commercial buildings demand landscaping, and any building in a hot climate is greatly improved by trees and vegetation.

Many books are written on landscaping, and there are several schools of thought regarding the arrangement of plantings. To the person specially interested in landscaping, good books on the subject are available at any library. Check one out.

Relationships between Landscaping and Orientation

This chapter is closely related to the chapter on orientation, and the two should be considered together. Only the functional side of landscaping can be presented here. Its important uses are protecting from sun and wind, screening objectionable views and framing desirable ones, and using trees and shrubs as fences and to set off the lines of the building (Fig. 7-1).

1. Trees and shrubs as sun and wind protection (mainly covered in "Orientation"). A knowledge of the path of the sun and direction of prevailing winds is of first importance in planning the location of plantings. To merely shut out the sun or wind, plant a dense hedge or row of trees in the proper spot. To provide a comfortable shaded area near the house, plant a large tree. For summer shade and winter sun, plant a tree that loses its leaves in winter; for constant shade, plant evergreens.

2. Trees and shrubs in relation to the view. The view from any window may be either improved or concealed by proper plantings. To conceal it, plant a screen in front of it. To set it off, plant trees and shrubs to frame it. Usually a large, open, growing tree will greatly improve the effect of the view seen through it.

3. Trees and shrubs as fences. Many types of plants may be used in a hedge to make an excellent fence. Any thorny hedge will keep people and large animals out of a property as effectively as barbed wire. Most close-growing hedges are almost as good. One advantage of a growing fence is that it never needs painting, though it will need pruning. Usually it will look better than most cheap fence materials.

4. Trees and shrubs to set off the building. When planted in front of the building, trees and shrubs provide soft lines to offset and soften the lines of the structure. They also give a feeling of space and scale to the architectural features of the building.

Treatment of the Ground

In addition to large plantings, ground covers, grass, and paving areas are extremely important to the design of a good landscape plan.

1. Ground covers. Ivy, strawberry, and other low-

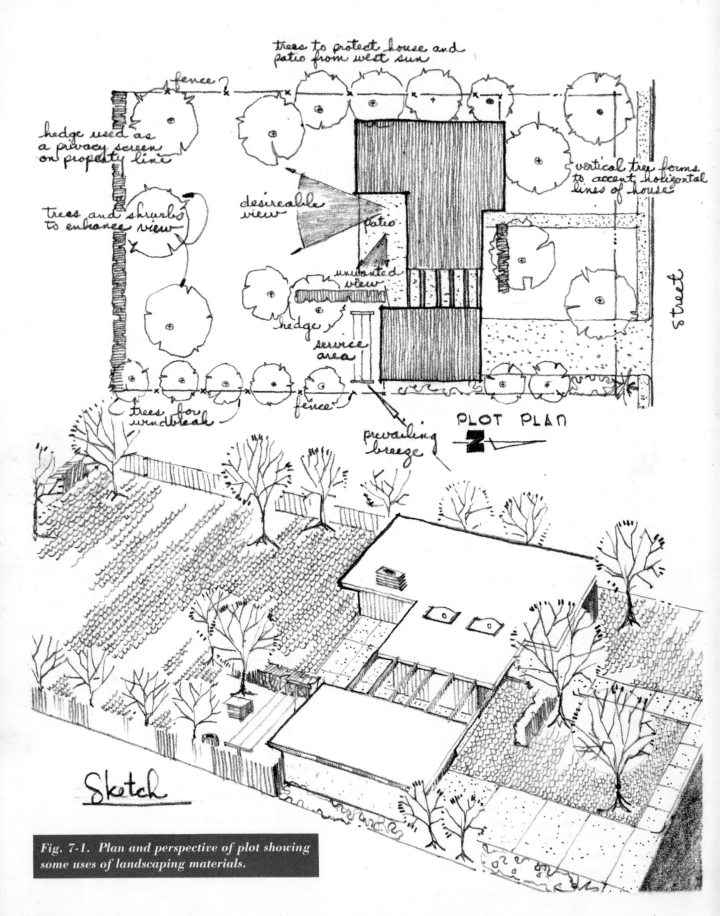

trees to protect house and patio from west sun

fence?

hedge used as a privacy screen on property line

desireable view

patio

vertical tree forms to accent horizontal lines of house

trees and shrubs to enhance view

unwanted view

hedge

service area

street

trees for windbreak

fence

prevailing breeze

PLOT PLAN

Sketch

Fig. 7-1. Plan and perspective of plot showing some uses of landscaping materials.

growing plants provide ground protection, color, and texture in areas away from traffic.

2. Grasses and other lawn materials. These will serve the same purposes as ground covers and, in addition will withstand foot traffic.

3. Brick and natural stone. Suitable for walks, patios, and walls, they provide a rich color and texture, and will take a great deal of traffic.

4. Concrete. It can be used in the same ways as stone and is extremely durable, but it lacks the richness of natural materials.

5. Plant-mix surfacing, or black top. A useful material for large areas of paving because of its economy.

Design

When planning the landscape, keep it simple and functional. Avoid "pretty" patterns and complicated arrangements of plantings. Remember that a beautiful geometric design, as seen on a plan, does not guarantee a beautifully landscaped plot. From the usual points of view, the observer is aware of space and volume as well as area in a landscaped plot.

In mild or hot weather, outdoor spaces can be used to advantage for dining, entertaining, or simple enjoyment. Well-designed outdoor spaces can add greatly to the useful living area of any project.

REVIEW QUESTIONS

1. Why are trees often better for the control of the sun than manufactured sunscreens?
2. In landscape painting and photography, why are trees often used to frame a view?
3. In your own part of the country, what deciduous trees are most often planted? What evergreens?
4. Where could an additional tree be used to advantage near your own home? What type?

STUDY SUGGESTIONS

1. Read a book on landscaping, and try to work the ideas you like into your own project.
2. Identify some of your local trees, and decide which ones will work best for specific conditions.

Chapter
8
Regional Differences in Design and Construction

Local Conditions

Many different types of construction are found throughout the country. The differences are brought about principally by climate, availability of materials, and regional architectural trends and tastes. Because these factors overlap in many ways and their effects are further complicated by local and personal factors, the student should investigate conditions and preferences in his own area.

Many weather factors have already been treated in Chap. 6. Other construction and design features affected by weather will be pointed out here. Hot and cold weather affect overall design, particularly regarding outdoor living, insulation, structure, and heating and cooling requirements. The frost line in winter affects the depth of footings, perimeter insulation at foundation walls, and insulation of plumbing lines. Basements are used in cold climates principally because the foundation walls must be excavated to basement depth anyway. Older houses in these areas used gravity heating, and gravity heating works best with a basement. The extra storage of basements plus personal preferences also favor their use. Basements are seldom used in the hot desert areas of California and Arizona. Cold weather also limits the use of large window areas. Rain and snow conditions affect the building greatly. Foundation drains, gutters, downspouts, and well-protected outdoor areas may all be needed in an area of severe winters. In arid sections, drains, gutters, and downspouts are usually omitted.

Wind, particularly hurricanes and cyclones, must be considered in the design of the structure. A basement or shelter is usually included in the plan as a safety factor, and the entire structure must be strengthened to withstand the extreme forces expected. Wall and roof bracing, foundation and roof ties, etc., normally exceed the requirements for other geographical areas.

Earthquakes, while not related to weather, are a regional factor which has to be considered. Foundation ties, wall bracing, and roof bracing must be made stronger to resist seismic forces.

Even though all other design considerations are the same, the easy availability and economy of certain local materials, and the dearth of others, have a large effect on the structure. For instance, redwood is most used in California and other west coast areas because it is grown only there. Structural brick walls are seldom used in areas far from a brickyard. These are only a few of the obvious examples.

Local Design Restrictions

Architectural and constructional details of many buildings are limited by local pressures and tastes. People in certain areas feel compelled to build of brick, wood, or another particular material because most buildings in the area are so built. Some clients are forced by local custom to build in Cape Cod, Spanish Provincial, Ranch, or some other style; the feeling in other localities seems to encourage experiment and originality in construction. Many regional design and construction features, however, can be effectively adapted to other areas; tradition and lack of imagination tend to limit their use.

These factors are impossible to ignore and are not usually noticed by the average person until he has reason to move from one part of the country to another. A draftsman, however, should always be aware of these factors in order to understand the differences between his drawings and those produced in other regions.

REVIEW QUESTIONS

1. Look at the drawings and photos in a national magazine of buildings in other parts of the country. Are they different in appearance and construction from comparable buildings in your own area? Why?
2. Why are many residences in northern Maine quite square in shape? Why are many residences in Arizona rambling in shape?
3. Do you think there are many commercial buildings of Spanish Colonial design in Boston, Massachusetts? Why?
4. Would you expect to find a newly constructed one-story wood-frame commercial building in the financial district in New York City? Why?
5. Why are coal-fired basement furnaces seldom found in San Diego, California?

STUDY SUGGESTIONS

1. Make a study of residential building practices and types in three widely distant parts of the country. This information can be found in any national architectural magazine.
2. In view of what you have learned from the above, try to adapt some of these practices to your own locality.

Chapter
9
Presentation Drawings

Definition and Purpose

Upon the completion of a set of preliminary drawings which seem to satisfy the client, the usual practice is to prepare a presentation drawing for the client's approval (Fig. 9-1). The purpose of the presentation drawing is to bring together on one sheet the solution thus far to the client's problem. If it is approved, work can then start on the working drawings; if not, changes may easily be made before any further time and expense are involved. Presentation drawings are not working drawings, and the building contractor seldom sees them. If the student plans to do such a drawing before the working drawings, this chapter should be studied; if not, he should proceed to the next chapter.

Composition of Presentation Drawings

The types of drawings which may appear on the presentation drawing, named in the order of their importance, are floor plan, elevations, plot plan, sections, interior elevations, and exterior or interior perspectives. A very simple drawing might include only a floor plan and an elevation or two; an elaborate one might use all of the drawings mentioned. A good format for a student drawing would include a floor plan, two elevations, and a structural section. Usually the drawings are not completely dimensioned, because it is reasonable to expect that changes will be made before working drawings are started. At this stage, the effect of the total project should be emphasized rather than completeness of detail. One purpose of a presentation drawing is to "sell" the client.

Characteristics of the types of drawings used on presentation drawings are described here:

1. Floor plans show only overall dimensions and room sizes, the walls are sometimes filled in very dark for visibility, and all the rooms are identified. Prevailing breeze and north arrows should be included as well as front and rear entrance indications. Electric outlets are omitted. Furniture and equipment, patios, parking areas, and landscaping close to the building should be shown. The roof overhang is generally drawn as a dashed line. Scale is indicated, usually $\frac{1}{8}$ or $\frac{1}{4}$ in. to the foot.

2. While one or more exterior elevations may be shown, the front elevation is always drawn. To indicate scale, conventionalized human figures are placed close to the building. Shrubs and trees, sometimes "transparent," are indicated. For realism shadows are drawn in, particularly the shadow of the roof overhang. It is good practice, but not necessary, to draw elevations to the same scale as the floor plan for ease in relating the two drawings.

3. The plot-landscaping plan should be quite complete, eliminating only dimensions and utilities, except the septic tank where required. Usually great care is taken in drawing in the landscaping, paving and streets, and fences or screens. Sometimes the plot and floor plan are combined, drawn at a scale larger than the usual plot plan. The usual scale varies between $\frac{1}{50}$ and $\frac{1}{16}$ in. to the foot.

4. When a cross section through the building is shown, important dimensions such as plate

height, beam and rafter sizes, and roof pitch should be given. The scale may be $\frac{1}{4}$ to $\frac{3}{4}$ in. to the foot. Indicate all surface materials used.

5. When interior elevations are used they commonly show only important wall areas. The scale is $\frac{1}{8}$ to $\frac{1}{4}$ in. to the foot.

6. Exterior or interior perspectives are usually drawn of the entrance or other important features of the building and sometimes of the entire project. The perspective is usually approximate rather than projected, and a viewpoint is chosen which will enhance the architectural features of the building.

Media

Presentation drawings may be done in pencil, crayon, colored pencil, charcoal, ink, pastels, water colors, or oil colors, depending upon the purpose of the drawing and the budget involved. The style of drawing is much more casual than that used on working drawings. Pencil is most often used, generally on tracing paper so that the drawing may be duplicated. However, if the job is a large one it may be done in color, particularly pastels, water colors, or tempera.

Many different materials are used: tracing paper, drawing paper, illustration board, or textured papers. Common sizes used are 20 by 30 in. and 30 by 40 in., although any available paper size is suitable. A special type of presentation drawing is the brochure type, assembled in book form on standard-size sheets, usually $8\frac{1}{2}$ by 11 in. Each sheet has one drawing, and the sheets are bound in an attractive folder.

Format

Certain printed information is required on the presentation drawing for identification, such as the title preceded by the word *proposed*, e.g., "Proposed Residence for J. Jones." The client's address and/or the location of the building should be shown, as well as the name and address of the architectural firm or student involved.

The composition of the material on a presentation drawing is more a matter of artistic taste than formula or rule. The student should examine the work of a professional and try to achieve a similar effect in technique and organization (Fig. 9-2). A pleasing, artistic style of drawing is more important to the success of a presentation drawing than it is to a working drawing. Good style requires artistic ability and constant practice.

REVIEW QUESTIONS

1. In your own words define a presentation drawing.
2. Do any of the building trades use presentation drawings in their work?
3. What is the principal advantage of doing presentation drawings on tracing paper?
4. What types of drawings, e.g., floor plan, may appear on a presentation drawing?
5. A presentation drawing will show exactly how the proposed building will look. True or False? Explain.

STUDY SUGGESTIONS

1. Cut some presentation drawings out of magazines or newspapers and study them. Pick a style you like, and apply it to a practice drawing of your own.
2. Practice sketching shrubbery, trees, conventionalized human figures, and automobiles whenever you have a little free time.

Chapter
10
Working Drawings

Definition and Purpose

From this point on, all drawings described are called *working drawings*. The term working drawing is used in all fields of drafting, and the general definition, as stated in French and Vierck's "Fundamentals of Engineering Drawing," (McGraw-Hill Book Company, 1960) is: "A working drawing is any drawing used to give information for purposes of manufacture, construction, or erection of a machine or structure. Complete knowledge for the production of a machine or structure is given by a set of working drawings conveying all the facts fully and explicitly, so that further instruction is not required." (See Figs. 10-1 and 10-2.) To satisfy this definition, architectural working drawings must include:

1. *Orthographic projection:* The true shape of all features described.
2. *Proper dimensioning:* The true size of all features described.
3. *Call-outs:* Complete notes regarding items not fully described by size and shape.
4. *Construction details, sections:* Enlarged drawings of construction features not completely shown in small-scale drawings or of features which are hidden.
5. *Electrical plan, plumbing plan, heating and ventilating plan, etc.:* Classification of different kinds of information for clarity and completeness of description.
6. *Specifications:* Bid documents, general information, and specific instructions.

In other words, a perfect set of working drawings would contain all the information needed by a builder to complete a building exactly as specified by the architect. In practice, however, continual inspection of the structure is made by the architect, city or county building inspectors, and sometimes the client to ensure compliance with the drawings. Specifications are included in any complete set of working drawings; they will be covered in Chap. 26.

Materials and Equipment

On the assumption that students in the class have had at least a year of mechanical drawing before using this book, terms such as *orthographic projection* and descriptions of objects such as *45° triangle* will be omitted from the following discussion on working drawings. Explanation will be made only when terms peculiar to architectural drawing are encountered.

Tools and equipment used by architectural draftsmen:

1. Pencils: Wood or automatic. Weight of lead varies according to individual preference; H to 4H are commonly used.
2. Pencil pointer: Sandpaper or mechanical type.
3. Triangles: Average sizes, 45° by 10 in., 30°-60° by 10 in.
4. T square or drafting machine: Both used. This is a matter of personal preference.
5. Scale: Architect's and engineer's.
6. French curves, circle, ellipse, plumbing and electrical templates: To cut drafting time and improve the appearance of the drawing.
7. Erasers, erasing shields, erasing machines, dry cleaner, and brush: For use in correcting mistakes and keeping drawings clean.

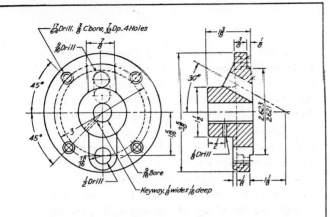

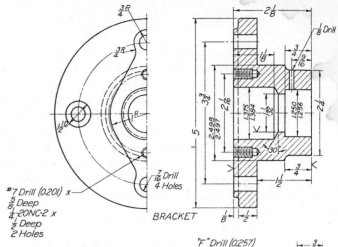

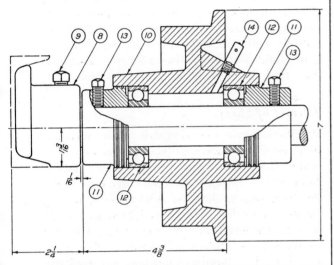

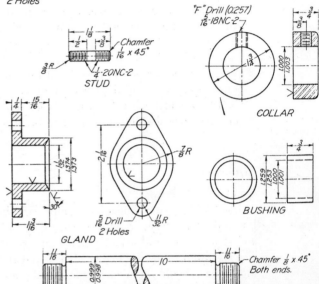

BRACKET

#7 Drill (0.201) x
$\frac{5}{8}$ Deep
$\frac{1}{4}$-20NC-2 x
$\frac{1}{2}$ Deep
2 Holes

STUD

"F" Drill (0.257)
$\frac{5}{16}$-18NC-2

COLLAR

GLAND

BUSHING

SHAFT

Fig. 10-1. *Examples of working drawings (from French and Vierck, "Fundamentals of Engineering Drawing").*

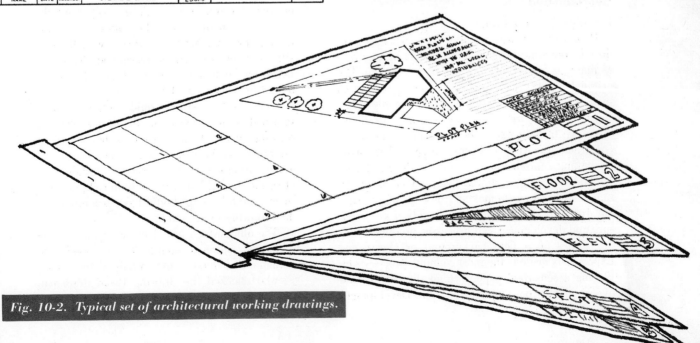

Fig. 10-2. *Typical set of architectural working drawings.*

8. Drawing boards, drafting tables: Common sizes of boards, 20 by 26 in., 24 by 30 in., 30 by 40 in. A table can be made by putting legs on a flush door. Size and type are determined by storage space available or the sheet size desired. For school use, where storage is a problem, 20 by 26 in. is the usual size, and an 18- by 24-in. sheet size is convenient. These are, however, much smaller than the 24- by 30-in. sheet size often used in professional practice.

Types of paper used:

1. Opaque or transparent paper: Used for rough studies until the final outlines of the drawing are determined. The finished drawing may be traced from this copy.
2. Tracing paper or plastic film: Used for finished drawings. Use of good-quality paper is important. No matter what the price, paper is much cheaper than the drafting time expended on it.

Linework

Standards of linework:

Use ASA recommendations; emphasize black linework, consistency in drawing each type of line, and cleanliness, or absence of stains and smudges. The style of drawing is a matter of taste and ability; the student should copy some professional example. Never sacrifice legibility for "style." For speed and accuracy, use electrical, plumbing, and other templates wherever possible.

Reproduction

Reproduction of drawings:

Practically all working drawings must be reproduced; sometimes when a large project is involved, as many as 50 sets of drawings may be made. The originals, or tracings, are kept on file and changes may later be made on them, while the reproductions, or "blueprints" as the layman calls them, are given to the contractors or workmen for actual construction purposes. There are several methods of making reproductions. However, the most-used methods have basic similarities, and all have the same end in view—to make a true copy of an original drawing. The two processes involved are exposure and development. All processes produce either dark lines on a light background or vice versa. Exposure is made in the most common processes by placing a sensitized paper behind the tracing and exposing them both to a strong light. Development

is a result of either exposing this sensitized sheet to a gas, usually ammonia, or wetting it with a chemical solution. The portion of the sheet which was covered by a pencil mark will develop and show as dark on light, or light on dark, depending upon the process.

A discussion of each type of reproduction process and its advantages and disadvantages is not of great importance, inasmuch as every city of fair size has a blueprint service which offers a choice of at least two common processes. Of great importance, though, is a knowledge of one step in the procedure, namely, exposure. As the machine cannot tell the difference between an important line and a stain, spot, or smudge, it reproduces them all. Also, a faint or indistinct pencil line will reproduce as a faint or indistinct line on the reproduction. This is the main reason for using black, consistent linework and keeping the drawing clean. Any drawing that is not entirely legible or lacks any small detail is not a good working drawing. Remember, the building is built from the reproductions, not the originals.

Format of Sheet

A suitable format—the size, style, and arrangement of material on the drawing—should be chosen which will be complete, economical of space, and pleasing to the eye (see A-4). It should be used consistently on all drawings in the set so that the person reading the drawings will be able to find desired information quickly. The format may be copied from an existing drawing, or the student may decide to develop his own; if so, the following factors must be considered.

1. Margins: $\frac{1}{2}$ in. on the top, bottom, and right side, and 1 in. on the left side. Margins are provided not only for appearance, but also to prevent the loss of information near the edges in case the tracing does not register perfectly with the sensitized sheet. The larger margin at the left is necessary so that the set of drawings may be bound together at the left.
2. A record or title strip should contain essential information not shown on the actual working drawing. It should be placed so that it will be prominent as the reader turns each sheet while going through the set; therefore, it should be placed at the bottom or the bottom right of every sheet. The title strip should have as a minimum the following information:
   a. The office which produced the drawing, firm name, address, architect's (or student's) name and initials, and initials of the person who checked the drawing (head draftsman or instructor).

b. The client for whom the drawings were produced, job number and title of each drawing, and address of the job.

c. The title of the drawing itself, revisions, the date completed, and the sheet number, e.g., sheet 4 of 7 (usually placed at the lower right corner for easy reference). The title, e.g., Plot Plan, is usually placed in the record strip and also within the margins under the drawing, since there may be more than one type of drawing to a sheet. Each drawing on the sheet should be clearly labeled.

d. The scale should always appear within the margins under the title of each drawing or detail.

Arrangement of Drawings

The following information on procedures and order of linework refers to all drawings in the set, not to any one drawing in particular. Before starting the working drawings, it is good practice to decide in advance which information should be placed on each sheet; then to make an outline of the full set. To do this, it is necessary to know only the total number of views or drawings per sheet, their overall size (with allowance for dimensioning where necessary), and the working space available. The sheets should be arranged generally in the order of their use on the job. A typical arrangement of a simple set of drawings with their sheet numbers might be (Fig. 10-2):

1. Sheet 1, Plot Plan
2. Sheet 2, Foundation Plan
3. Sheet 3, Floor Plan
4. Sheet 4, Elevations
5. Sheet 5, Interior Details

They are arranged in this way because they are used in this order from the start of actual construction. On a large project it is necessary to classify drawings to a greater degree than this. On a small job it is assumed that foundation details are on the same sheet as the foundation plan; the window, door, room finish, and electrical schedules are on the floor plan; the structural sections are on the elevations; and cabinet details are on the interior details. When special sheets are needed for structural, electrical, plumbing, or similar information, they may be inserted where desired. In any case, the system of detail references later described will make reference between one sheet and another easy and clear.

Procedure

Before starting any sheet, a study should be made of the various symbols and conventional practices to be used on that particular drawing. This will shorten drafting time considerably and eliminate much erasing. Check the dimensions of the drawing for overall size. Next, space the views on the working area for appearance, room for dimensioning, and titles. Generally a large drawing on a sheet will be more pleasing to the eye if it is spaced equally at the sides with slightly more space at the bottom than the top. This will frame the drawing effectively and leave room for the title and scale below. Using construction lines, indicate the major outlines of the drawing and the location of the title. At this point check with the instructor; he may be able to point out some small error or suggest an improvement.

The order of linework suggested here should be followed generally; however, minor changes may be made to suit individual preference (Fig. 10-3). The principal object of this method is to avoid unnecessary corrections and erasures of hard, black lines which are difficult to get rid of completely.

Using construction lines:

1. Place all major outlines of drawing on the sheet.
2. Locate center lines and edge lines of important features, walls, doors, and openings.
3. Draw in smaller details—trim, mullions, small footings, etc.
4. Check with instructor.

Using finished lines:

1. Draw in main outlines, partitions, openings, etc. (object lines).
2. Draw in minor details (object lines).
3. Dimension (dimension lines).
4. Letter in notes and dimensions, particularly where they occur within the outlines of the drawing.
5. Draw in textures and shading.
6. Profile the drawing if desired. Profiling consists of drawing a heavy line around the outline of the view.
7. Complete lettering on drawing and record strip.
8. Check with instructor.

This procedure will apply to any working drawing, and reference will be made to this chapter in the chapters which follow.

Reversed Tracing

Many drawings are superimposed on the outline of the floor plan—plumbing, electrical plans, etc. On

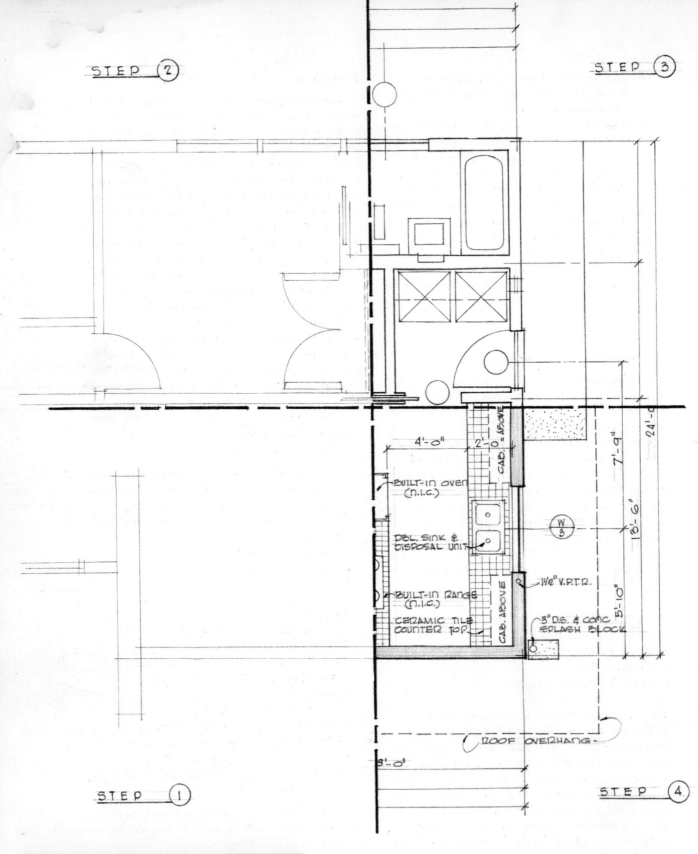

STEP ②

STEP ③

STEP ①

STEP ④

4'-0" 2'-0" CAB. ABOVE

7'-9"

24'-0

BUILT-IN OVEN
(N.I.C.)

13'-6"

W
3

DBL. SINK &
DISPOSAL UNIT

1½" V.P.T.R.

5'-10"

BUILT-IN RANGE
(N.I.C.)

3" D.S. & CONC
SPLASH BLOCK

CERAMIC TILE
COUNTER TOP

CAB. ABOVE

ROOF OVERHANG

3'-0"

Fig. 10-3. Steps in the development of a floor plan. (All other working drawings should proceed in the same order of work.)

a large project, the outline of the floor plan is printed several times on a special transparent paper. These copies can be drawn on like tracing paper and all information printed at once. The plumbing,

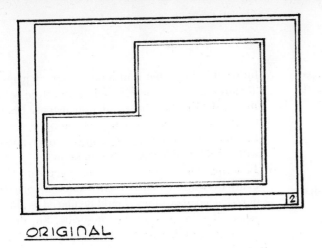

ORIGINAL

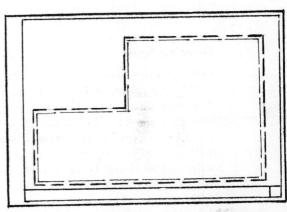

STEP 1 - INVERT ORIGINAL

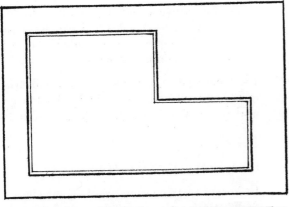

STEP 2 - TRACE ON NEW SHEET

STEP 3 - INVERT NEW SHEET

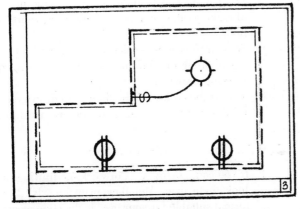

STEP 4 - PLACE DESIRED IN-FORMATION.

NOTE : THIS DRAWING NOT TO ANY SCALE. LINES ON TOP SURFACE OF PAPER ARE SHOWN SOLID. LINES ON BACK ARE SHOWN DASHED.

electrical, heating, or other information can be placed as desired. The principal reason for using this method is the economy of reproducing a drawing rather than redrawing it.

Fig. 10-4. Method of tracing a plan on the back of the sheet for use with electrical and other plans.

In cases where only a small number of drawings are to be made, the following method works well (Fig. 10-4).

1. Turn the tracing of the floor plan over.
2. Trace the walls, windows, doors, and locations of large appliances on a new piece of tracing paper. Ignore all lettering.
3. Put the original tracing away, and place the second copy, penciled side down, on the board.
4. Draw in the desired information.

The reason behind this procedure is that any correction or erasure of, for instance, the electric circuits will not disturb the lines of the walls, etc., which are on the other side.

Drafting Styles

Drafting styles vary greatly, depending upon the locality, the office, and the individual draftsman. Any style is good if the drawings are legible, accurate, and complete. Most offices try to standardize the appearance of their drawings; therefore, the draftsman should keep an open mind regarding his style, and he should be prepared to learn another when he goes to work.

The factors which produce a pleasing, readable style of drafting are simple to state but demand constant practice to develop. An artistic style is not an end in itself. Drawings are read by many people of varying degrees of experience and intelligence; therefore, readability is the most important requirement. Some of the devices which create a style are:

1. The artistic ability of the draftsman. Probably the most important factor, it guides him in his use of the various devices.
2. Varying weights of line. Used consistently for each symbol, they make a drawing pleasing and easy to read. Lines slightly thinner or heavier than those in the alphabet of lines may be used for particular symbols, such as thin object lines for structure beyond the section, extra-heavy object lines for outlines and profiling.
3. Arrangement of drawings on the sheet. Space should be efficiently used, yet plenty of room must be left for titles, notes, and call-outs.
4. Distinctive titling for drawings. The judicious use of stenciled letters, underlining, and visible guide lines will enhance the appearance of any drawing.
5. Delineation of gratings, wood, brick, and stone textures on all drawings. This device is most use-ful on elevations, but is also often used on plans. Textures must not be allowed to interfere with the readability of notes and dimensions. Practically speaking, textures are not required, since the outline of each material plus proper notes will tell the builder all he has to know.
6. Lettering shape, size, and arrangement. On many drawings extensive notes must be placed in restricted areas; they should be placed as close as possible to the spot they describe. For these reasons the draftsman should be able to produce small, compressed, and legible notes when they are needed.
7. Pencil technique. Crossed corners, increased pencil pressure at the ends of lines, graceful call-outs, attractive arrows, etc., all have to do with the way a person holds and handles a pencil. These techniques are the product of artistic ability and constant practice.

Until the student acquires the skill and taste required to develop his own style, he should copy the work of a professional architect (Figs. 10-5 to 10-7).

REVIEW QUESTIONS

1. Name five architectural working drawings.
2. What are two reasons why a draftsman should use templates?
3. Is the use of cheap tracing paper a wise economy?
4. Describe in your own words what good linework looks like.
5. What is the most important step in the process of making either a dark or a white line reproduction?
6. Why are margins needed on drawings?
7. What order of linework will you use on your working drawings?
8. Why is the outline of the floor plan drawn on the back of the tracing paper for the electrical plan?

STUDY SUGGESTIONS

1. If you can, borrow a set of working drawings and look them over. Did they print clearly? Is the format suitable for your use? Is the style pleasing to you? Is the lettering architectural and legible? Is the reference system easy to use? Remember, your drawings will be judged in the same way.
2. Draw some details on a sheet using several weights of line. Place a piece of tracing paper on top and trace each of the details. Note the weight

(continued on page 62)

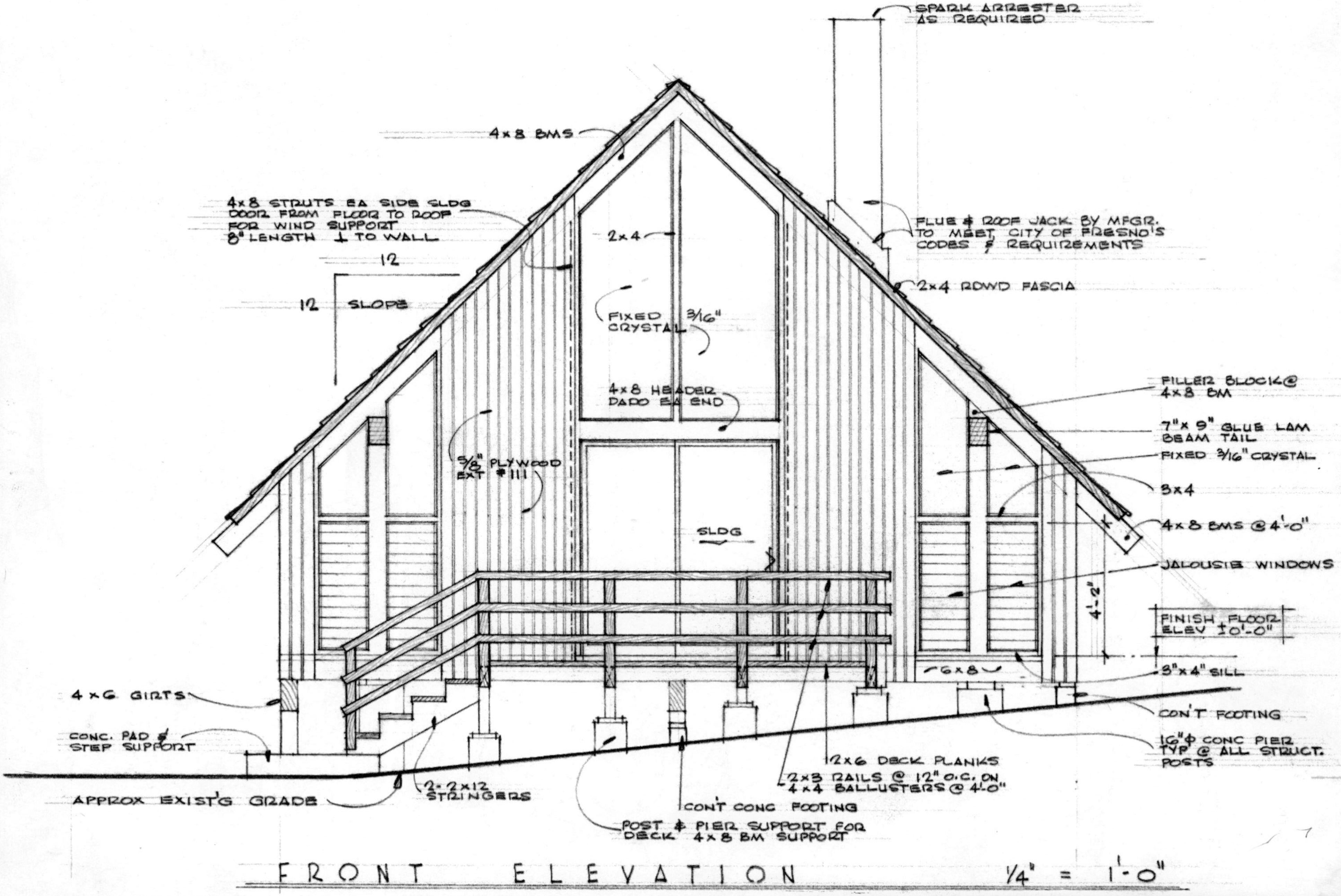

FRONT ELEVATION   ¼" = 1'-0"

SPARK ARRESTER AS REQUIRED

FLUE & ROOF JACK BY MFGR. TO MEET CITY OF FRESNO'S CODES & REQUIREMENTS

2×4 ROWD FASCIA

FILLER BLOCK @ 4×8 BM

7"× 9" GLUE LAM BEAM TAIL

FIXED 3/16" CRYSTAL

3×4

4×8 BMS @ 4'-0"

JALOUSIE WINDOWS

FINISH FLOOR ELEV. ± 0'-0"

3"×4" SILL

CON'T FOOTING

16"ø CONC PIER TYP @ ALL STRUCT. POSTS

(6×8)

12×6 DECK PLANKS

2×3 RAILS @ 12" O.C. ON 4×4 BALLUSTERS @ 4'-0"

CON'T CONC FOOTING

POST & PIER SUPPORT FOR 4×8 BM SUPPORT

FIXED 3/16" CRYSTAL

2×4

4×8 HEADER DADO EA END

SLDG

5/8" PLYWOOD EXT #111

4×8 BMS

4×8 STRUTS EA SIDE BLDG DOOR FROM FLOOR TO ROOF FOR WIND SUPPORT 8' LENGTH ⊥ TO WALL

12

12

SLOPE

2-2×12 STRINGERS

4×6 GIRTS

CONC. PAD & STEP SUPPORT

APPROX EXIST'G GRADE

59

Fig. 10-5. Example of professional drafting technique.

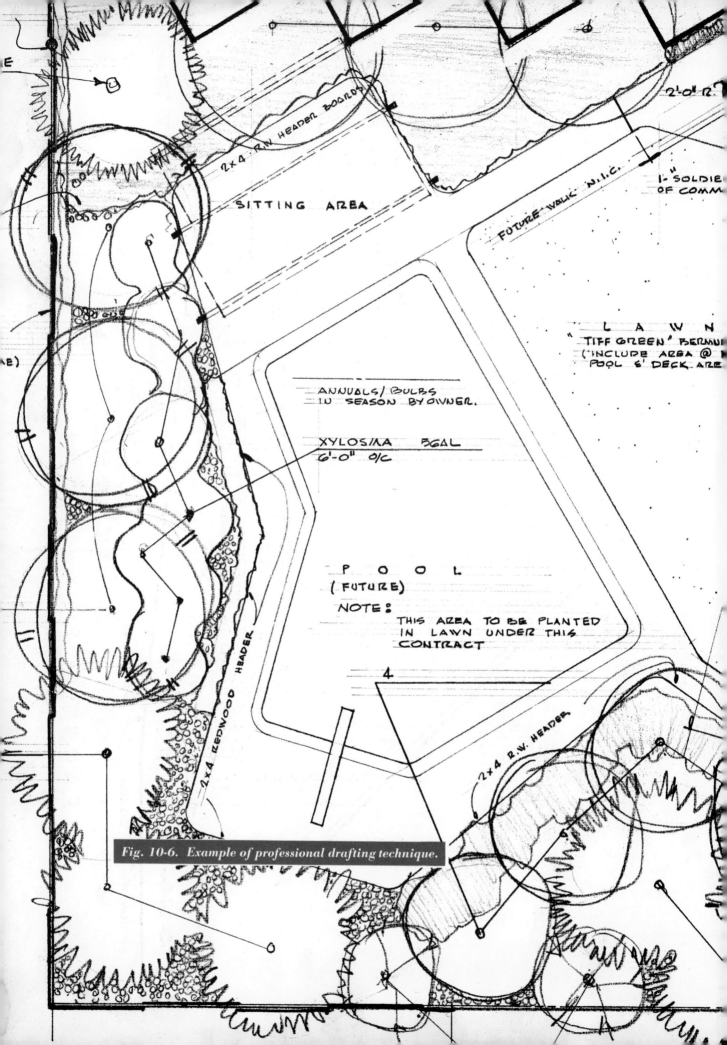

Fig. 10-6. *Example of professional drafting technique.*

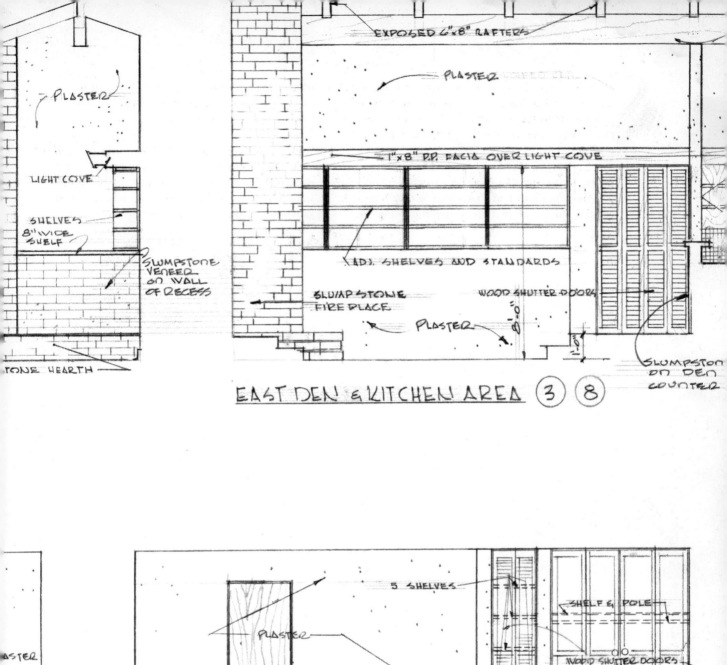

PLASTER

LIGHT COVE

SHELVES 8" WIDE SHELF

SLUMPSTONE VENEER ON WALL OF RECESS

STONE HEARTH

EXPOSED 6"x8" RAFTERS

PLASTER

1"x8" R.P. FACIA OVER LIGHT COVE

ADJ. SHELVES AND STANDARDS

SLUMPSTONE FIRE PLACE

PLASTER

WOOD SHUTTER DOORS

SLUMPSTONE ON DEN COUNTER

EAST DEN & KITCHEN AREA (3) (8)

5 SHELVES

SHELF & POLE

PLASTER

WOOD SHUTTER DOORS

(4)   SOUTH MASTER BEDROOM (4) (REVERSED)

Fig. 10-7. Example of professional drafting technique.

SL. PLASTIC PANEL

TILE

PLASTER

SLID. PLASTIC PANEL

WOOD SHUTTER DOORS

SHELF & POLE

MIRROR

of line required to read the drawing easily through the tracing paper. It is very important to make drawings traceable, because much time can be wasted by constantly lifting the top sheet to check.

3. Draw or trace a few details on a sheet of tracing paper; try to copy the styles of several drawings you like. You will find that pleasing techniques require study and analysis to determine exactly what it is that creates the effect. You will notice that consistent linework is the common element in all successful styles.

4. Practice several types of lettering at all sizes from $\frac{1}{16}$ to $\frac{1}{4}$ in. in height. Try extended and compressed lettering, long notes in small spaces; experiment with underlines and visible guide lines. When you find a type of lettering that satisfies you, practice it until it becomes a habit.

Chapter

11

Relationships among Drawings

Agreement among Drawings

No working drawing can be drawn in isolation from the others. Neither can changes in one be made without considering the effect of the change on the others (Figs. 11-1 and 11-2). The major drawings of a set, such as plot plan, foundation plan, structural sections, floor plan, elevations, and interior elevations, must agree in all respects. Other drawings, such as electrical, plumbing, ventilating and air-conditioning plans, are closely related to one another and the floor plan especially. Some drawings, such as particular miscellaneous details, are related closely to only one or two of the others. For instance, cabinet details must agree with the interior elevations and the floor plan. These are only a few of the possible combinations. Some obvious reasons for being careful are: Many drawings are traced in part from the floor plan; agreement in projection must exist among all drawings; clearance must be maintained among footings, beams, pipes, ducts, etc.; and plumbing, electrical, and duct connections must be provided for appliances.

Preliminary Planning

Certain construction features must be checked closely; e.g., stairs usually require a minimum of 6 ft 6 in. of headroom from the tread. This problem must be worked out orthographically in the preliminary drawings, because the working drawings cannot easily be changed later. An error in the size of the stairwell could be an expensive mistake to correct. Another common problem is providing adequate clearance for pipes and ducts in restricted

attic spaces. Though the drawings sometimes indicate plenty of clearance, the sheet-metal man and the plumber often find that their jobs conflict because of a draftsman's oversight. Other problems arise because of the space requirements of under-the-floor and under-the-slab ducts and footings, roof bracing, ducts, plumbing vents, and wall thickness. Problems which are more difficult to anticipate involve the intersections of oblique roof and ceiling planes with sloping pipes or ducts. These are difficult to detail exactly.

Changes in Drawings

The following is an example of the amount of work caused by a change. If the location of the heating-refrigerating plant were changed after completion of the working drawings, changes would have to be made in the floor plan, foundation plan, plumbing plan, electrical plan, heating and air-conditioning plan, and possibly the roof and floor framing plans, elevations, and plot plan. In case of conflict among drawings, large-scale details take precedence over other drawings because of the obvious increase in accuracy achieved by drawing at larger scale.

In many situations it is necessary to start drawing a detail from some existing or otherwise fixed point. This point could be the height of a canopy, from which window heights would be derived, or the corner studs in a frame wall, which would locate the edge of a window jamb. Sometimes the size of a door or window frame will determine the spacing of the module lines of an entire building. The size of any modular building material, such as cinder block, will restrict the size and location dimensions of the building to multiples of this module.

Drafting-room Problems

Agreement among drawings becomes more complicated in a large drafting room in which several draftsmen may be working on different drawings of a set at the same time. Although the main responsibility for solving this problem lies with the architect or head draftsman, each draftsman, in the interest of his employer's reputation and his own job, should be aware of the relationship of the drawing on which he is working to all the other drawings.

Most of the drawings of the set are developed together in normal office practice to avoid conflict and unnecessary changes, since a minor change in one drawing could affect several others to a great degree. The most important drawings in the set from the standpoint of their influence on all of the others are the floor plan, structural sections, schedules, plot plan, exterior elevations, and stair and fireplace sections. In unusual structures some large piece of equipment, such as a hoist or a large machine, may also have a great effect on the total structure.

See Fig. 11-2, which shows the relationships among drawings. It can be seen that the basic drawings must be accurately worked out at the start, even though they may be completed in some other order.

REVIEW QUESTIONS

1. Name three working drawings affected by an inside staircase.
2. Point out some possible points of conflict between the heating and air-conditioning plan and the second-floor plan.
3. Name a fixture or appliance used in a residence which if moved would affect at least three working drawings.
4. How many working drawings in a set are supplemented by the specifications?
5. How many working drawings in a set are affected by a fireplace?
6. In view of your answers to the above questions, can you see the reason for using care in drawing the preliminaries?
7. Does the draftsman have any responsibility for the agreement of his own drawing with others?

Fig. 11-1 Relationships in projection among some of the more important drawings in a set.

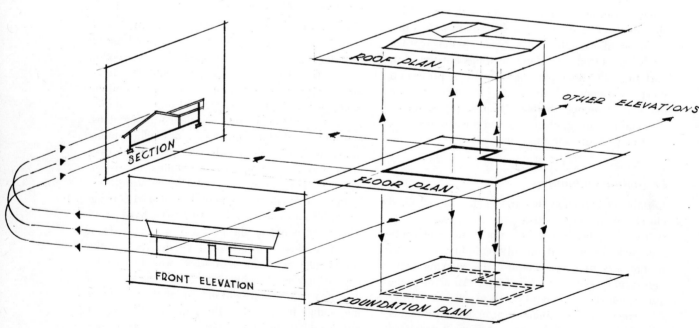

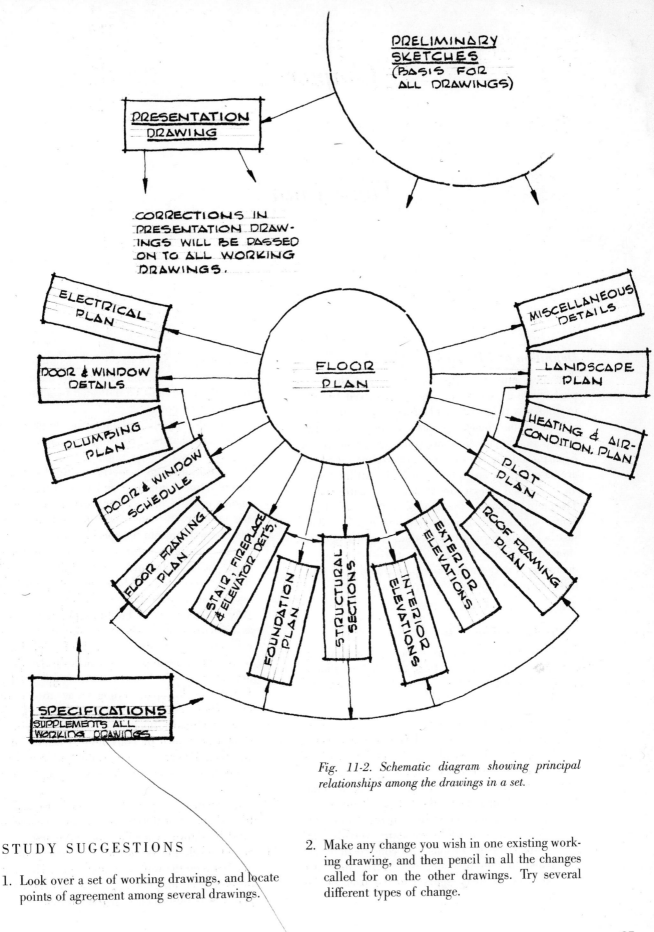

Fig. 11-2. Schematic diagram showing principal relationships among the drawings in a set.

STUDY SUGGESTIONS

1. Look over a set of working drawings, and locate points of agreement among several drawings.

2. Make any change you wish in one existing working drawing, and then pencil in all the changes called for on the other drawings. Try several different types of change.

Chapter
12
Floor Plan

Definition and Purpose

The most important drawing of a set is the floor plan, since all other drawings are derived from it in some way (Figs. 12-1 and 12-2). For instance, the outline of the foundation plan is traced from the floor plan, the elevations are projected or measured from it, and the sizes of roof and ceiling members are based on the spans between walls. All the building trades find at least part of their information on it. The main purpose of the floor plan, which is a horizontal section through the building usually taken just below the tops of the windows and doors, is to show the location of the walls, partitions, and all openings. A very simple floor plan would show only this, but most show much more detail.

Drafting the Floor Plan

The floor plan is copied from the final preliminary drawings, but before starting, the student should check with Chap. 10. The procedure for drawing the floor plan is as follows:

1. A one-line floor plan is drawn in light lines. Lines for outside walls indicate the outside face of studs or the outside face of masonry. Lines for interior partitions indicate the center lines of walls. It is best to place the drawing with the main entrance facing the bottom of the sheet.
2. The thickness of the walls showing doors, windows, etc., is shown by standard symbols. The symbols for the various wall constructions are listed in the Appendix (see A-5). Note: All pochéing is to be applied to the back of the tracing.

3. Landings, steps, walks, and handrails are shown in outline and noted. Any change in floor elevation must be indicated by a line plus a call-out or note.
4. Fireplaces, masonry planters, or dividers are shown crosshatched. Hearths are shown in outline and described by note.
5. The locations and sizes of heating and air-conditioning equipment and water heaters are shown in solid lines. Type, capacity, and catalog number are noted near the equipment or may be written into the specifications.
6. Large plumbing fixtures are drawn to scale, while hose bibbs and other small items are drawn as symbols. Where needed, plumbing access panels are called out by note.
7. Any cabinet work or built-in equipment, such as a stove or oven, is shown in solid lines; upper cabinets are normally indicated as dashed lines (here conventional practice violates the rules of projection).
8. Furred, or lowered, ceiling areas are shown by dashed lines and called out by note.
9. The individual rafters in an open-beam ceiling should be shown by conventional center lines and their size and spacing called out. Supporting beams are shown as dashed lines and called out.
10. The extent of floor materials, such as carpet, tile, slate, or materials of varying thickness, must be shown by a solid line and noted.
11. Sound insulation is indicated by a serpentine line between the wall lines and noted. Thermal insulation is not generally drawn on the floor plan but is described in a general note.

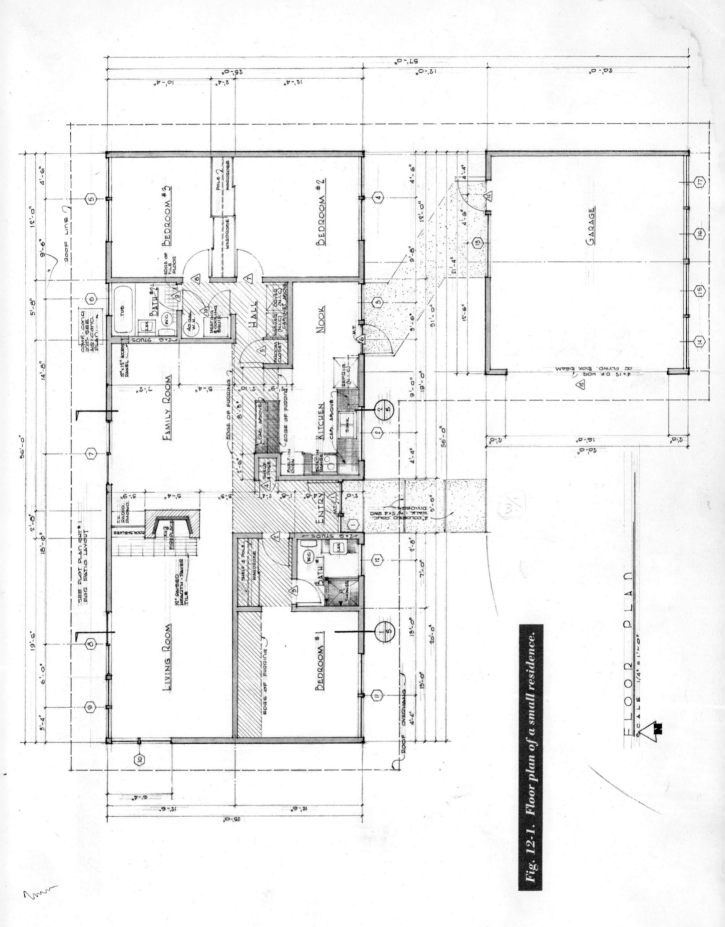

Fig. 12-1. Floor plan of a small residence.

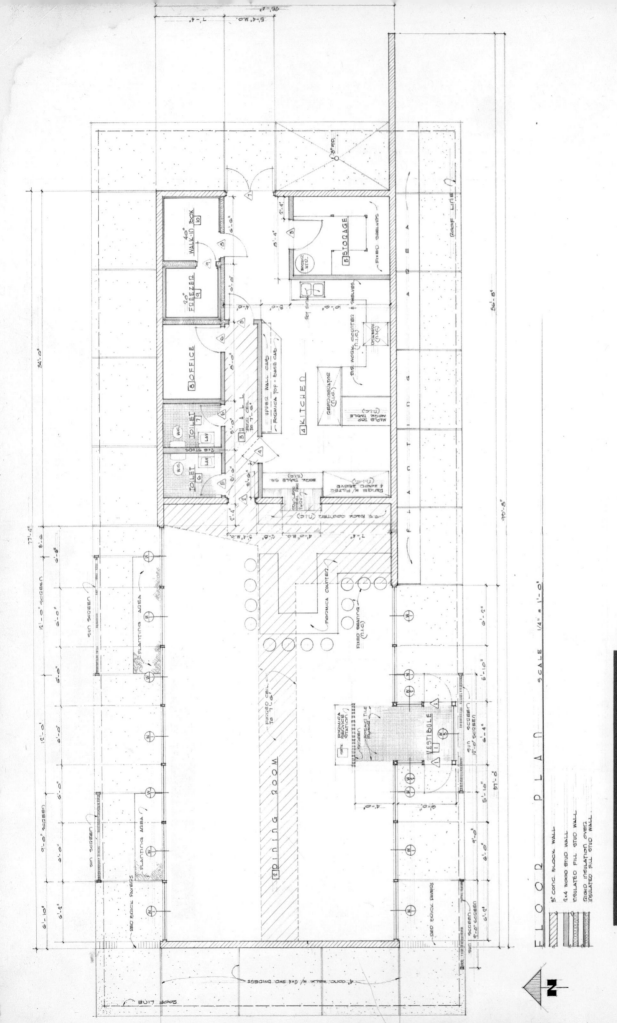

FLOOR PLAN SCALE 1/4" = 1'-0"

Fig. 12-2. Floor plan of a small restaurant.

12. Attic access doors, or scuttles, are indicated by dashed lines and called out by note. They are generally located in hall ceilings, storerooms, or other inconspicuous places.

13. Where space is reserved for equipment which is not included in the bid, the equipment is drawn in outline and noted NIC (not in contract).

14. The dimension lines are drawn in.

15. All lettering, notes, reference symbols, title, and scale are placed. The full-scale extracts from the floor plan show the use of most of these symbols (Fig. 12-3).

Simple Floor Plans

In a complete set of plans for a large project such information as plumbing, electrical, heating, and air-conditioning is placed on separate sheets, i.e., plumbing plan, electrical plan, and heating and air-conditioning plan. On small jobs, this information may be placed on the floor plan. Separate sections in this book are devoted to these special drawings, but when the information is to be placed on the floor plan, the following instructions should be used (Fig. 12-4):

1. Electrical. Electric outlets, switches, and switch legs are shown by the symbols listed in the Appendix. Any outlet, whether on the floor, ceiling, or wall, is merely located where desired. The only wiring generally indicated is the switch leg from the outlet, or outlets to the switch, or switches controlling them. If special light fixtures are desired, the manufacturer's name and catalog number are placed beside the outlet. The location of the service-entrance switchgear should be shown, generally at the rear of the building, and the size of the main fuses and number of branch circuits noted. The symbols used are described in the electrical schedule on the same sheet. For speed and consistency in drafting, use a template for all symbols. For more complete information see Chap. 19.

2. Heating and air-conditioning. Heating and air-conditioning units are shown in actual size by outline, and the manufacturer, catalog number, type of unit, and capacity are noted. Heating and cooling registers, return-air grilles, radiators, fans, etc., are located by note and described by size and type. For additional information see Chap. 20.

3. Plumbing. Plumbing fixtures are shown true size

in outline. Care must be taken to provide adequate space around each fixture as required by local building codes and ordinances. Plumbing lines are not usually shown on the floor plan. Use a plumbing template for all fixtures. For additional information see Chap. 21.

4. Schedules. Although the use of window, door, and room-finish schedules is preferred on most drawings, when there are only a few windows and doors this information may be placed beside each opening on the floor plan. Type, brand, and material of windows should be written in the form of a general note beside the plan. The size of the door is noted at each door symbol, and the material and type of finish are also in the form of a general note. The description of wall, floor, and ceiling finish is lettered near the room name. A complete treatment of the use of the various schedules is given in Chap. 13.

Dimensioning

Dimensioning is extremely important and should be consistent. If the drawing is small compared with sheet size, the spacing between dimension lines may be large; if the area is limited, the spacing must be smaller. The clear space between the wall line and the nearest dimension line should be at least $\frac{3}{4}$ in. so that notes may be entered close to the building. Space between dimension lines may be $\frac{1}{4}$ to 1 in., depending upon space, to avoid crowding the figures. For a neat appearance, use the same spacing on all sides of the building.

In architectural practice, dimension lines are continuous, with figures above the line (Fig. 12-1). This practice increases speed in drafting. All lettering should read from the bottom or right-hand edge of the sheet; figures are placed above the line. One may use conventional arrows, small circles, or slant lines (hash marks) through the intersection of the dimension line with the center line or extension line. Hash marks are recommended because of speed in drafting. Circles and arrows have special meanings in modular dimensioning. Distances are always expressed in feet and inches. Whenever distances are in even feet, zero inches has to be shown. For distance less than a foot, place zero feet before the number of inches. Each continuous row of dimensions must add up to the overall dimension. It is possible to have gaps in the row of dimensions as long as all important points are located.

Although there are variations in practice, dimen-
(continued on page 74)

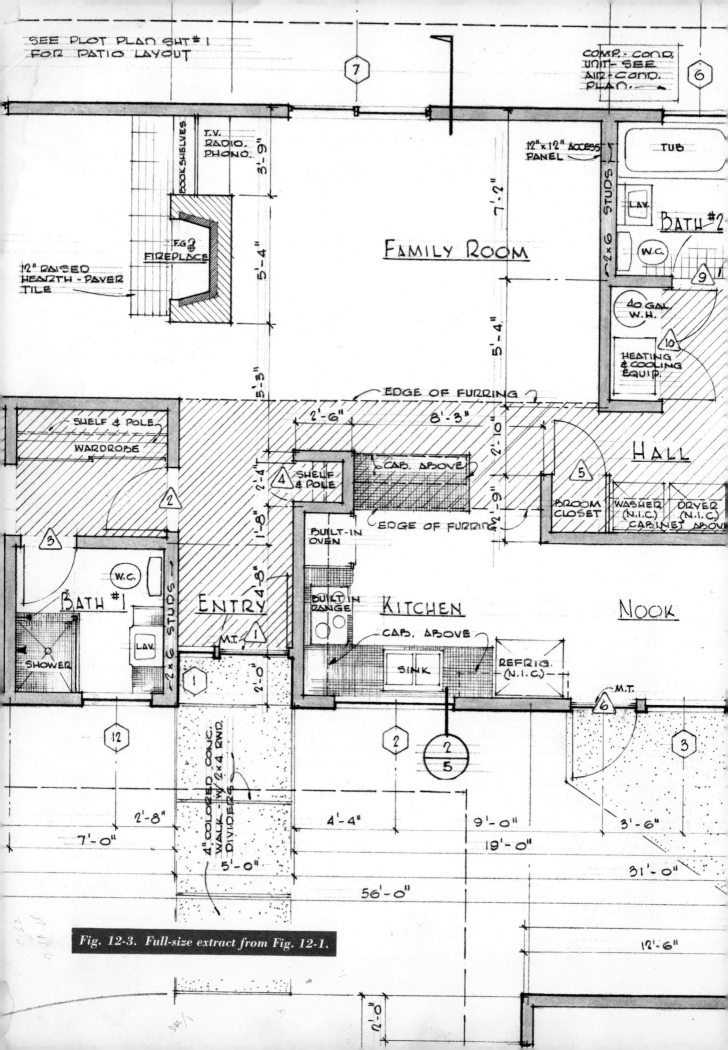

Fig. 12-3. Full-size extract from Fig. 12-1.

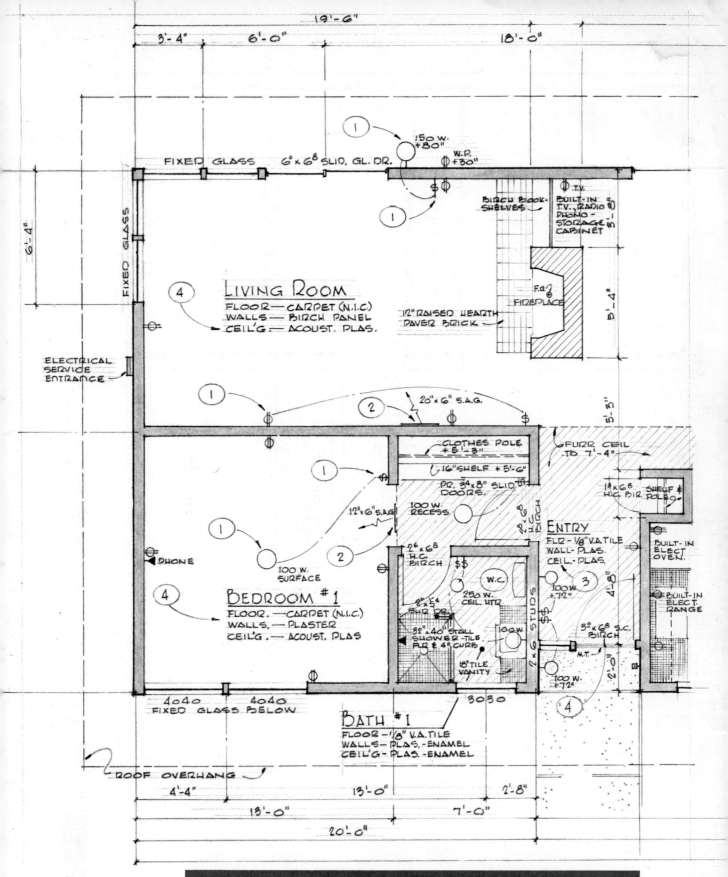

Fig. 12-4. *Floor plan showing door, window, and finish information on plan.*

71

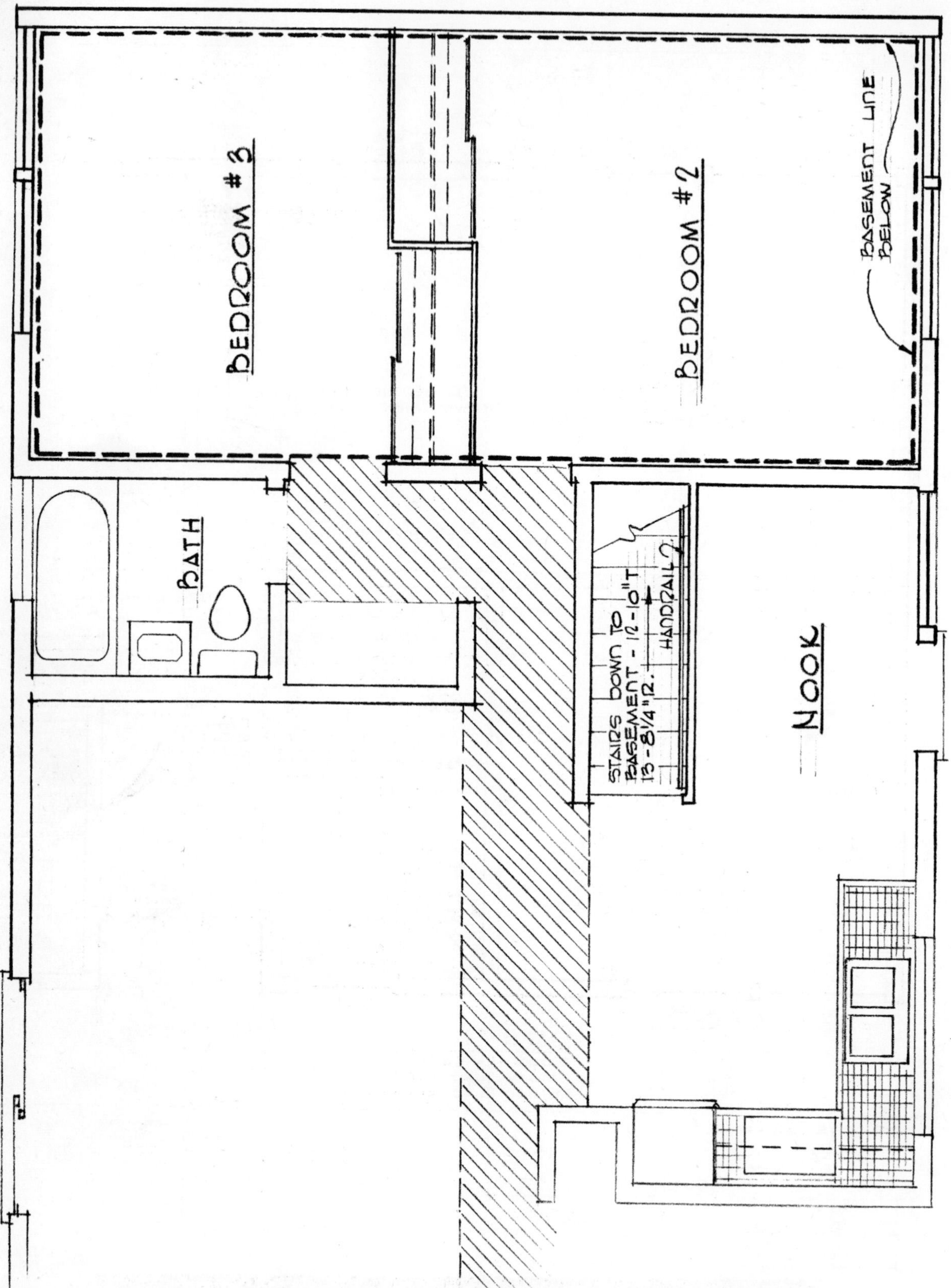

BEDROOM #3

BEDROOM #2

BASEMENT LINE BELOW

BATH

STAIRS DOWN TO
BASEMENT - 12'-10"T
13 - 8¼"12.

HANDRAIL

NOOK

Fig. 12-5. Method of representing basement and stairs on first-floor plan.

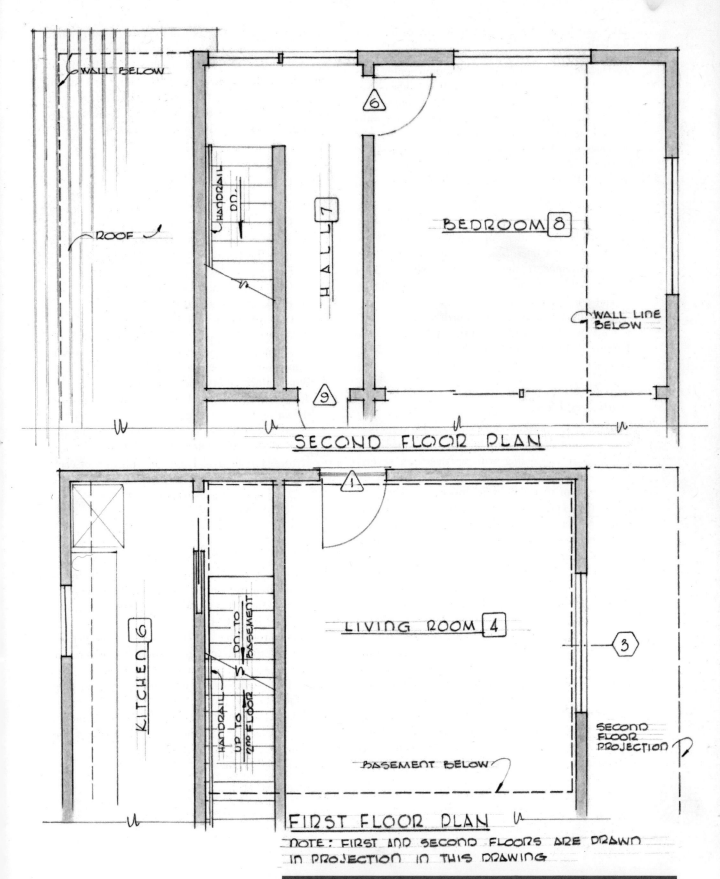

WALL BELOW

ROOF

HANDRAIL DN.

⑥

HALL 7

BEDROOM 8

WALL LINE BELOW

⑨

SECOND FLOOR PLAN

①

KITCHEN 6

HANDRAIL UP TO 2nd FLOOR

Dn. TO BASEMENT

LIVING ROOM 4

③

SECOND FLOOR PROJECTION

BASEMENT BELOW

FIRST FLOOR PLAN

NOTE: FIRST AND SECOND FLOORS ARE DRAWN IN PROJECTION IN THIS DRAWING

Fig. 12-6. *Methods of representing stairs, basement, setback, and cantilevered second story.*

sions can be arranged in the following order from the wall line:

1. Distance between door and window center lines and the outside of the end walls or offsets (see illustrations for examples of dimensioning)
2. Distances between center lines of interior walls and outsides of end walls
3. Distances between wall breaks and outside of end walls
4. Overall dimensions, outside wall to outside wall

All outside walls and wall breaks are shown by extension lines to the faces of studs, not to the surface finish. All centers of openings or walls are shown by center lines. Short interior partitions may be dimensioned in the floor plan, while cabinet work, drainboards, and similar features are dimensioned on the detail sheets.

One important symbol, the north-pointing arrow, should be placed with the title and scale at the bottom of the drawing on all floor plans. Place an entrance symbol at the main entrance.

Multistory Plans

Thus far it has been assumed that the building is of one-story construction. In the case of a two-story building or a building with a basement, several factors must be considered (Figs. 12-5 and 12-6). The first-floor plan should be drawn first. The basement and second story can then be traced from the first-floor plan. The exterior walls of the basement and second story may be in a line with the first-floor walls or set back from them, or the second floor may be cantilevered out from the first-story walls. If the walls of an upper floor are set back, structural support must be provided underneath and shown by dashed lines on the floor below. If the top floor is cantilevered, a dashed line is used to show the location of the wall below. Interior walls do not necessarily have to line up unless they are used as bearing walls or unless they contain vents or piping from the wall below. Stairways must be carefully lined up and provision made for head room. Remember to provide space for vertical heating ducts from the basement to the second floor. Basements may be equal to the size of the first floor or smaller. They may be completely below ground or may have one or more walls exposed, as on a sloping site. In any case, floor plans of the basement and second floor are required. The same procedures are used for drawing the second-floor and basement as for the first-floor plan. Further information regarding basements will be found in Chap. 17.

REVIEW QUESTIONS

1. Which one drawing is used by the most building tradesmen? Explain.
2. At $\frac{1}{4}$ in. = 1 ft 0 in. scale, draw a 10-ft section of the following types of wall in plan.
   a. Stud wall
   b. Post and beam, 32 in. between posts
   c. Brick veneer over stud wall
   d. Concrete block wall, 8 in. thick
3. What are three types of specialized information which may either appear on the floor plan or be placed on separate drawings?
4. What information concerning a door or a window, aside from its plan-view symbol, must be shown on the floor plan?
5. Draw a typical row of dimensions showing the proper use of center lines, extension lines, arrows, and figures. Label the function of each line of dimensions with a call-out and note, e.g., "overall dimensions."

STUDY SUGGESTIONS

1. Look over a completed floor plan drawn by an architect or draftsman; try to identify the various symbols for walls, fixtures, etc. See how well you can read the drawing.
2. Visit a residence which is under construction, and ask the foreman if you might compare his drawings with the actual construction.
3. Study the symbols and notes used on a floor plan before starting the drawing.
4. Make a freehand floor plan of your own kitchen and one other adjacent room. Use all of the proper symbols and notes.
5. Practice lettering!

Chapter

13

Door, Window, and Room-finish Schedules

Definition and Purpose

The door, window, and room-finish schedules furnish much information which is often difficult to place elsewhere on the working drawings (Fig. 13-1). The principal advantage of using schedules is that the information concerning the doors, windows, and finish is organized logically and can be found in one place. Though schedules are usually used, some floor plans contain such a small amount of other detail that this information can be placed on the drawing as notes (Fig. 12-4). It is the draftsman's responsibility to decide upon the method which will work best for each set of drawings. There are two types of door and window schedules, pictorial and tabular.

Types

Pictorial door and window schedules are simply scale drawings, at $\frac{1}{4}$ or $\frac{1}{2}$ in. $= 1$ ft 0 in., of each of the types of doors and windows used (Fig. 13-2). Each unit is designed specially for the job or the needed information is copied directly from manufacturers' catalogs. Each illustration is further described by a note giving the manufacturer's name and catalog number, type, material, and finish of the unit.

Tabular door and window schedules use verbal descriptions in place of pictures, and the information is broken down into several categories for easy reference (Fig. 13-3). Though there are many variations in practice, the schedules described here are typical and include all of the necessary information.

Window Schedules

The headings used on a window schedule (Fig. 13-4) are listed here:

1. *Symbol:* The keying symbol or number
2. *Size:* The dimensions of the window
3. *Type:* Casement, double-hung, horizontal, sliding, fixed, etc.
4. *Manufacturer and catalog number:* Taken from the catalog
5. *Glazing:* Single- or double-strength crystal, plate, obscure, etc.
6. *Material:* Wood, steel, aluminum
7. *Remarks:* Any further description

Door Schedules

The headings used on a door schedule (Fig. 13-5) are listed here:

1. *Symbol:* The keying symbol
2. *Size:* The dimensions of the door
3. *Thickness:* Front to back
4. *Type:* Panel, flush, dutch, sliding, overhead, rolling, folding, etc.
5. *Manufacturer and catalog number:* Taken from the catalog if required
6. *Material:* Wood, steel, aluminum, plastic, etc.
7. *Finish:* Varnish, paint, lacquer, etc.
8. *Jamb:* Wood, steel, etc.
9. *Remarks:* Any further description

Room-finish Schedules

The room-finish schedule may be arranged similar

(continued on page 78)

ROOM FINISH SCHEDULE

REMARKS

- (n) NATURAL FINISH
- (E) 3 COAT ENAMEL
- (W) 3 COAT FLAT WALL PAINT
- (S) STAIN FINISH
- (P) PRE-FINISHED
- (XS) EXTERIOR STAIN
- (XE) EXTERIOR TRIM PAINT.

NOTES

1. PAINT CONC. BLOCK FIREPLACE WITH TWO COATS-VINYL WALL PAINT.

NO.	NAME	FLOOR: EXPOSED CONCRETE	FLOOR: CARPET (N.I.C.)	FLOOR: VINYL ASBESTOS TILE	BASE: HARDWOOD	BASE: PINE	BASE: 4" VINYL TOPSET	WALLS SOUTH: 1/2" GYPSUM BD.	WALLS SOUTH: HARDWOOD PANELING	WALLS SOUTH: TEXTURE ONE-ELEVEN PLYWD	WALLS SOUTH: MARLITE PANEL	WALLS SOUTH: D.F. PLYWD. WARDROBE	WALLS SOUTH: UNFINISHED
1	ENTRY		○		E								
2	LIVING ROOM		○		n				P				
3	FAMILY ROOM		○		E			W					
4	KITCHEN			○			○	E					
5	NOOK			○			○	E					
6	HALL		○		E			W					
7	BEDROOM #2		○		E			W					
8	BEDROOM #3		○		E							E	
9	BATH #2			○			○				P		
10	BATH #1			○			○				P		
11	BEDROOM #1		○		E								
12	GARAGE	○				E							○
	EXTERIOR.									XS			

NO.	NAME	WALLS WEST: 1/2" GYPSUM BD.	WALLS WEST: TEXTURE ONE-ELEVEN PLYWD.	WALLS WEST: MARLITE PANEL	WALLS WEST: D.F. PLYWOOD WARDROBE	WALLS WEST: UNFINISHED	WALLS NORTH: 1/2" GYPSUM BD.	WALLS NORTH: HARDWOOD PANELING	WALLS NORTH: TEXTURE ONE-ELEVEN PLYWD.	WALLS NORTH: MARLITE PANEL	WALLS NORTH: D.F. PLYWD. WARDROBE	WALLS NORTH: UNFINISHED	WALLS EAST: 1/2" GYPSUM BD.	WALLS EAST: TEXTURE ONE-ELEVEN PLYWD.	WALLS EAST: MARLITE PANEL	WALLS EAST: UNFINISHED
1	ENTRY		S										W			
2	LIVING ROOM	W						P								
3	FAMILY ROOM							P					W			
4	KITCHEN	E														
5	NOOK						E						E			
6	HALL	W					W						W			
7	BEDROOM #2	W									E			S		
8	BEDROOM #3	W					W							S		
9	BATH #2			P						P					P	
10	BATH #1			P						P					P	
11	BEDROOM #1		S													
12	GARAGE					○						○				○
	EXTERIOR.		XS						XS					XS		

NO.	NAME	CEILING: 1/2" GYPSUM BD.	CEILING: 12"x12" ACOUSTICAL TILE	CEILING: UNFINISHED	CLG. HT.	WAINSCOT	WAINS. HT.	CABINETS & DOORS: PINE CASEWORK	CABINETS & DOORS: WHITE ASH CASEWORK	CABINETS & DOORS: CERAMIC TILE COUNTER TOP	CABINETS & DOORS: NOVOPLY DOORS	CABINETS & DOORS: BIRCH DOORS	CABINETS & DOORS: WHITE ASH DOORS	TRIM: PINE	TRIM: HARDWOOD	TRIM: REDWOOD	NAME	NO.
1	ENTRY	W			7'-4"							E		E			ENTRY	1
2	LIVING ROOM		○		VARIES				n						n		LIVING ROOM	2
3	FAMILY ROOM		○		VARIES				n					E			FAMILY ROOM	3
4	KITCHEN	E			VARIES				n	○							KITCHEN	4
5	NOOK	E			VARIES							E		E			NOOK	5
6	HALL	W			7'-4"			E				E		E			HALL	6
7	BEDROOM #2	W			VARIES			E			E	E		E			BEDROOM #2	7
8	BEDROOM #3	W			VARIES			E			E	E		E			BEDROOM #3	8
9	BATH #2	E			VARIES							E		E			BATH# 2	9
10	BATH #1	E			VARIES			E		○		E		E			BATH # 1	10
11	BEDROOM #1				VARIES			E			E	E		E			BEDROOM #2	11
12	GARAGE			○	VARIES							E		E			GARAGE	12
	EXTERIOR.															XE	EXTERIOR.	

WINDOW SCHEDULE

SYM.	SIZE WDTH x HT.	TYPE	MANUFACTURE & CATALOG NO.	GLAZING	MATERIAL	REMARKS
1	1'-6" x 7'-4"	FIXED	JOB MADE	OBSCURE	REDWOOD	CUSTOM SIZE
2	5'-0" x 3'-0"	HORIZ. SLID.	E-Z SET ROLLING WINDOWS #5030	D.S. "B"	ALUM.	CUSTOM SIZE
3	3'-6" x 4'-0"		#3640			
4	4'-0" x 4'-0"		#4040			PAIR - WOOD MULLION BETWEEN
5	4'-0" x 4'-0"		#4040			
6	3'-0" x 3'-0"		#3030	OBSCURE		
7	6'-0" x 6'-8"	SLID. DOOR	ACME - 500 SERIES #6068-XO	1/4" PL.		
8	6'-0" x 6'-8"		#6068-OX	1/4" PL.		
9	5'-6" x 6'-8"	FIXED	JOB MADE	3/16" CRY.	REDWOOD	
10	6'-0" x VARIES			3/16" CRY		
11	4'-0" x 4'-0"	HORIZ. SLID.	E-Z SET ROLLING WINDOWS #4040	D.S. "B"	ALUM.	PAIR - WOOD MULLION BETWEEN
12	3'-0" x 3'-0"		#3030	OBSCURE		
13	6'-0" x 3'-0"		#6030	D.S. "B"		
14	5'-0" x VARIES	FIXED	JOB MADE	OBSCURE	REDWOOD	
15	5'-0" x VARIES					
16	5'-0" x VARIES					
17	5'-0" x VARIES					

DOOR SCHEDULE

SYM	SIZE WDTH x HT	THK	TYPE	MANUFACTURE & CATALOG NO.	MATERIAL	FINISH	JAMB	REMARKS
1	3'-0" x 7'-4"	1 3/4"	FLUSH-SOLID	"SIMPSON"- 5 PLY SOLID CORE	BIRCH	ENAMEL	WOOD	PAINT GRADE - BIRCH VENEER.
2	2'-8" x 6'-8"	1 3/8"	FLUSH-HOLLOW	"SIMPSON"- 5 PLY HOLLOW CORE				
3	2'-6" x 6'-8"							
4	1'-8" x 6'-8"							
5	2'-4" x 6'-8"							
6	2'-10" x 6'-8"	1 3/4"	FLUSH-SOLID	"SIMPSON"- 5 PLY SOLID CORE				
7	2'-8" x 6'-8"	1 3/8"	FLUSH-HOLLOW	"SIMPSON"- 5 PLY HOLLOW CORE				
8	2'-8" x 6'-8"							
9	2'-6" x 6'-8"							
10	PR. 2'-4" x 6'-8"		FULL LOUVER					
11	3'-0" x 6'-8"	1 3/4"	FLUSH - SOLID					
12	16'-0" x 7'-0"		OVHD. GARAGE	"FILUMA" FIBERGLASS GARAGE	ALUM			FIBERGLASS FACE SKIN

Fig. 13-1. Door, window, and room-finish schedules for a small residence.

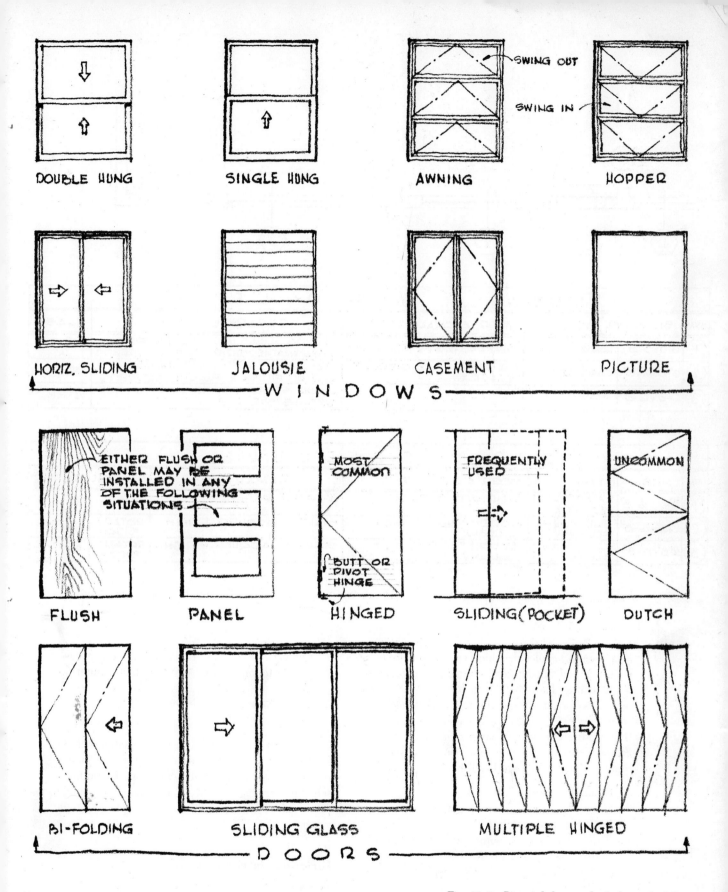

Fig. 13-2. Pictorial door and window schedules.

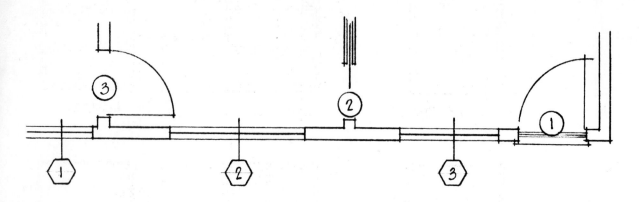

			WINDOW	SCHEDULE	
SYM	SIZE	TYPE	MFGR. & CATALOG NO.	REMARKS	GLASS
①	6'-0"x3'-0"	HORIZ. SLID.	"TRIMVIEW" - TYPE T-2 #500-6030	SLIDING ALUMINUM, LACQUER FINISH VINYL WEATHERSTRIP, PLASTIC SCREENS	D.S. "A"
②	6'-0"x4'-0"	CASEMENT	"E-Z SET" DELUXE CASEMENT #3424 XW	DBL. VENT, ROTARY OPERATOR, LAQUER FINISH & PLASTIC SCREENS	7/32" OBSC.
③	4'-0"x6'-0"	FIXED		WOOD STOPS SET IN MASTIC. SEE DETAILS SHT. A-9	1/4" P.P.

			DOOR	SCHEDULE			
SYM	SIZE	TYPE	MFGR. & CATALOG NO.	REMARKS	MATERIAL	THK	HDWE. TYPE
①	3'-0"x6'-8"	S.A. ENTRANCE TWO PANEL	"SIMPSON" SONATA	3 COATS EXT. TRIM PAINT	PINE	1¾"	A
②	2'-6"x6'-8"	SLIDING, H.C. FLUSH	"RODDIS" HOUSEMART HOLLOW	STAIN & LACQUER FINISH	ROTARY BIRCH	1⅜"	F
③	2'-8"x6'-8"	S.A., H.C. FLUSH	"RODDIS" HOUSEMART HOLLOW	STAIN & LACQUER FINISH.	ROTARY BIRCH	1⅜"	C

Fig. 13-3. Window and door schedules for a small residence, showing method of keying to the floor plan.

to a door schedule, in which case descriptions of materials and finishes are lettered in opposite the room names. The type shown here lists all of the materials and finishes at the top of the sheet, and small circles are used to key them to the rooms (Fig. 13-6). This system saves space and lettering. Either method is suitable. The headings used on a room-finish schedule are listed here:

1. *Room:* The name of the room
2. *Floor:* Hardwood, concrete, carpet, tile, etc.
3. *Base:* Size and material
4. *Walls:* North, east, south, and west; gypsum-board, plaster, tile, plywood, etc.
5. *Ceiling:* Plaster, open-beam, suspended, acoustic-tile, etc.
6. *Wainscot:* Tile, plywood, plastic, etc., plus height of wainscot

7. *Cabinets and doors:* Pine, birch, or ash case-work; tile, micarta, or stainless-steel countertop, etc.
8. *Trim:* Door casing, window trim, ceiling molding, etc.

The room-finish schedule is used together with the appropriate interior elevation to get a true picture of the inside walls of the building. Room-finish schedules are usually keyed to the floor plan by the room name, but some offices use a special keying symbol.

Variations in Form

The sizes of the columns used with any schedule depend upon the amount of information to be placed within them as well as the space available.

(continued on page 82)

WINDOW SCHEDULE

SYM.	SIZE (WDTH × HT.)	TYPE	MANUFACTURE & CATALOG NO.	GLAZING	MATERIAL	REMARKS
1	1'-6" × 7'-4"	FIXED	JOB MADE	OBSCURE	REDWOOD	CUSTOM SIZE
2	5'-0" × 3'-0"	HORIZ. SLID.	E-Z SET ROLLING WINDOWS #5030	D.S. "B"	ALUM.	CUSTOM SIZE
3	3'-6" × 4'-0"		#3640			
4	4'-0" × 4'-0"		#4040			PAIR - WOOD MULLION BETWEEN
5	4'-0" × 4'-0"		#4040			
6	3'-0" × 3'-0"		#3030	OBSCURE		
7	6'-0" × 6'-8"	SLID. DOOR	ACME - 500 SERIES #6068-XO	1/4" PL.		
8	6'-0" × 6'-8"		#6068-OX	1/4" PL.		
9	5'-6" × 6'-8"	FIXED	JOB MADE	3/16" CRY.	REDWOOD	
10	6'-0" × VARIES			5/16" CRY		
11	4'-0" × 4'-0"	HORIZ. SLID.	E-Z SET ROLLING WINDOWS #4040	D.S. "B"	ALUM.	PAIR - WOOD MULLION BETWEEN
12	3'-0" × 3'-0"	"	#3030	OBSCURE		
13	6'-0" × 3'-0"		#6030	D.S. "B"		
14	5'-0" × VARIES	FIXED	JOB MADE	OBSCURE	REDWOOD	
15	5'-0" × VARIES					
16	5'-0" × VARIES					
17	5'-0" × VARIES					

Fig. 13-4. Full-size extract from Fig. 13-1 (tabular window schedule for floor plan of Fig. 12-1).

DOOR SCHEDULE

SYM	SIZE WIDTH × HT	THK	TYPE	MANUFACTURE & CATALOG NO.	MATERIAL	FINISH	JAMB	REMARKS
1	3'-0" × 7'-4"	1¾"	FLUSH - SOLID	"SIMPSON"- 5 PLY SOLID CORE	BIRCH	ENAMEL	WOOD	PAINT GRADE - BIRCH VENEER.
2	2'-8" × 6'-8"	1⅜"	FLUSH - HOLLOW	"SIMPSON"- 5 PLY HOLLOW CORE	→	→	→	→
3	2'-6" × 6'-8"	→	→	→	→	→	→	→
4	1'-8" × 6'-8"	→	→	→	→	→	→	→
5	2'-4" × 6'-8"	→	→	→	→	→	→	→
6	2'-10" × 6'-8"	1¾"	FLUSH - SOLID	"SIMPSON"- 5 PLY SOLID CORE	→	→	→	→
7	2'-8" × 6'-8"	1⅜"	FLUSH - HOLLOW	"SIMPSON"- 5 PLY HOLLOW CORE	→	→	→	→
8	2'-8" × 6'-8"	→	→	→	→	→	→	→
9	2'-6" × 6'-8"	→	→	→	→	→	→	→
10	PR. 2'-4" × 6'-8"	→	FULL LOUVER	→	→	→	→	→
11	3'-0" × 6'-8"	1¾"	FLUSH - SOLID	→	ALUM	→	→	FIBERGLASS FACE SKIN
12	16'-0" × 7'-0"		OVHD. GARAGE	"FILUNA" FIBERGLASS GARAGE				

Fig. 13-5. Full-size extract from Fig. 13-1 (tabular door schedule for floor plan of Fig. 12-1).

Fig. 13-6. Full-size extract from Fig. 13-1 (tabular room-finish schedule for floor plan of Fig. 12-1).

REMARKS legend:
- (n) NATURAL FINISH
- (E) 3 COAT ENAMEL
- (W) 3 COAT FLAT WALL PAINT
- (S) STAIN FINISH
- (P) PRE-FINISHED
- (XS) EXTERIOR STAIN
- (XE) EXTERIOR TRIM PAINT

NO.	NAME	FLOOR: Exposed Concrete	Carpet (N.I.C.)	Vinyl Asbestos Tile	BASE: Hardwood	Pine	4" Vinyl Topset	SOUTH: 1/2" Gypsum Bd.	Hardwood Paneling	Texture One-Eleven Plywd	Marlite Panel	D.F. Plywd. Wardrobe	Unfinished	WEST: 1/2" Gypsum Bd.	Texture One-Eleven Plywd	Marlite Panel	D.F. Plywood Wardrobe	Unfinished	NORTH: 1/2" Gypsum Bd.	Hardwood Paneling	Texture One-Eleven Plywd	Marlite Panel	D.F. Plywd. Wardrobe	Unfinished	EAST: 1/2" Gypsum Bd.	Texture One-Eleven Plywd
1	ENTRY		●		E																				W	
2	LIVING ROOM		●		n				P					W	S					P						
3	FAMILY ROOM		●		E															P					W	
4	KITCHEN			●			●	W						E												
5	NOOK			●			●	E											E						E	
6	HALL		●		E			E						W					W						W	
7	BEDROOM #2		●		E			W						W									E			S
8	BEDROOM #3		●		E			W						W												S
9	BATH #2			●			●				P					P			W			P				
10	BATH #1			●			●				P					P						P				
11	BEDROOM #1		●		E							E			S											
12	GARAGE	●				E							●					●						●		

It is better to use a separate sheet for schedules than to try to crowd them into a small space. The schedules described here are broken down into seven to nine columns; other schedules are simpler but may still be adequate.

REVIEW QUESTIONS

1. Name two different types of door schedules.
2. Which of the above types of schedule takes the most drafting time?
3. How many types of doors and windows, based on the manner in which they operate, can you name? Use "Sweet's File" as a reference.
4. What advantages are inherent in each type of door and window as listed above?
5. How many applications can you think of in which acoustic tile would be superior to plaster for a ceiling? Vice versa?
6. Why is smooth-finished plaster used in kitchens and baths? Why is rougher-textured plaster used for other rooms?
7. Concrete, hardwood, linoleum, plastic tile, carpet, and terrazzo are all common flooring materials; discuss the reasons why each material should or should not be used in your own project.

STUDY SUGGESTIONS

1. Look over a set of drawings for a large building, and note the extent of the schedules.
2. Check back and forth in these drawings between the interior elevations and the schedules to see how they are related.
3. Visit a building-supply firm and look at various types of doors, windows, and surface materials. Sketch them as they would be shown in plan, elevation, and section.

Chapter

14

Structural Sections

Definition and Purpose

Structural sections are views taken through the building at points which will best show the relationships of all structural and architectural parts of the building (Figs. 14-1 and 14-2). All important dimensions are shown, such as plate height and roof pitch. Points of connection between various structural parts are shown, and all members are noted concerning size and material (Fig. 14-3). Often, when the building is complex, several sections may be needed. Wherever there is a change in shape or construction methods, a new section must be drawn. Generally the structural sections are drawn on a separate sheet; however, on a small project they may be placed with another drawing. Structural sections are drawn at a fairly large scale to show detail—about $\frac{1}{2}$ to 1 in. $= 1$ ft 0 in.

As construction practices and materials vary greatly from one part of the country to another, instruction in structural systems must be applicable to all areas. To this end, the phases of construction will be broken down into their logical parts—foundation, floor, wall, ceiling, and roof systems. With a few exceptions, any type of foundation may be used with any type of floor, with any type of wall, and so on. Obviously though, masonry materials should not be placed above wood construction. It is best to use those types of constructions which are in common use locally.

Design

In the structural design of a building it is necessary to work from the top down, because each member below must be designed to support the weight of the structure above. For drafting purposes though, it is better procedure to start below grade and work toward the top in the same order that the structure is erected. This is effective because all parts of the structure will have been sized by the time the working drawings start. For this reason, when any statement concerning the design of a part is made, remember that the necessary data are derived from the structure above.

Structures in Contact with Ground

Concrete and masonry are the only materials approved by building codes for foundations. Concrete, plain or reinforced, is the most common material used. The decision about what material to use depends upon many factors: the type of construction above, availability of materials and labor, building codes, weather conditions, type of soil, cost, etc.

FOOTINGS

The base of any structure is the footing, which distributes the weight of the building over the soil. The size of the footing varies with the type of soil and the weight of the building above. The decision whether or not to use reinforcing steel depends on the building code and design considerations. In general, it is best to use reinforcing rods, at least, in the footing.

FOUNDATION WALL

The foundation wall transmits vertical forces from above to the footing. Walls may be extended up or

(continued on page 87)

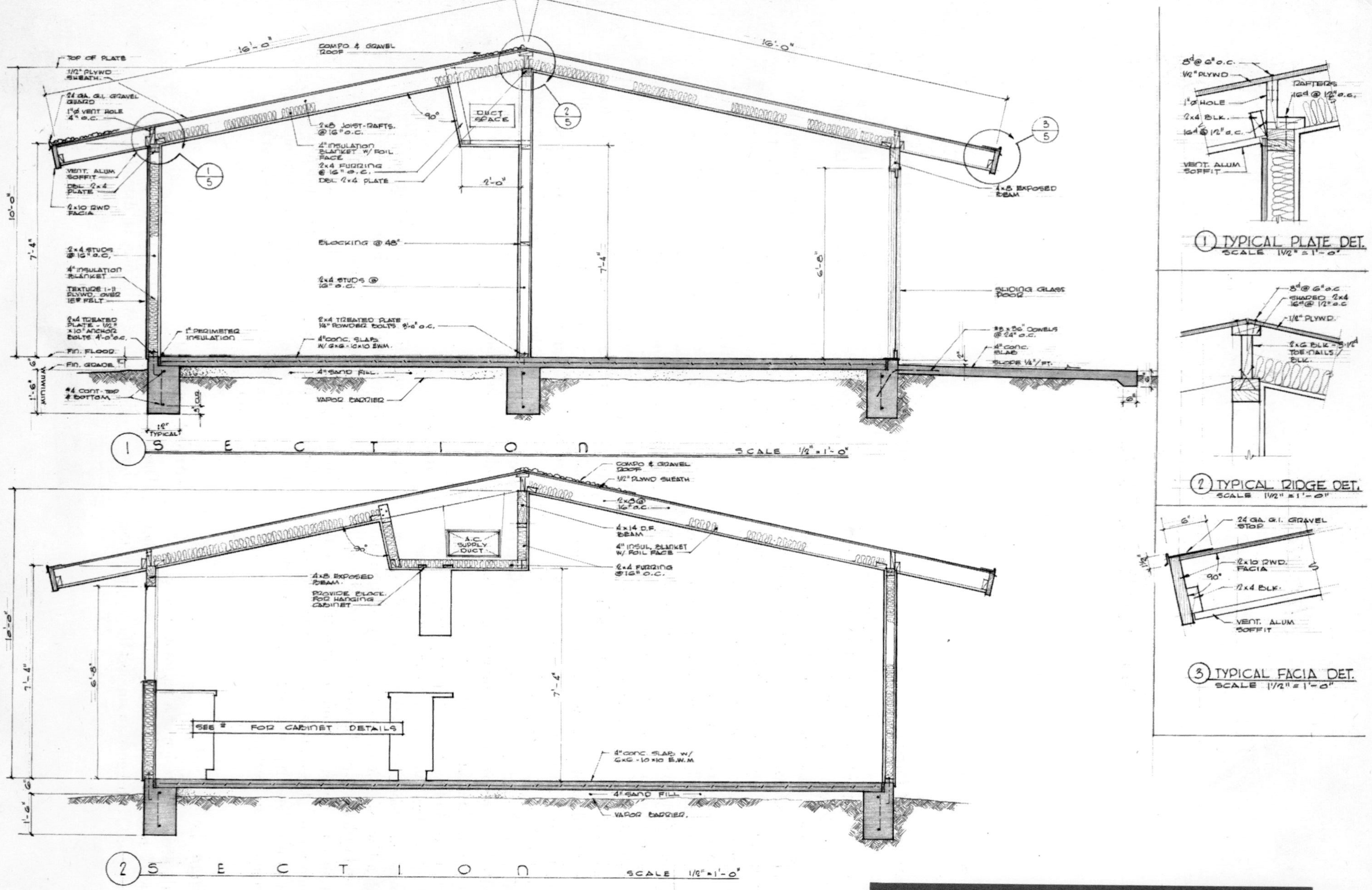

Fig. 14-1. Structural section of a small residence.

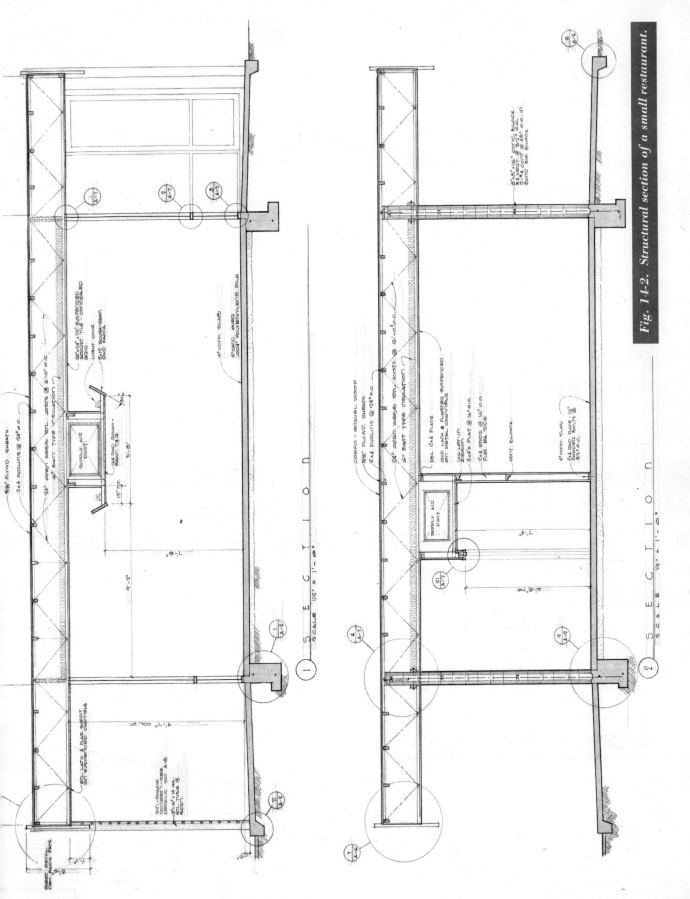

Fig. 14-2. Structural section of a small restaurant.

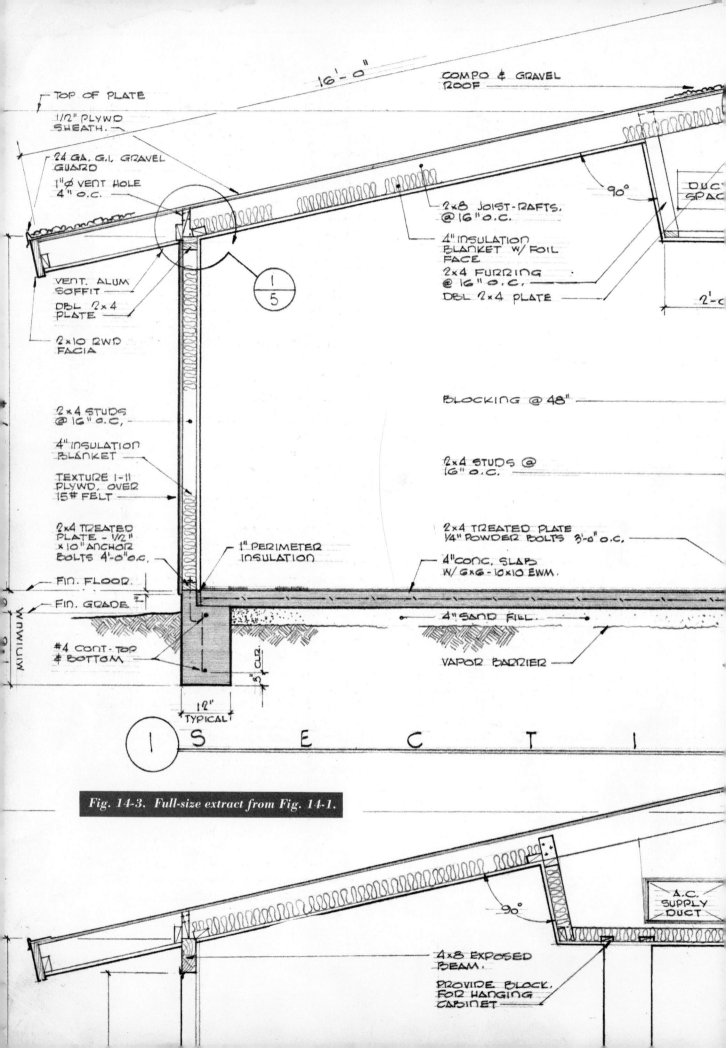

TOP OF PLATE

1/2" PLYWD SHEATH.

24 GA. G.I. GRAVEL GUARD

1"ø VENT HOLE 4" O.C.

VENT. ALUM SOFFIT

DBL 2×4 PLATE

2×10 RWD FACIA

2×4 STUDS @ 16" O.C.

4" INSULATION BLANKET

TEXTURE 1-11 PLYWD. OVER 15# FELT

2×4 TREATED PLATE - 1/2" × 10" ANCHOR BOLTS 4'-0" O.C.

FIN. FLOOR.

FIN. GRADE.

#4 CONT. TOP & BOTTOM

16'-0"

COMPO & GRAVEL ROOF

2×8 JOIST-RAFTS. @ 16" O.C.

4" INSULATION BLANKET W/ FOIL FACE

2×4 FURRING @ 16" O.C.

DBL 2×4 PLATE

90°

DUCT SPAC

2'-0

BLOCKING @ 48"

2×4 STUDS @ 16" O.C.

1" PERIMETER INSULATION

2×4 TREATED PLATE 1/4" POWDER BOLTS 3'-0" O.C.

4" CONC. SLAB W/ 6×6 - 10×10 EWM.

4" SAND FILL.

VAPOR BARRIER

5" CLR.

12" TYPICAL

1' - 6" MINIMUM

1 / 5

1   S E C T I

Fig. 14-3. Full-size extract from Fig. 14-1.

90°

A.C. SUPPLY DUCT

4×8 EXPOSED BEAM.

PROVIDE BLOCK. FOR HANGING CABINET

down to form retaining walls or basement walls. They also isolate the wood construction from the effects of water, insects, and rot.

The thickness of foundation walls varies with the material in the wall, loads on the wall, and the footing below. The height of foundation walls varies from the usual minimum of 6 in. above grade to any desired height. Many building codes establish minimum wall heights and thicknesses. The use of reinforcing steel in walls increases strength and reduces mass. Size and spacing of steel in the foundation wall are determined by building code or local engineering practices (see A-6 and A-7). All of the foregoing applies equally well to solid concrete or masonry construction.

CONCRETE FLOORS

On- or below-grade concrete floors may be cast separately or integrally with the foundation footing or wall (Fig. 14-4). The usual thickness of a concrete floor is $3\frac{1}{2}$ in. (4 in. nominal), and it is often reinforced with welded wire fabric for strength and control of cracking.

WATERPROOFING

The footings, walls, and on-grade floors are all in contact with the earth and must be protected from ground water. Below-grade walls, concrete floors, and footings are waterproofed on the earth side by the application of an impervious membrane. These films may be asphaltic or bituminous products (applied hot or cold, with or without a membrane) or plastic films or solutions. Concrete floors are sometimes further protected by a layer of gravel or crushed rock below the membrane. The large spaces between the rocks prevent the rise of water due to capillary action. In areas of poor soil drainage or excessive ground water, footing draintiles should be placed to conduct water away from the load-bearing surfaces.

Other types of footings include spread footings, piles, and caissons (Fig. 14-4). These are used to support concentrated loads of posts, columns, piers, and pilasters. Grade beams which carry wall loads bridge the spaces between footings; they are, however, partially supported by the soil. This completes the list of structural members which are in direct contact with the earth.

Floor Systems

Any floor system is designed to transmit live and dead loads from above, as well as its own weight, to the footings (Fig. 14-5). A dead load is the weight of the structure. A live load is any movable load. The most common types of floor systems include on- and above-grade concrete, wood-joist, steel-joist, and plank-and-beam. On-grade concrete floors have already been described. Above-grade concrete floors in this discussion refer to floors not in contact with the earth. They must be designed to support their own weight plus live and dead loads from above. They must be supported by bearing walls, girders, or beams. These may be separate from or integral with the floor. Such floors always require reinforcing steel. This type of floor is an engineering problem beyond the scope of this book.

WOOD-JOIST FLOORS

Wood-joist floors are quite common in all parts of the country (Fig. 14-6). They are extremely simple to design and build. Tables are available which give the size and spacing of joists for any span and loading (see A-8). Any carpenter understands this type of construction. Joists are supported by bearing walls, girders, or beams of any common material. The size and spacing of the joists is related to the load, the span between supports, and the type of wood. The live and dead loads are specified in the local building code (usually 40 psf live load for a residence), and the span is equal to the distance between supports. The type of wood depends upon the locality.

Where spans between bearing walls are great, wood-joist floors are supported over basementless spaces on dwarf walls or piers and girders. They are supported over a basement or lower floor by girders or beams. Second-story floor joists serve as the ceiling joists over the first floor; they are found in a separate column of the joist table. Cross bridging is used between joists over long spans to stiffen the structure. Spans up to 8 ft do not require bridging. Solid blocking is placed between joists over dwarf walls or other supports and also under bearing walls at an angle to the joists. If the bearing wall is parallel to the joists, the joists are doubled under the wall. Basementless spaces must be ventilated; the requirements are set forth in local building codes. Subfloor materials used over wood joists are straight or diagonal wood sheathing, tongue and

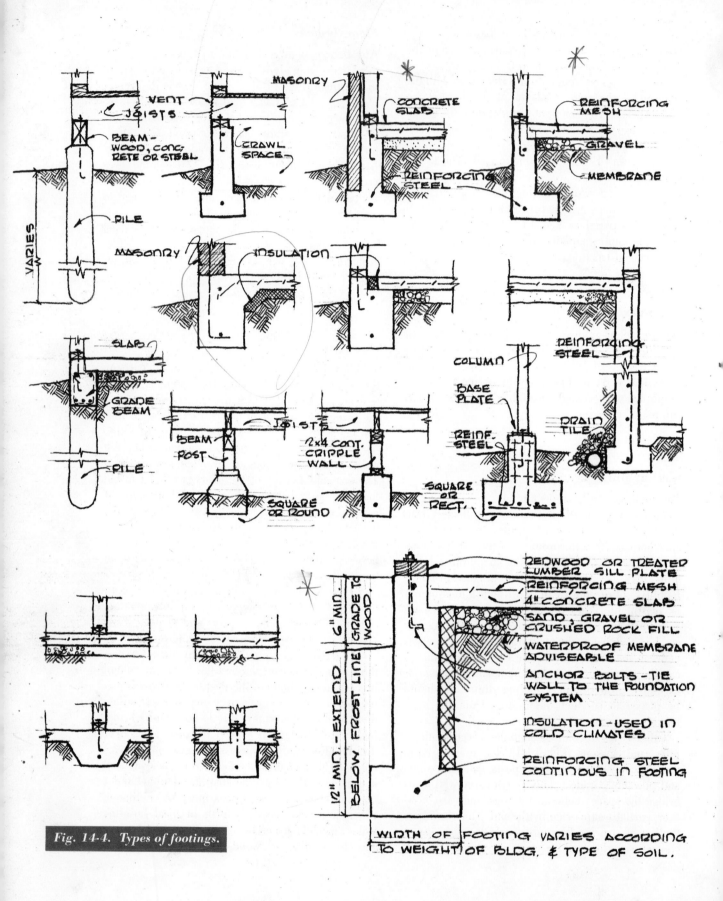

Fig. 14-4. Types of footings.

Labels within the figure:

VENT
JOISTS
MASONRY
CONCRETE SLAB
REINFORCING MESH
BEAM—WOOD, CONCRETE OR STEEL
CRAWL SPACE
GRAVEL
REINFORCING STEEL
MEMBRANE
PILE
VARIES

MASONRY
INSULATION
REINFORCING STEEL

SLAB
GRADE BEAM
PILE
BEAM
POST
JOISTS
2×4 CONT. CRIPPLE WALL
SQUARE OR ROUND
COLUMN
BASE PLATE
REINF. STEEL
SQUARE OR RECT.
DRAIN TILE

REDWOOD OR TREATED LUMBER SILL PLATE
REINFORCING MESH
4" CONCRETE SLAB
SAND, GRAVEL OR CRUSHED ROCK FILL
WATERPROOF MEMBRANE ADVISEABLE
ANCHOR BOLTS – TIE WALL TO THE FOUNDATION SYSTEM
INSULATION – USED IN COLD CLIMATES
REINFORCING STEEL CONTINOUS IN FOOTING
6" MIN. – EXTEND GRADE TO WOOD.
12" MIN. BELOW FROST LINE
WIDTH OF FOOTING VARIES ACCORDING TO WEIGHT OF BLDG. & TYPE OF SOIL.

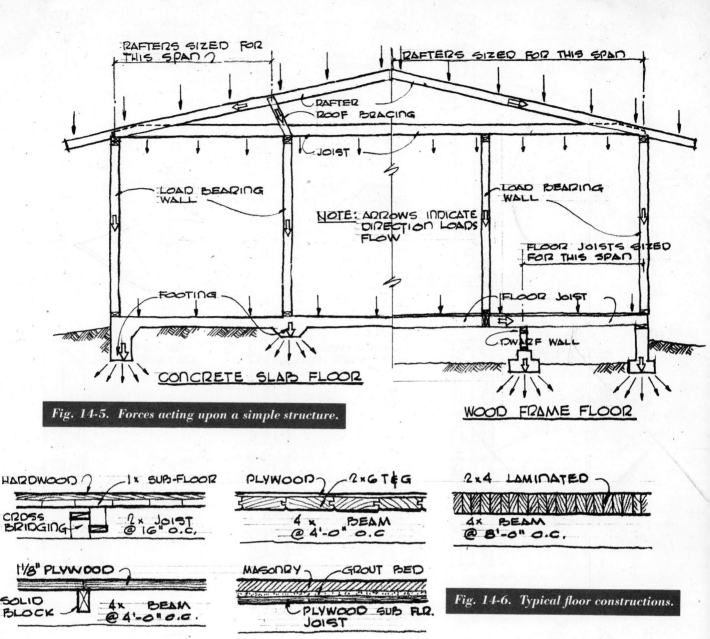

Fig. 14-5. *Forces acting upon a simple structure.*

Fig. 14-6. *Typical floor constructions.*

groove sheathing, and plywood. Finish floor materials used over the subfloor may be hardwood, plastic, ceramic tiles, or carpet.

STEEL-JOIST FLOORS

Steel joists perform the same functions as wood joists and, in addition, will span larger distances for their weight, are incombustible, and will not rot. They are used most often in commercial structures. AISC tables are available for the use of steel joists (see A-9). Floor materials used over steel joists are the same as those used over wood joists; in addition, metal floor materials are available (Fig. 14-6).

Some steel joists use bolted or welded clips to fasten other materials to them, while others are nailable with ordinary carpenters' tools and fastenings.

PLANK-AND-BEAM FLOORS

The plank-and-beam floor system differs from the joist system in that the supports (beams) are widely spaced, and heavy floor sheathing (planks) is used to span the larger spaces (see A-9). Tongue-and-groove sheathing permits the use of wider spacing of beams than ordinary lumber. The beams are supported by the exterior wall, dwarf walls, posts, or piers.

89

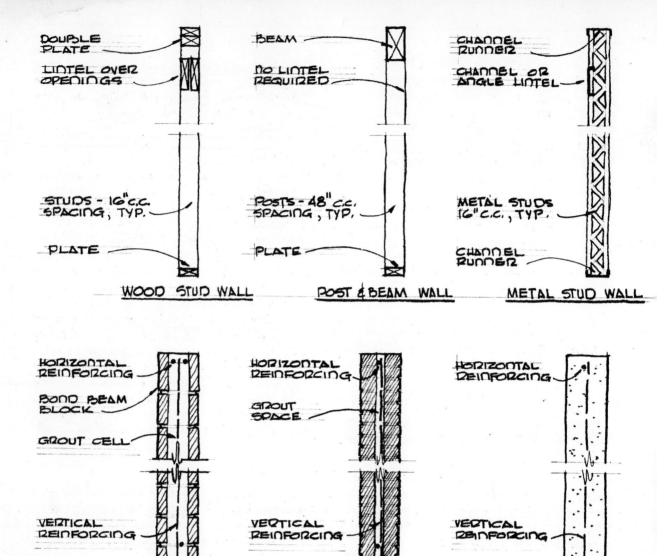

DOUBLE PLATE

LINTEL OVER OPENINGS

STUDS - 16" C.C. SPACING, TYP.

PLATE

WOOD STUD WALL

BEAM

NO LINTEL REQUIRED

POSTS - 48" C.C. SPACING, TYP.

PLATE

POST & BEAM WALL

CHANNEL RUNNER

CHANNEL OR ANGLE LINTEL

METAL STUDS 16" C.C., TYP.

CHANNEL RUNNER

METAL STUD WALL

HORIZONTAL REINFORCING

BOND BEAM BLOCK

GROUT CELL

VERTICAL REINFORCING

CONCRETE BLOCK

HORIZONTAL REINFORCING

GROUT SPACE

VERTICAL REINFORCING

BRICK

HORIZONTAL REINFORCING

VERTICAL REINFORCING

CONCRETE

Fig. 14-7. Typical wall constructions.

In a system using wood, a rot- and insect-resistant wood sill or plate must be placed between the concrete or masonry and the wooden structure above. The sill is bolted to foundation bolts which are embedded in the concrete or masonry. In a structure with a concrete floor, the bottom plate of the wall is bolted to the concrete.

Wall Structures

In the usual frame construction the exterior, and sometimes the interior, walls are designed to support roof loads. Conventional 2- by 4-in. or 2- by 6-in. stud walls consist of a bottom plate, studs, and a double top plate. Intermediate bracing, or fire blocking, is placed horizontally near the middle of the studs. The double plates are overlapped at joints and all corners for continuity. This construction provides a strong ring around the top of the wall and also supports those rafters which fall between the studs. Spacing of studs is usually 16 in., but may be 12 or 24 in. Interior and exterior finish materials are nailed to the studs (Fig. 14-7).

POST-AND-BEAM WALLS

Post-and-beam walls are similar to stud walls with a few exceptions. The bottom plate is the same, but the vertical members are 4 by 4s at wider spacing, often 32 or 48 in. The top plate is a 4 in. beam—

4 by 4, 4 by 6, or 4 by 8. The size of the beam depends upon the size of the largest opening in the wall. These plates are joined with a simple lap joint at joints and corners. Advantages claimed for post and beam construction over stud construction are that the finished building has a neat modular appearance; there is less cutting and waste of finish materials; most lintels, trimmers, etc., are eliminated; and, when properly designed and built, construction goes faster. When openings such as doors, windows, arches, or fireplaces occur in a bearing wall, loads above the opening must be supported (Fig. 14-8). The problem of transferring the weight above the opening down to the floor is solved by the use of a stiff lintel which is supported by trimmers at each side. When the top plate in a post-and-beam wall is large enough, no header is required for an opening. Sizes of lintels vary with the size of the opening (Fig. 14-8 and A-10).

METAL-STUD WALLS

Metal studs are available which can be used with wood, masonry, or all-metal construction. They serve the same purposes as conventional studs and may be used at the same spacings. A U-shaped floor runner takes the place of the bottom plate; it is fastened to the floor with bolts, nails, or powder bolts. The studs are welded or wired to this channel. Blocking or cross bridging is used as fire blocking and stiffening. A U channel similar to the floor runner is used at the top. Finish materials may be fastened by wire, bolts, screws, or welding, some types of studs will take nails.

NONBEARING WALLS

To this point, all the frame wall systems mentioned are suitable for use as bearing walls, exterior or interior. This same construction can be used for nonbearing walls. However, since nonbearing walls do not have to carry any vertical loads but their own weight, they may be lighter in construction than bearing walls, and lintels may be omitted over openings. It is permissible to use studs turned sideways in a nonbearing wall if space is critical. The resulting gain of 2 in. is sometimes important. In some parts of the country, nonbearing walls may consist of plywood, wood-fiber, or gypsum-board panels glued together without the use of studs. These walls are not usually recommended where noise between rooms is a problem, and since they are not standard wall thickness, their use is not advisable where doors must be framed in.

MASONRY WALLS

Masonry walls consist of modular, incombustible units laid up in courses, and they may be solid or grouted, with or without reinforcing (see A-11). There are hundreds of different masonry materials, and no attempt will be made to list all of them or to

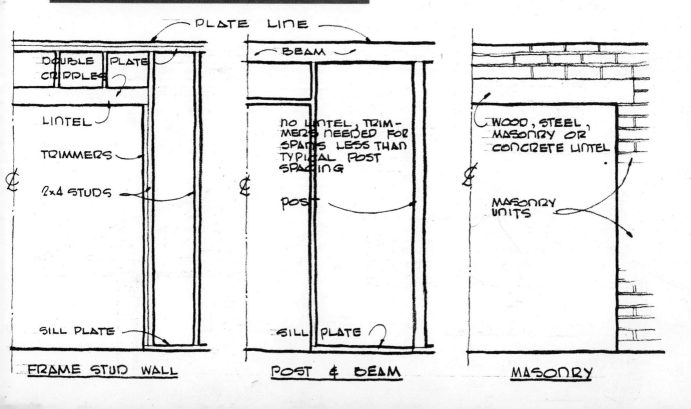

Fig. 14-8. Typical supports above openings in walls.

evaluate their merits. There are several general statements which can be made about the usual masonry construction, however, and it is the student's responsibility to decide upon a suitable material which is locally used.

All masonry must be "keyed" or tied to the foundation wall or footing. This is done by the use of a depression, or "key," cast into the footing or slab. If the wall is to be reinforced with steel, reinforcing rods or dowels must be cast into the foundation at the proper spacing. Later, the spaces around the steel are grouted in. In earthquake areas, horizontal bond beams are required at the bottom, midpoint, and top of the wall (Fig. 14-7).

Most masonry walls require a mechanical tie completely around the wall at the plate line at least. This tie can consist of a complete ring of reinforcing rods grouted into the cavity or a concrete bond beam on top of the masonry. Anchor bolts are set into a steel or wood plate to which a wood or steel roof may be fastened. When a concrete roof is used, reinforcing dowels extend from the bond beam into the roof slab.

Following are examples of the many types of masonry units:

1. Concrete blocks. Usual sizes are 16 by 8 by 8 in., 16 by 8 by 6 in., 16 by 8 by 4 in., and 12 by 8 by 8 in., but some manufacturers produce many other sizes. They are available in numerous shapes designed for particular purposes.
2. Fired-clay bricks. Usual sizes are 8 by $3\frac{3}{4}$ by $2\frac{3}{4}$ in., $2\frac{1}{16}$ by $5\frac{1}{2}$ by $11\frac{1}{2}$ in., and 2 by 4 by 12 in., though many others are made. Hundreds of colors, materials, and finishes are available.
3. Terra-cotta tiles. These are available in many sizes, shapes, materials, and finishes; it would be difficult to describe an average specimen. Some of these materials may not be used in many areas of the country for structural walls.
4. Natural stone. Stone-masonry materials are available in an infinite variety depending upon locality; they are usually not imported except in the case of expensive materials. Some stone is used only in walls as a structural material, while others are used as facings and veneers. For further information refer to "Architectural Graphic Standards."

OPENINGS

Windows, doors, and other openings require lintels above to carry vertical loads. These lintels may be made of masonry, steel, or wood, depending upon the local building code.

Roof-ceiling Structure

The roof-ceiling structure above the walls serves several purposes. It provides shelter, supports the surface materials, and ties the walls together. In some cases it provides space for heating, ventilating, plumbing, and electric equipment and conductors (Fig. 14-9).

Fig. 14-9. Typical roof-ceiling constructions.

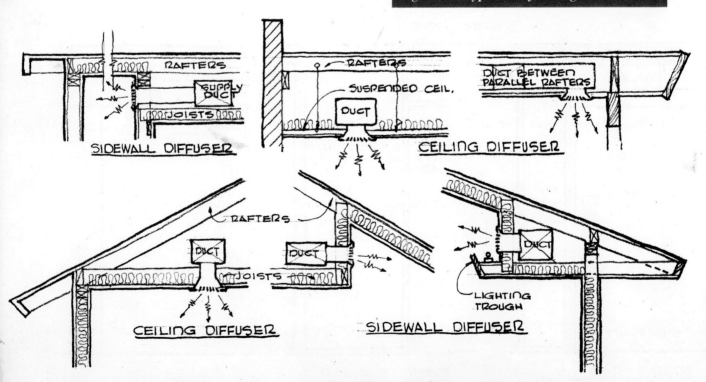

ATTIC SPACE

Two roofs which appear to be the same from the outside may be quite different in structure if one has an attic space and the other does not (Fig. 14-10). The one with the attic has a flat ceiling hung from joists, which also act as ties across the building. When the ties are omitted, as is usual with a cathedral ceiling, a beam or beams must be provided to support the rafters between the walls (see A-14). When an open-beam ceiling is desired, either exposed beams or rafter ties must be used. In either case the bottom of the roof decking usually shows as the ceiling finish. If desired, the bottoms of the rafters may be covered by plaster or some other finish material.

ROOF SHAPES

Hundreds of different combinations of roof shapes and materials can be developed, but the design of some of these systems requires an extensive engineering background. For this reason, the roof types discussed here will be limited to wood and metal with some mention of concrete. Through the use of these materials many architectural effects can be achieved. The structural shapes possible include everything from a flat roof to an A frame, a butterfly section, or a warped surface (Fig. 14-10). Various types may be modified or combined to produce clerestory windows or skylights. The possibilities are limited only by the requirements of the structure and the designer's ingenuity.

The most commonly used roof systems can be divided into two general groups, flat and pitched. Any roof steeper than 4:12 pitch is called a pitched roof. Any roof shallower than 4:12 is called a flat roof. These two groups can be further classified into systems, such as a simple-span system and a trussed system.

SIMPLE-SPAN SYSTEM

In the simple-span system, the main structural member may be a rafter or a beam. Rafters and 1-in. sheathing are most often used for ordinary gable-and-hip roofs. Rafters and 2-in. tongue-and-groove decking are often used for open-beam ceilings. There are many other possible constructions. Wood or metal rafters and wood, metal, or concrete decking can be used. Such roofs are common on residences and some small commercial structures; 24 ft is usually the maximum span used for this type of construction. The sizes of all structural parts of the roof can be found in tables based on the spans involved and the materials used (see A-12 and A-13).

TRUSSED SYSTEM

Trussed systems permit large clear spans and speed up construction on large projects (Fig. 14-10). For this reason trusses are often used in large commercial buildings or large tracts of residences; they are seldom used in custom residences. Trusses are usually designed by engineers and fabricated and erected with special equipment. Many types of wood and metal trusses are available for various spans; they are listed in "Sweet's File." The design of trusses is beyond the scope of this book.

OTHER SYSTEMS

Warped-surface systems are the least common types of roofs in use. Concrete is a perfect material for most complex shapes such as conoids, domes, vaults, and hyperbolic paraboloids. Wood and metal can be used for simple warped surfaces, while plywood is especially suitable for barrel vaults and folded-plate roofs.

One type of structure which does not fit readily into the foregoing discussion is the A frame (Fig. 14-10). This system is adaptable to cabins and certain types of commercial buildings.

Surface Materials for Roofs

Many methods of weatherproofing the roof are available. Students should choose materials and methods used locally. A brief list of the most common roof materials follows (Fig. 14-11):

1. Overlapping units: Including wood shingles and shakes, asphalt shingles, slate, flat and mission tiles, asbestos shingles, and plywood sheets. These materials must be placed on a sloping surface to avoid leaking. Building codes and manufacturers' recommendations concerning the degree of slope must be followed.
2. Membrane roofs: Including built-up building paper and asphalt, fiber glass and plastic binder, and concrete. Many other types of fibers are used with many types of binders or waterproofing. These materials may be applied by painting, rolling, spraying, or hot mopping. Membrane roofs may be placed flat or at any desired angle. Some types, particularly bituminous roofs, may be covered with a layer of small rock. This

(continued on page 96)

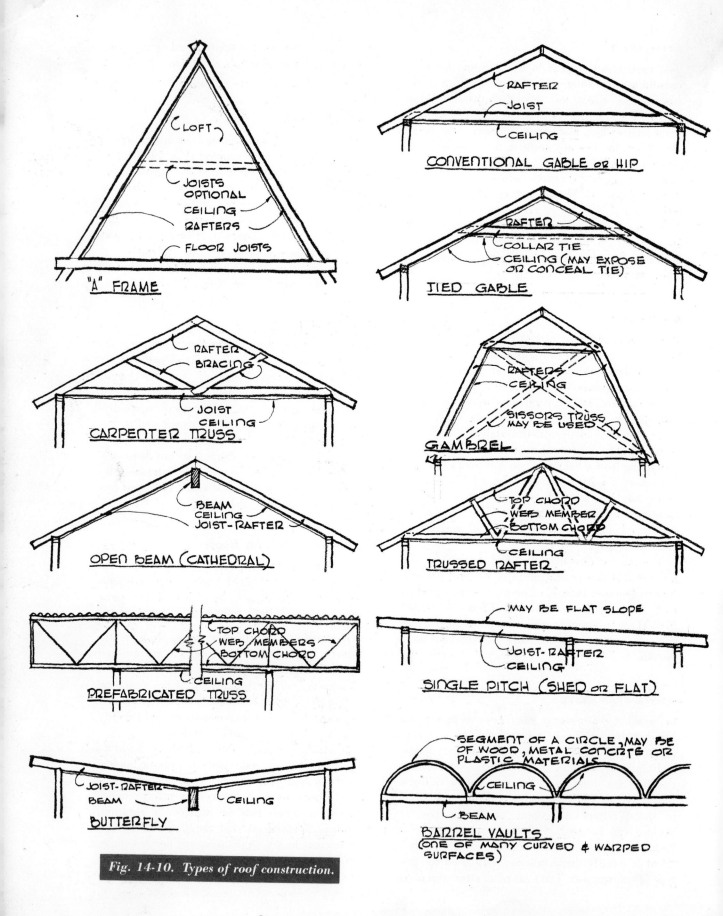

Fig. 14-10. Types of roof construction.

Labels within the figure:

"A" FRAME — LOFT, JOISTS OPTIONAL, CEILING RAFTERS, FLOOR JOISTS

CONVENTIONAL GABLE or HIP — RAFTER, JOIST, CEILING

TIED GABLE — RAFTER, COLLAR TIE, CEILING (MAY EXPOSE OR CONCEAL TIE)

CARPENTER TRUSS — RAFTER, BRACING, JOIST, CEILING

GAMBREL — RAFTERS, CEILING, SISSORS TRUSS MAY BE USED

OPEN BEAM (CATHEDRAL) — BEAM, CEILING, JOIST-RAFTER

TRUSSED RAFTER — TOP CHORD, WEB MEMBER, BOTTOM CHORD, CEILING

PREFABRICATED TRUSS — TOP CHORD, WEB MEMBERS, BOTTOM CHORD, CEILING

SINGLE PITCH (SHED or FLAT) — MAY BE FLAT SLOPE, JOIST-RAFTER, CEILING

BUTTERFLY — JOIST-RAFTER, BEAM, CEILING

BARREL VAULTS (ONE OF MANY CURVED & WARPED SURFACES) — SEGMENT OF A CIRCLE, MAY BE OF WOOD, METAL, CONCRETE OR PLASTIC MATERIALS, CEILING, BEAM

94

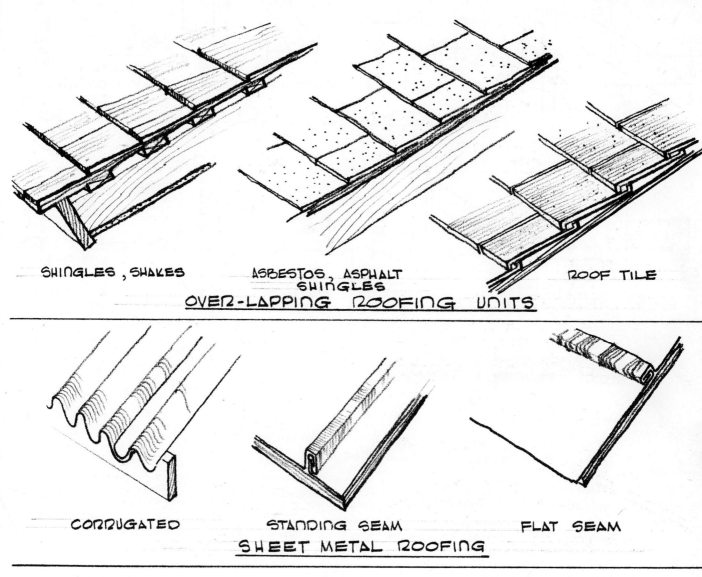

SHINGLES, SHAKES   ASBESTOS, ASPHALT SHINGLES   ROOF TILE

OVER-LAPPING ROOFING UNITS

CORRUGATED   STANDING SEAM   FLAT SEAM

SHEET METAL ROOFING

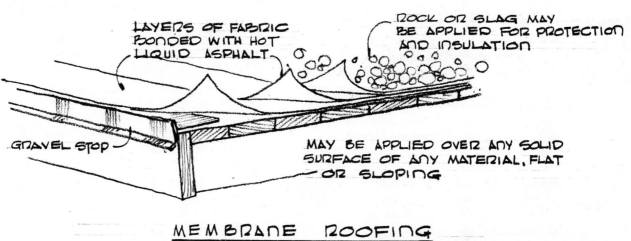

LAYERS OF FABRIC BONDED WITH HOT LIQUID ASPHALT

ROCK OR SLAG MAY BE APPLIED FOR PROTECTION AND INSULATION

GRAVEL STOP

MAY BE APPLIED OVER ANY SOLID SURFACE OF ANY MATERIAL, FLAT OR SLOPING

MEMBRANE ROOFING

Fig. 14-11. Types of roof coverings.

95

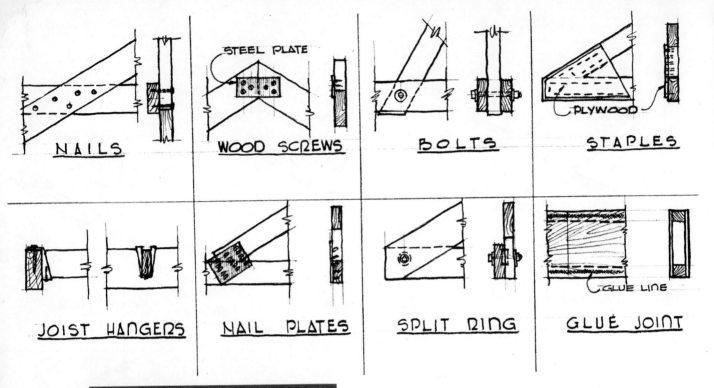

Fig. 14-12. Typical connecting devices.

provides mechanical protection and radiant insulation but will limit the pitch of the roof to less than 3 in 12.

3. Metal roofs: Copper, terneplate, aluminum, lead, galvanized iron, etc., may be used in several ways. The most common joints are overlapping, standing-seam, flat-locked, and soldered. Other methods are also used.

Drains and Gutters

Gutters, drains, or scuppers must be placed at the eaves or low points of the roof. These are connected to downspouts. Pipes, vents, chimneys, etc., which pass through a roof must be provided with waterproof flashings. Flashings must be placed at all valleys in any type but a membrane roof. Gutters, flashings, etc., are described in Chap. 25.

In this discussion of roof systems, most of the methods of construction and special terms have been omitted; however, they are shown in the accompanying illustrations. This eliminates much difficult verbal description, since pictures are easier to understand. The student should avoid the use of any complex roof system in his drawings, because the design of such a roof demands a considerable engineering and practical background.

Fastenings

Many means of connecting the structural members of a building are available. For the purpose of this book, only methods applicable to wood will be discussed (Fig. 14-12).

1. Nails are widely used in small structures. They are cheap, available everywhere, and all workmen are familiar with their use. On the other hand, they sometimes split the wood, and the resulting joints are relatively weak.
2. Screws are less often used but are useful for attaching beam-seat connections, steel plates, etc. They are slower to use and more expensive than nails.
3. Bolts are often used in large structures for assembling trusses, attaching beams and plates, etc. They make possible very secure joints. They are expensive for some uses and require the drilling of holes.
4. Staples are adaptable to such uses as building box beams and plywood-gusseted trusses. Because air-driven guns are used, staples are faster to drive than nails.
5. Joist hangers are used to eliminate the notching of beams and to reduce carpentry labor.
6. Split-ring connectors may be used to join any

two or more intersecting members. The resulting joints are much stronger than nailed joints.

7. Nail plates, because of their tremendous holding power, make it possible to mass-produce trusses cheaply.

8. Adhesives of many types are produced which make it possible to use materials in new ways. Because of the large contact area, glued joints possess tremendous strength.

Some of these joints may be substituted for one another; others, because of design restrictions, building codes, and availability of special equipment are sometimes specifically indicated. The intelligent application of these methods demands a background of engineering design and practical experience.

Drafting the Structural System

After deciding on the type of foundation, wall, floor, ceiling, and roof to be used in the section, the actual drafting of the section is quite easy. The process follows (Fig. 10-3 and A-5):

1. Compute sizes of all members used in construction.
2. Decide on the scale to be used and the amount of space the drawing will occupy. Draw a full section or sections using the scale $\frac{1}{2}$ in. = 1 ft 0 in. or greater.
3. Establish the grade line, bottom of footing, top of foundation wall, finish-floor level, and top of plate as construction lines.
4. Establish the width of the footing and foundation wall, size of the floor joists or thickness of the slab, thickness of the wall, and thickness and pitch of the roof structure.
5. Darken outlines of all structural parts.
6. Draw in all structural connections.
7. Draw in all sheathing and finish materials.
8. Dimension all important parts above and below finish floor.
9. Profile outline of section if desired.
10. Place all call-outs and notes.
11. Draw large-scale details showing structural connections.

Note: Check illustrations for method of dimensioning and location of notes. Refer to the pictorial drawings which define the various structural parts of the building (Fig. 14-3).

REVIEW QUESTIONS

1. Look at a picture of a building in a magazine. Can you draw a reasonably accurate cross section of it based on what is visible from the outside? You will have to make a few educated guesses about certain construction features.

2. In a simple gable roof, why do the ceiling joists run in the same direction as the rafters?

3. Does the term *flat roof* always refer to a horizontal roof?

4. Does the building code in your area require that footings for residential construction go deeper than 12 in. below grade? Why?

5. Are concrete floors often used locally in residential construction? Why?

6. Compare brick, wood-frame, and hollow concrete-block wall sections. What parts perform similar functions at the top and bottom of the walls?

7. In a simple gable roof, what similar functions do the ceiling joists (flat ceiling) and central beam (open-beam ceiling) perform?

8. Why must shingle roofs be steeper than 4 in 12 pitch?

9. *a.* If the total uniformly distributed weight on the perimeter wall of a building is 225,000 lb, the length of the wall is 150 ft, and the bearing capacity of the soil is 2,000 psf, what is the minimum width of continuous running footing which would support the building? (No tables are required.)

   b. Using a bearing capacity of 3,000 psf, what would be the width of the footing?

   c. Under local building codes, what is the minimum width of footing permissible?

10. Assume a 12- by 24-ft rectangular office building with no interior bearing partitions for the following questions. The walls are 8 ft high, and the gable ends are on the 12-ft walls. All joists bear on the 24-ft walls; the roof is 9:12 pitch with a 2-ft overhang all around. The soil is sandy clay. The building materials are slate roof covering, wood-joist roof structure, wood-joist and acoustic-tile ceiling, 2- by 4-in. stud with lath and plaster walls, wood-joist and $\frac{3}{4}$-in. wood floor, and a concrete foundation. Draw a quick perspective sketch of the building for reference, and answer the following questions. (Use A-6a to d.)

    a. What is the weight of the slate roof material? (Remember that the proportions of the roof-pitch triangle are 3:4:5.)

    b. What is the weight of the supporting roof structure?

    c. What is the weight of the ceiling structure?

    d. What is the weight of the wall structure on the long walls?

e. What is the weight of the wall structure on the gable ends?

f. What is the weight of the floor structure?

g. What is the weight of the concrete foundation on the long walls? (Assume a cross section close to the size expected—in this case, 6-in. wall, 6 in. above grade; 12- by 6-in. footing, 24 in. below grade. Use 1.5 cu ft per running foot of wall.)

h. What is the weight of the concrete foundation on the gable-end walls?

11. What are the live loads on the building?

   a. On the roof? (No snow load. Use horizontal distance from eave to eave.)

   b. On the floor?

   c. What is the maximum allowable bearing value of sandy clay?

12. What is the minimum allowable width of the footing on the long walls? (These walls must bear the live and dead loads of the floor and roof, the dead load of the long walls, and the weight of the concrete in the foundations under the long walls.)

13. What is the minimum allowable width of the footing on the gable-end walls? (These walls need only bear the weight of the gable-end wall and the concrete foundation.)

14. What is the minimum width of footing allowed by code?

15. Assume a foundation footing of the following dimensions: $d = 6$ in., $w = 23$ in., $t = 6$ in. Will it be necessary to use reinforcing steel in this footing? (Refer to A-7.) How many No. 4 bars would be needed?

16. What size and spacing of joists is required to span 21 ft under the following conditions: no plaster below (therefore deflection is not critical), 1,450-lb fiber stress, 40-lb live load, 12-in. joist spacing? (Refer to A-8.)

17. What size and spacing of joists is required to span 21 ft under the following conditions: plaster below (therefore deflection must be limited to 1/360 of span), 40-lb live load, 12-in. joist spacing? (Refer to A-8.)

18. What is the allowable load on a built-up girder under the following conditions: 1,450-lb fiber stress, 2 by 10, span 17 ft? (Refer to A-13c.)

19. What is the maximum span permitted with 3 by 6 sugar-pine decking with a live load of 50 psf? (Refer to A-9.)

20. What is the maximum span permitted using 2 by 6 joists at 16 in. o.c. when there is access to the attic? (Refer to A-13.)

21. What is the maximum span permitted using 2 by 6 joists at 16 in. o.c. when there is no access to the attic? (Refer to A-13.)

22. What size lintel would be required to span 9 ft 0 in. in a single-story frame building? (Refer to A-10.)

23. *a.* What size wood rafter is required to span 10 ft under the following conditions: 24-in. spacing, 1,200-psi fiber stress, roof slope $2\frac{1}{2}$:12, 20-lb live load + 8-lb dead load? (Refer to A-12.)

   b. What size wood rafter is required to span 10 ft under the above conditions but with a fiber stress of 1,000 psi?

   c. What distance can a wood rafter span under the following conditions: 12-in. spacing, 1,500-psi fiber stress, roof slope 9:12, 16-lb live load + 8-lb dead load?

24. What is the maximum distance between supports in any direction of an 8-in. reinforced-masonry exterior bearing wall? (Refer to A-11.)

STUDY SUGGESTIONS

1. Compare the drawings of a partially completed building with the actual construction. Try to identify all the structural parts, and describe their functional purposes.

2. Visit the building sites of structures of several different types of construction. Try to determine the practical reasons for the use of each structural system for the particular job.

3. The questions in this section are extremely simple and are based on the use of tables. To get a more comprehensive picture of what is involved, get a textbook on elementary design and study further.

Chapter
15
Stair and Fireplace Details

Place in Drawings

Fireplace and stair construction have no necessary relationship to each other; they are grouped together here only for convenience. Because these drawings have such a great effect on the total structure and affect other drawings in the set to such an extent, they are discussed separately. In a set of drawings, however, the stair and fireplace details are grouped with the miscellaneous details.

Definition of Stair Details

Stair details show the structure, stair size, posts, rails and balusters, materials, and method of attachment to the structure. Sizes and clearances are dimensioned, and all materials are called out by note. The usual scale is full section $\frac{1}{2}$ in. = 1 ft 0 in., small sections, baluster, post, rail, newel, etc., $1\frac{1}{2}$ in. = 1 ft 0 in. to 3 in. = 1 ft 0 in. (Fig. 15-1).

PRELIMINARY DRAWINGS

Staircases must be carefully planned before working drawings are started. The procedure for laying out the longitudinal section follows (Fig. 15-2):

1. Establish the two floor levels.
2. Draw the thickness of the flooring and joists of the floor above to scale.
3. Divide the vertical distance from finish floor to finish floor into equal increments of rise (approximately 7 in. is comfortable, 9 in. is maximum). Determine the run. (A simple formula is Run = 75 in./Rise. This works well for average stairs.)

4. Establish the angle of the staircase based on the dimensions of total rise and run.
5. Draw the outlines of the individual steps.
6. Place a construction line parallel to the staircase and 6 ft 6 in. vertically above the nose of the tread. This represents the minimum headroom. The open end of the stairwell will be at the point where this line passes through the bottom line of the top-floor construction. This method can also be used with a staircase which changes direction and with a circular staircase.

The working drawings will be based on the foregoing construction. Other drawings, such as the floor plan, floor framing plan, and interior and exterior elevations, are affected by the size, shape, and structure of the stairs.

DRAFTING OF THE STAIR DETAILS

The procedure in drawing the longitudinal stair section follows (Fig. 15-3):

1. Copy the construction just described.
2. Lay out the structural members of the staircase, e.g., stringer, tread, riser. Construction methods vary, so local methods should be followed.
3. Draw in treads, risers, and other members. (Construction lines show the *outline* of the stairs. Thickness of tread and riser must be subtracted to find the shape of the stringer).
4. Place all notes, dimensions, title, and scale.

TRANSVERSE SECTIONS

Transverse sections are drawn in the same order

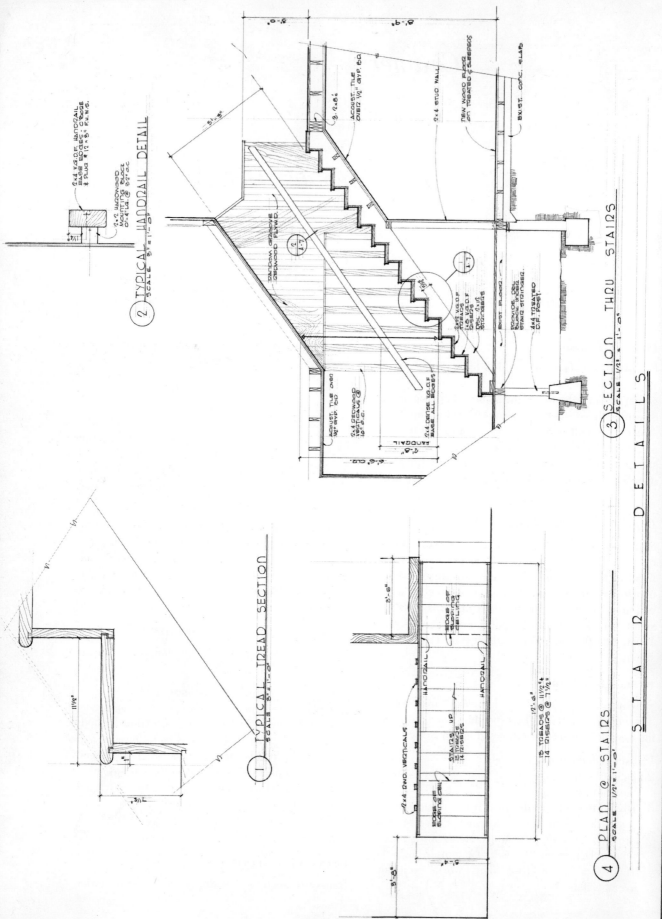

100

Fig. 15-1. *Stair details of a small residence. (This drawing has no relation to the set of drawings developed in this book.)*

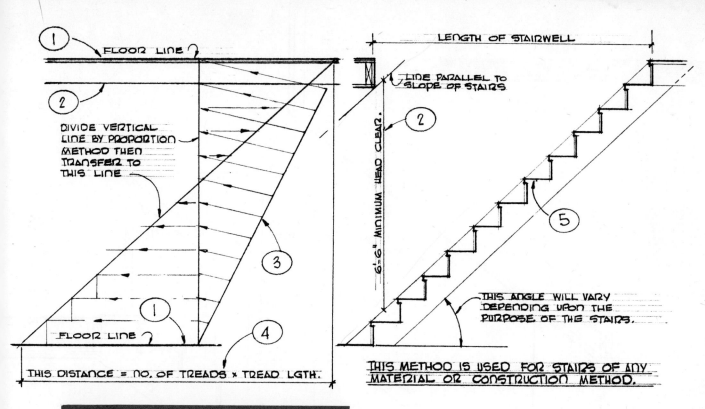

Fig. 15-2.   *Procedure in laying out a staircase.*

from Step 2 above; they must agree in projection with the longitudinal section. Elevations of the stairs appear on either the interior or exterior elevations or both. Posts, rails, balusters, and trim are shown in the elevations. Cross sections of these members are shown along with the other stair sections (Fig. 15-4).

Elevators, dumbwaiters, and hoists also affect the structure to a great extent. Because of the wide variety of such devices and their relatively infrequent use in residential and light-commercial structures, they will not be discussed here. Information is available in "Architectural Graphic Standards" and various manufacturers' catalogs.

Definition of Fireplace Details

Fireplace drawings show a section through the foundation, the fireplace, and the chimney to the cap, as well as transverse sections (Fig. 15-5). A fireplace may be built of most masonry materials or common metals. It may be a ready-built unit or built on the job. The only restrictive factors involved in fireplace design are the area of the fireplace opening, the flue area, and the height of the chimney. These factors may easily be derived from tables in the back of the book (see A-15). Hardware is available for practically any shape of fireplace

desired (Fig. 15-6). In addition, well-engineered metal fireplaces may be purchased from many sources and installation is a small problem. The drawing in Fig. 15-7 shows all construction— foundation, cleanout, hearth, firebox, smoke shelf, damper, flue, cap, and surrounding masonry. If the fireplace is a factory-built metal unit, installation drawings are available from the manufacturer. Dimensions are shown where needed; all materials are called out by note. Scale is usually $\frac{1}{2}$ in. = 1 ft 0 in.

DRAFTING OF THE FIREPLACE DETAILS

The procedure in drawing a vertical fireplace section follows:

1. Establish the groundline, or base, of the fireplace and the floor, roof, and ceiling structures as light lines.

2. Draw the inside of the firebox, smoke shelf, and flue.

3. Draw the outline of the masonry, or exterior finish, of the fireplace and the foundation.

4. Place smaller details such as damper, hearth, chimney cap, location of reinforcing steel, method of flashing, and chimney ties.

5. Dimension as needed.

(continued on page 108)

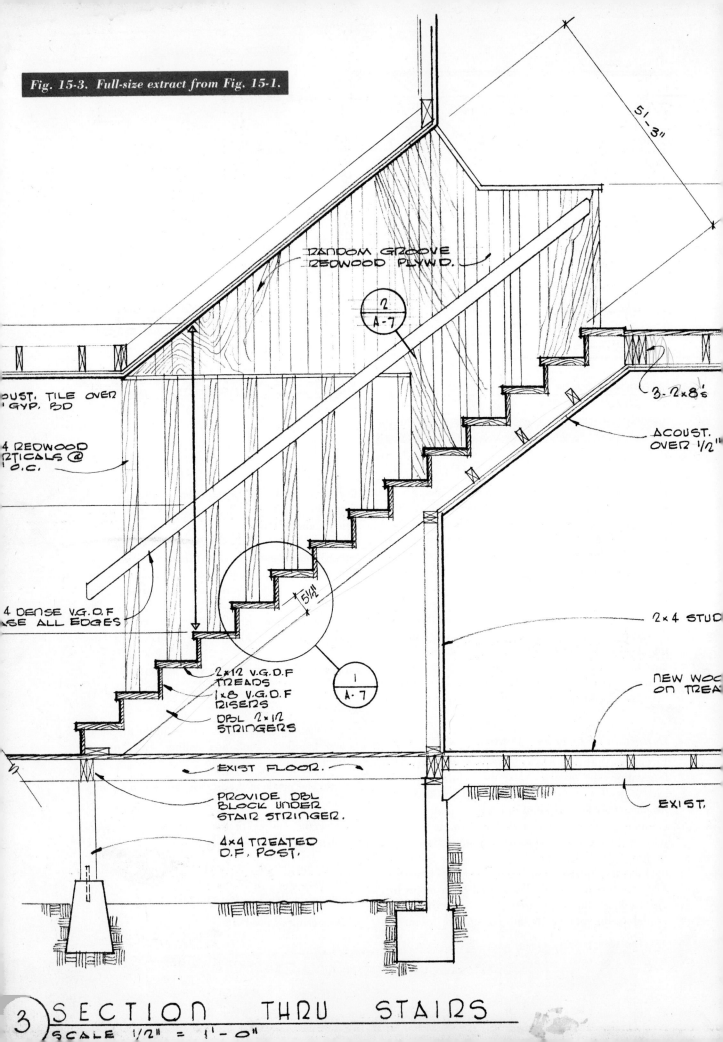

Fig. 15-3. *Full-size extract from Fig. 15-1.*

RANDOM GROOVE
REDWOOD PLYWD.

2 / A-7

COUST. TILE OVER
GYP. BD

4 REDWOOD
RTICALS @
O.C.

3-2×8's

ACOUST.
OVER 1/2"

4 DENSE V.G.D.F
ASE ALL EDGES

5½"

1 / A-7

2×4 STUD

2×12 V.G.D.F
TREADS
1×8 V.G.D.F
RISERS
DBL 2×12
STRINGERS

NEW WOO
ON TREA

EXIST FLOOR.

PROVIDE DBL
BLOCK UNDER
STAIR STRINGER.

4×4 TREATED
D.F. POST.

EXIST.

51-3"

3 SECTION THRU STAIRS

SCALE 1/2" = 1'-0"

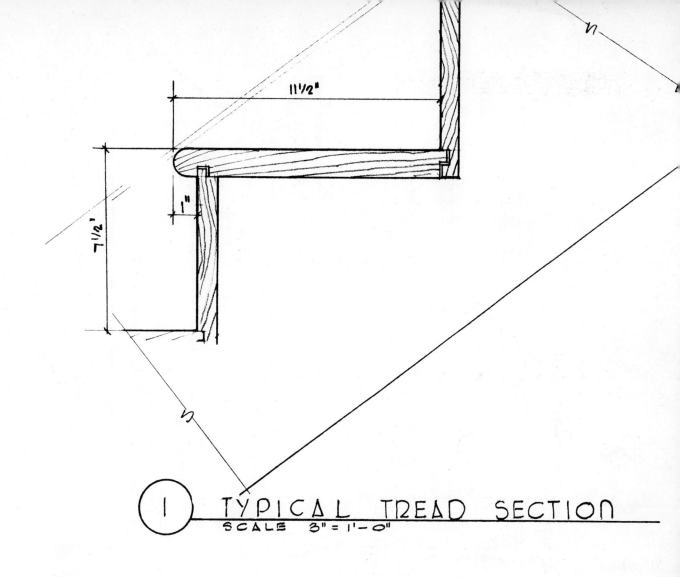

11½"

1"

7½"

N

N

① TYPICAL TREAD SECTION
SCALE 3" = 1'-0"

Fig. 15-4. Full-size extract from Fig. 15-1.

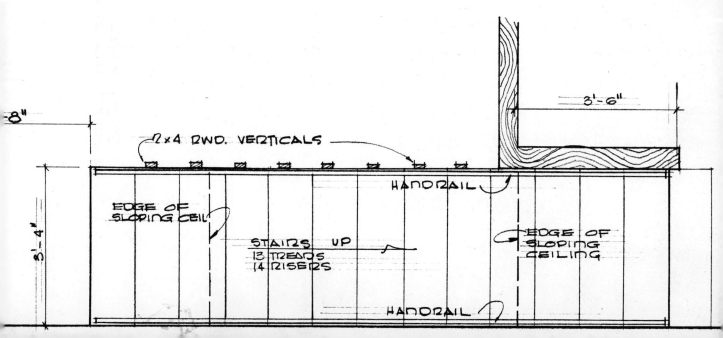

8"

3'-6"

2 x 4 RWD. VERTICALS

HANDRAIL

EDGE OF
SLOPING CEIL'

3'-4"

STAIRS   UP
13 TREADS
14 RISERS

EDGE OF
SLOPING
CEILING

HANDRAIL

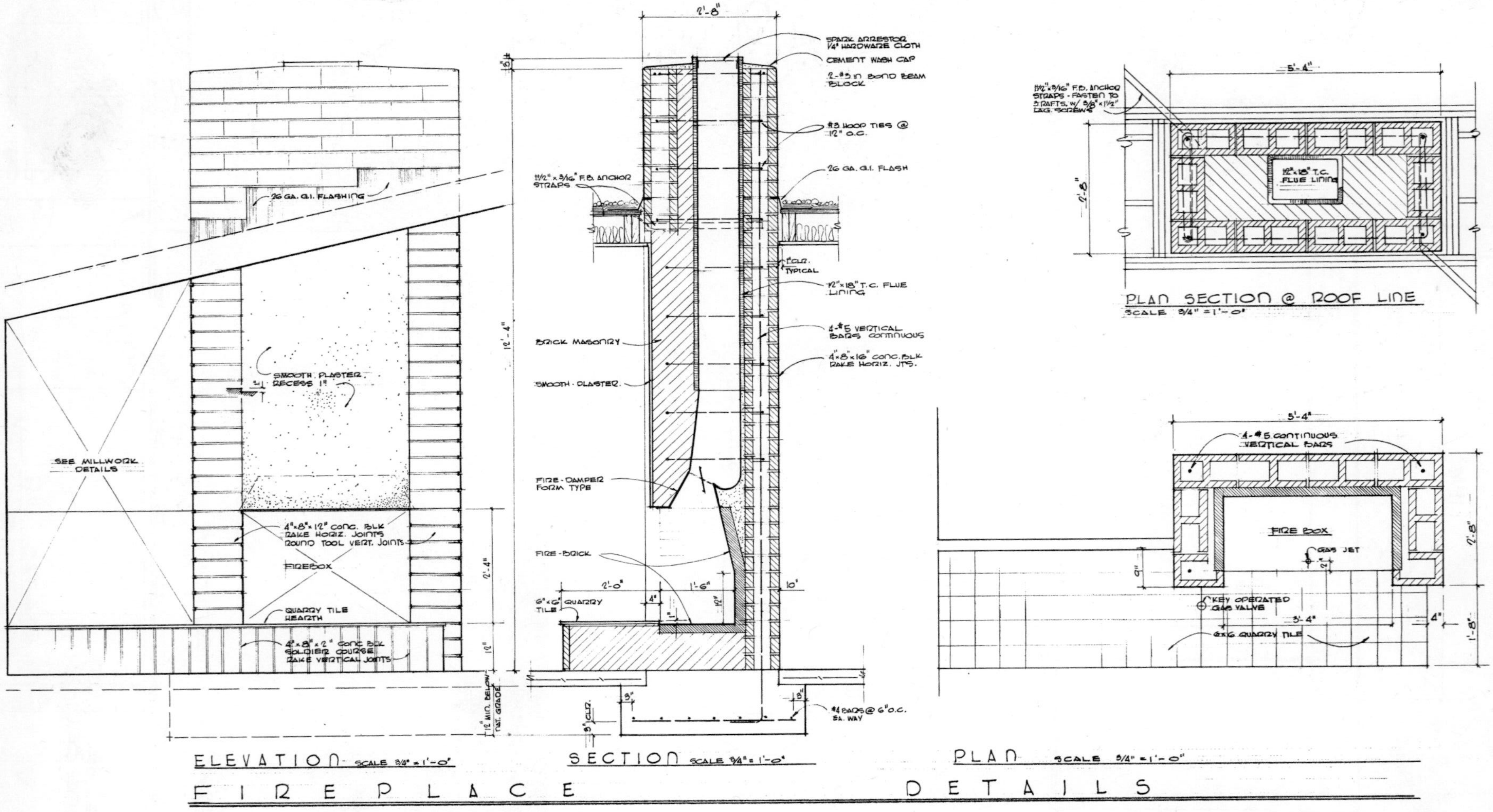

Fig. 15-5. Fireplace details of a small residence.

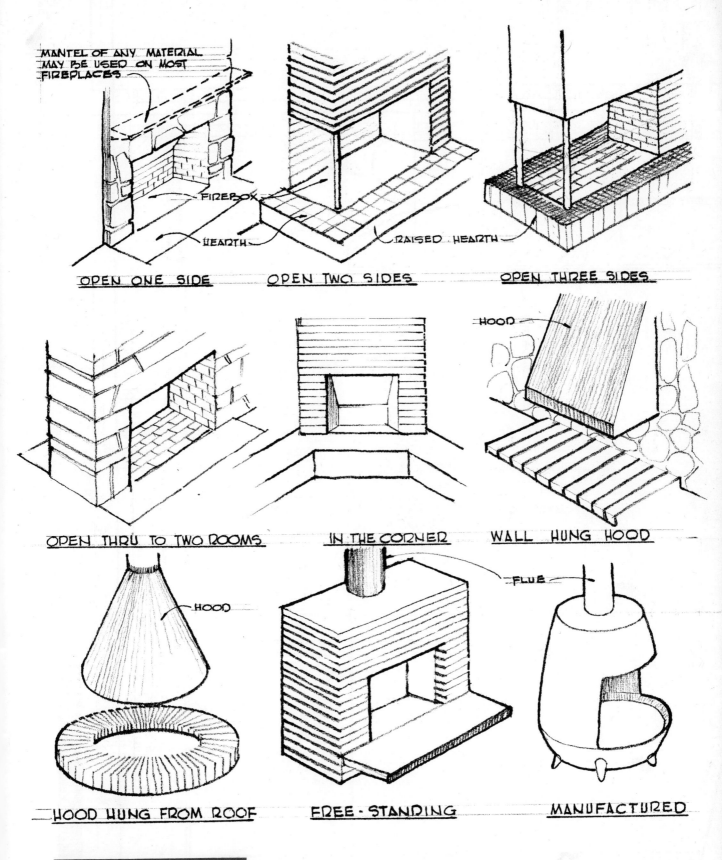

MANTEL OF ANY MATERIAL MAY BE USED ON MOST FIREPLACES

FIREBOX

HEARTH

RAISED HEARTH

HOOD

OPEN ONE SIDE   OPEN TWO SIDES   OPEN THREE SIDES

OPEN THRU TO TWO ROOMS   IN THE CORNER   WALL HUNG HOOD

HOOD

FLUE

HOOD HUNG FROM ROOF   FREE-STANDING   MANUFACTURED

Fig. 15-6. Types of fireplaces.

105

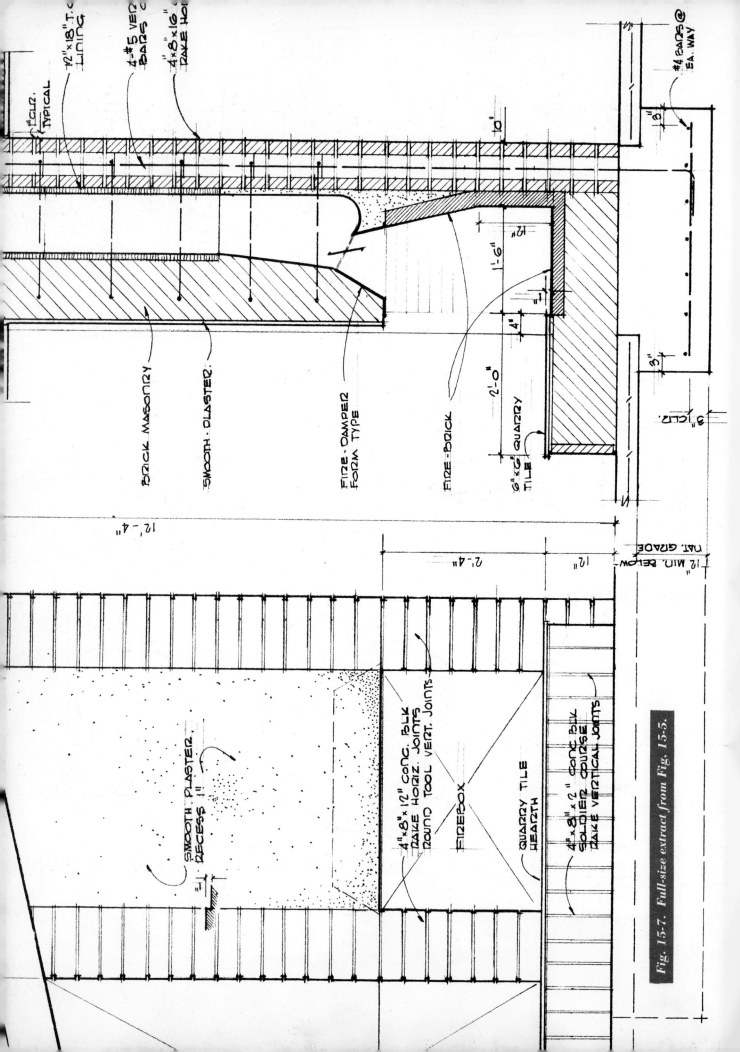

Fig. 15-7. Full-size extract from Fig. 15-5.

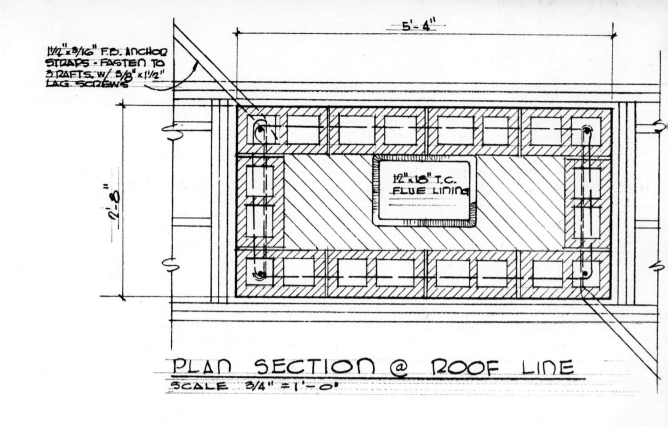

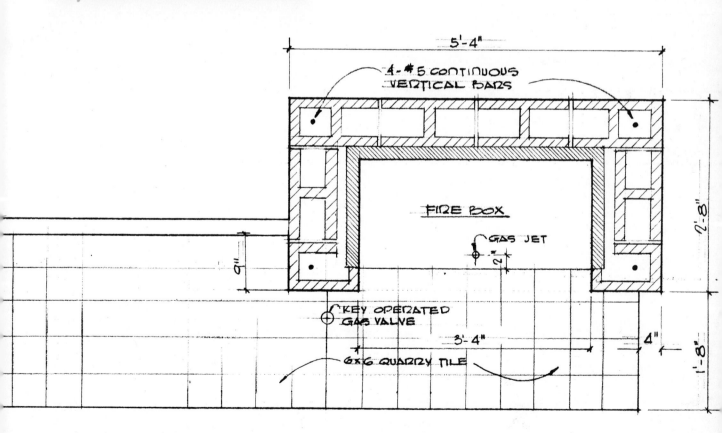

Fig. 15-8. Full-size extract from Fig. 15-5.

6. Letter in all notes, title, and scale. Because of the height of a fireplace section, break lines are sometimes drawn across the flue to reduce its height.

HORIZONTAL SECTIONS

Horizontal sections are also taken to show the plan shape and the construction of the fireplace at flue, cleanout, and firebox (Fig. 15-8).

REVIEW QUESTIONS

1. Outline the procedure in designing a staircase.
2. What drawings are affected by the staircase?
3. What are the functional parts required in any fireplace?
4. What is the rule for establishing the height of a chimney above a roof? (Uniform Building Code)

STUDY SUGGESTIONS

1. Check through an existing set of drawings to see the effects of the stairs and fireplace on each drawing.
2. Visit a building-supply house, and look at the fireplace and staircase hardware available, such as fireplace forms, dampers, hoods, complete fireplaces, metal treads, rails, and balusters.
3. Further tables and planning information are available from many sources, such as "Time-Saver Standards," and "Architectural Graphic Standards." Study these.

Chapter

16

Exterior Elevations

Definition and Purpose

The purpose of the exterior elevations is to show the finished appearance of all outside aspects of the building (Figs. 16-1 and 16-2). Each elevation is an orthographic projection of one view of the building based on the floor plan and the structural sections. Other drawings, for instance the roof plan, are occasionally needed to find points not easily derived from these two. All surface materials are indicated as well as the locations of important structural features—floor line, plate line, and window and door heights. Exterior elevations are usually drawn at the same scale as the floor plan.

Drawing by Direct Projection

When drawing the elevations, you may use either direct projection or measurement. To fix the relationships of the three drawings firmly in mind, it is a good idea for the beginner to try at least one job by direct projection. Basically, the procedure is the same as a "missing-view problem" in elementary drawing in which the floor plan is the top view, the structural section is the side view, and the elevation is the missing front view. This method is rather cumbersome with a large building but works easily with a small one.

REQUIRED DRAWINGS

Before starting, a copy of each of the different sections through the structure must be drawn at the same scale as the floor plan. These must be drawn on a separate sheet, not on the elevation drawings. It is important that the width of each section jibe with the width of the floor plan at the point the section is taken and that all height measurements, roof pitch, etc., be taken accurately from the structural sections. It is a good idea to draw the roof plan over the floor plan (first draft, not finished drawing) for more accurate projection. First decide how many elevations will be required to give a complete description of the building; then space them by light outlines on the sheet or sheets required. Leave room for a title and scale under each elevation.

DRAFTING THE EXTERIOR ELEVATIONS

The steps in drawing the elevations by direct projection follow in logical order (Fig. 16-3):

1. Place the floor plan, with the outside wall facing down, directly above the space desired. This is important; if projected upward, a mirror image of that wall will result. To one side and in line with the desired space, place the required structural section or sections. All elevations will be exactly the same height overall.

2. Project a series of light lines from the floor plan to the working space. These lines represent length, or horizontal features of the building, such as ends of walls, eaves, windows, and doors. Project a series of light lines across from the sections to represent height, or vertical features of the building, such as grade line, floor line, window and door height, plate line, and ridge line.

3. Darken the lines slightly as needed, and erase those which might later be misleading. The result at this stage is a rough elevation lacking detail but giving a good idea of the ultimate appearance of that particular wall.

4. Repeat this procedure for all the required elevations. Take care to rotate the floor plan for each

(continued on page 114)

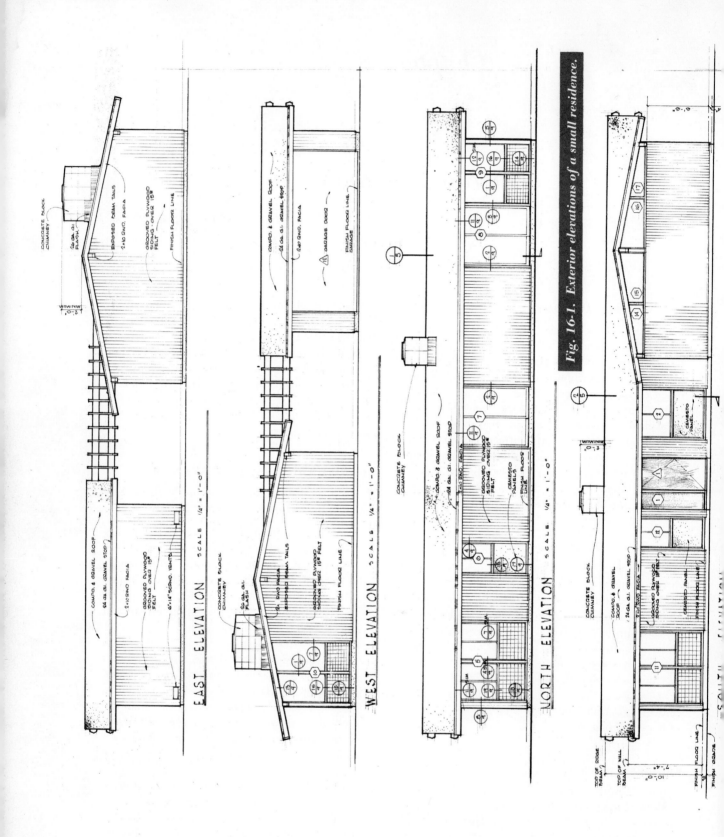

Fig. 16-1. Exterior elevations of a small residence.

110

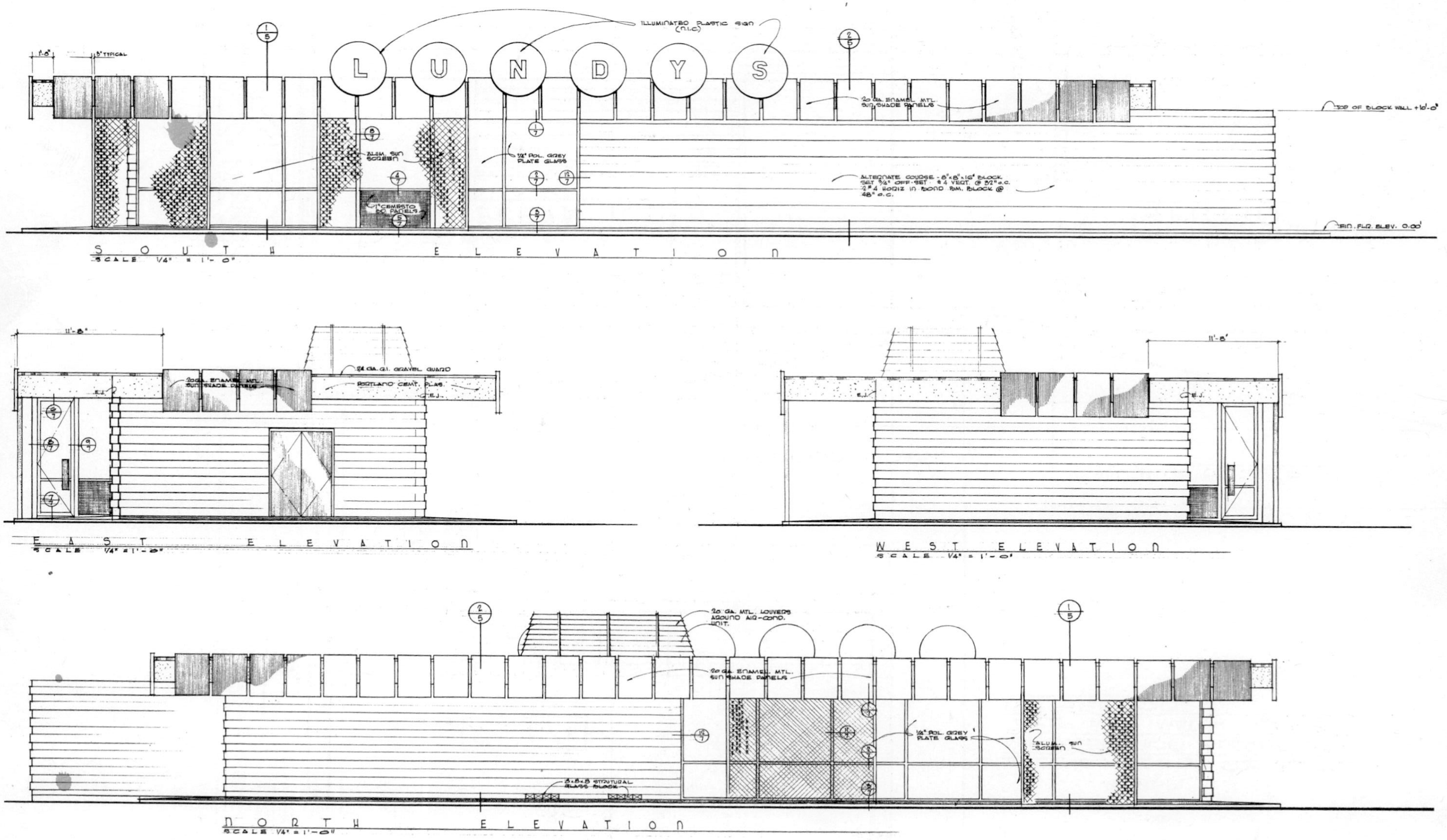

Fig. 16-2. Exterior elevation of a small restaurant.

111

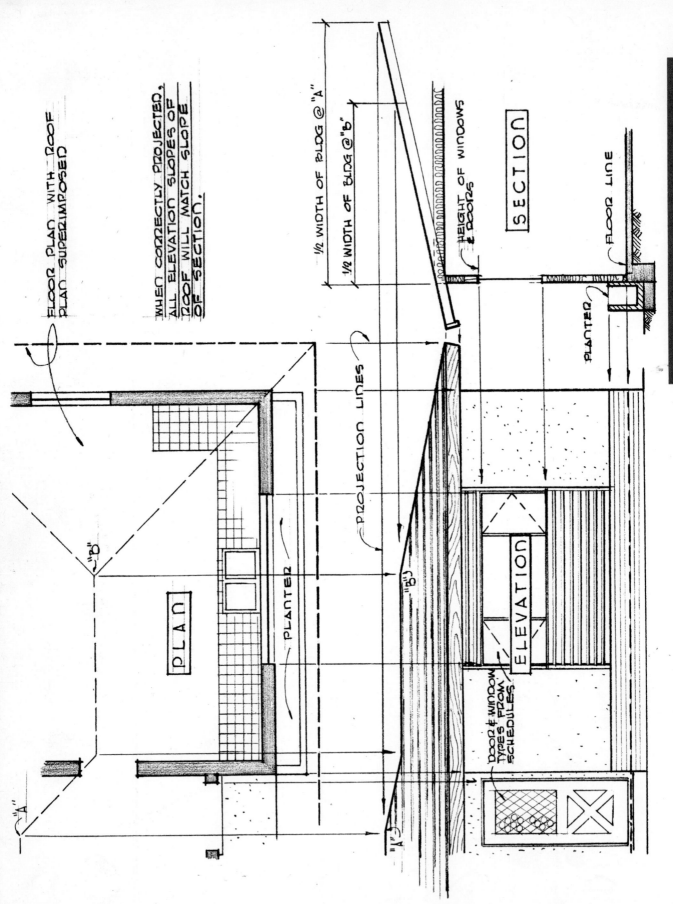

FLOOR PLAN WITH ROOF PLAN SUPERIMPOSED

WHEN CORRECTLY PROJECTED, ALL ELEVATION SLOPES OF ROOF WILL MATCH SLOPE OF SECTION.

½ WIDTH OF BLDG @ "A"

½ WIDTH OF BLDG @ "B"

HEIGHT OF WINDOWS & DOORS

SECTION

FLOOR LINE

PLANTER

"B"

"A"

PLAN

PLANTER

PROJECTION LINES

"B"

"A"

ELEVATION

DOOR & WINDOW TYPES FROM SCHEDULES

PLANTER

Fig. 16-3. Method of direct projection of elevations.

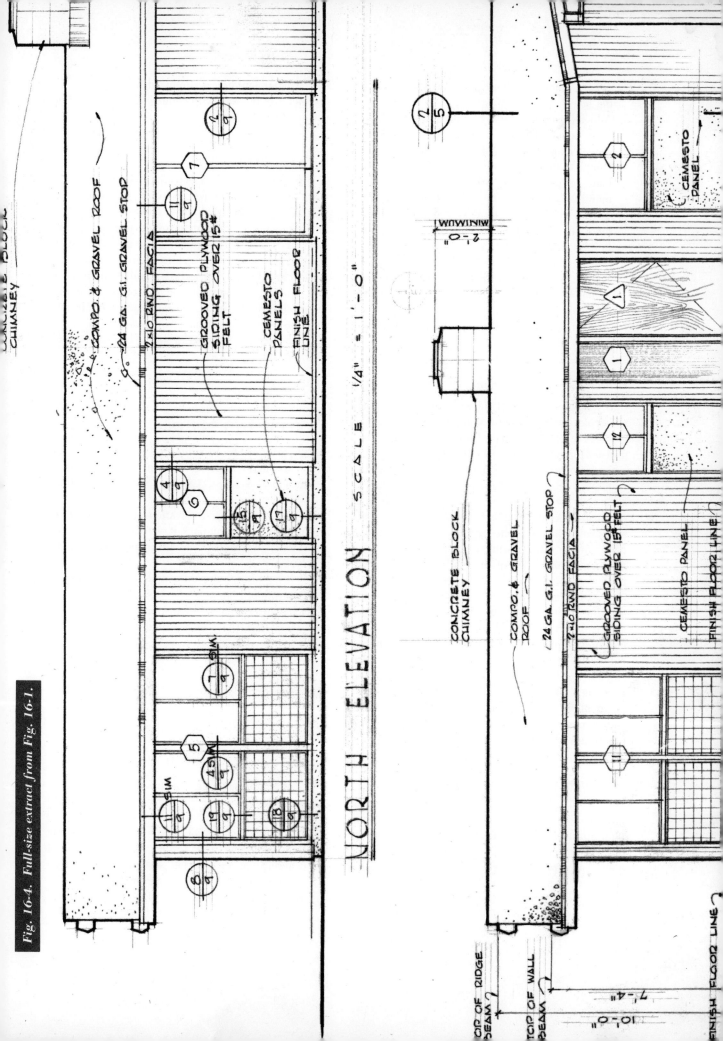

Fig. 16-4. Full-size extract from Fig. 16-1.

NORTH ELEVATION SCALE 1/4" = 1'-0"

CONCRETE BLOCK CHIMNEY

4" COMPO. & GRAVEL ROOF

24 GA. G.I. GRAVEL STOP

2×10 RND. FACIA

GROOVED PLYWOOD SIDING OVER 15# FELT

CEMESTO PANELS

FINISH FLOOR LINE

CONCRETE BLOCK CHIMNEY

COMPO. & GRAVEL ROOF

24 GA. G.I. GRAVEL STOP

2×10 RND FACIA

GROOVED PLYWOOD SIDING OVER 15# FELT

CEMESTO PANEL

CEMESTO PANEL

FINISH FLOOR LINE

FINISH FLOOR LINE

2'-0" MINIMUM

TOP OF RIDGE BEAM

TOP OF WALL BEAM

7'-4"

10'-0"

view. Remove the floor plan and sections from the board.

5. Add all porches, railings, chimneys, trim, and other small details in the order of their importance and line weight. Information needed to complete this part of the drawing is drawn from many sources. The arrangement of window muntins is found in the manufacturer's catalog. The chimney is usually designed by the draftsman, and its height is determined by local building codes. Other sources include "Time-Saver Standards," "Architectural Graphic Standards," "Sweet's File," construction details of the building, and the draftsman's judgment.

6. Place all notes, title, and scale.

7. Draw in textures of all materials, and profile the drawing if desired.

Drawing by Measurement

It is not mandatory that the elevations be directly projected from the floor plan and sections. The alternative is to measure from the drawings and transfer the required points to the sheet. A *tick strip*, or scrap of paper with "ticks" in line with walls, windows, etc., may be used to transfer distances accurately. It is important, however, that the right end of the elevation appear on the right side of the sheet and that absolute agreement in projection exist among all drawings concerned. For these reasons, a knowledge of the method of direct projection is considered desirable. A few quick tests, quite easy to understand, can be made as the drawing progresses which will detect serious error and avoid redrawing. For instance, if the north elevation happens to be high at the left side of the paper, the south elevation must be high at the right side. If the building has a pitched roof, say a hip roof, then the pitches of all roofs in all views will be identical with the roof pitch of the section. In addition, agreement in projection between selected points can be checked in all three drawings.

Developed and Rotated Elevations

If a building has a wing projecting from the main part at other than a right angle or if it has an odd plan form, say a circle, there are two ways of drawing the elevations. Direct projection, as shown above, is one way; development is the other. A developed elevation is produced merely by rotating the skewed section into the plane of projection and then projecting normally. A developed elevation

of a circular building is produced by laying out the perimeter of the wall with windows, doors, etc., laid out in a straight line.

Use of Texture

Texture can be used on elevations in either of two ways, i.e., complete rendition of all textures or partial rendition (Fig. 16-4 and A-5). Taste or office practice usually determines which is to be used. The use of complete texturing takes more drafting time, but some architects prefer its appearance. Partial texturing is faster and, if done well, will appeal to many people. Textures for many materials are shown in the reference section, and their use is self-explanatory. In either case, the areas of each type of material should be called out by note.

REVIEW QUESTIONS

1. Try to draw an elevation based on the floor plan of a small building without reference to a structural section. Can you do it accurately? Why?

2. Sketch a developed elevation of an odd-shaped building, and compare it with the normal elevation. What are the advantages and disadvantages of both methods?

3. Is it possible to draw a complete elevation from only a floor plan and a cross section? Explain.

4. What direct effect did the preliminary orientation sketches have on your elevation?

5. Is it possible to see a finished building as an accurate elevation? In other words, in orthographic projection?

6. Show how an elevation is related to several other working drawings.

STUDY SUGGESTIONS

1. Visit a building under construction, and compare the exterior of the building with the exterior elevations.

2. Try some sketches of your own project, using the floor plan and several cross sections of different shape, different sizes and proportions of doors and windows, and several combinations of exterior finishes. Some of these solutions may seem better to you than your first idea.

Chapter

17

Foundation Plan

Definition and Purpose

The foundation plan shows the extent and location of all concrete footings, flatwork, and underpinning of the building (Fig. 17-1). Masonry fences, masonry walls above grade, and swimming pools are not included; they are usually shown on separate sheets. The primary purpose of the foundation is to distribute the weight of the building over the soil. The Appendix contains formulas and data for use in simple foundation design. These should be used in unusual situations. Most students, however, will follow local building codes in determining the sizes of footings, walls, etc. Concrete is most often used in foundations, though stone and other masonry materials may be used.

Types of Foundations

Though there are many types of foundations and floor systems in use, only the two types most commonly used for residential and light-commercial structures will be discussed, i.e., wood-floor and concrete-floor construction. Wood-floor construction uses outside foundation walls and interior supports of one type or another to carry the wood construction above grade (Fig. 17-2). All forces from above are transmitted from these supports through the footings to the soil. In concrete-floor construction, wall loads are carried through the footings to the soil; the floor loads are carried by the soil beneath the concrete slab.

Each system has certain advantages and disadvantages. It is up to the individual to choose the one that suits his purpose best. Wood floors have a

texture and appearance that cannot be achieved with concrete. It is possible to work on the plumbing under a wood floor easily, and some people feel that a wood floor is more resilient than a concrete floor. Concrete floors are usually cheaper to build, warmer in winter, and cooler in summer than wood. They are quieter, because audible vibrations are not easily transmitted through concrete.

Required Information

All foundation plans should include:

1. Plan views of:
    - a. Foundation walls and footing of all buildings
    - b. Interior footing or dwarf walls
    - c. Piers and footing pads
    - d. Walls below grade (basements)
    - e. Locations of girders and beams supporting floors, walls, etc.
    - f. Walks, driveways, and paved outdoor areas
    - g. Other footings, curbs, gutters, and areaways
2. Cross-sectional details of all foundation work usually drawn at $\frac{3}{4}$ in. = 1 ft 0 in. scale
3. Complete dimensioning and notes to go with the above drawings

Preliminary Steps

The foundation plan is based on the floor plan as are all other plan views in the set. The best procedure is to trace the outline of the building from the floor plan in light lines. Show the center lines of any bearing walls, the locations of all outside entrances, and any isolated columns as light lines.

(continued on page 118)

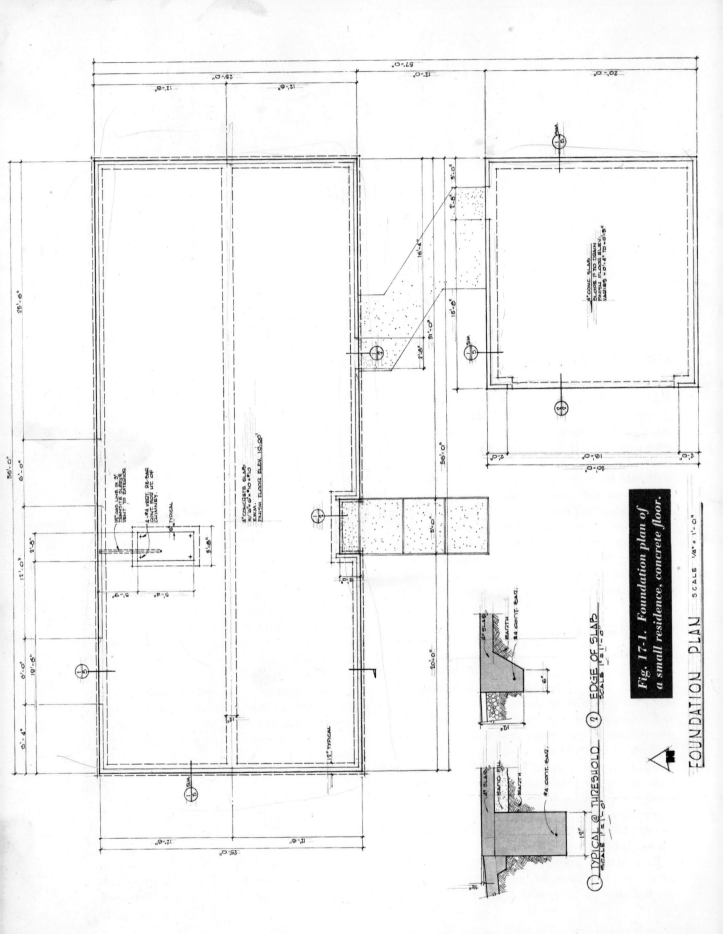

Fig. 17-1. Foundation plan of a small residence, concrete floor.

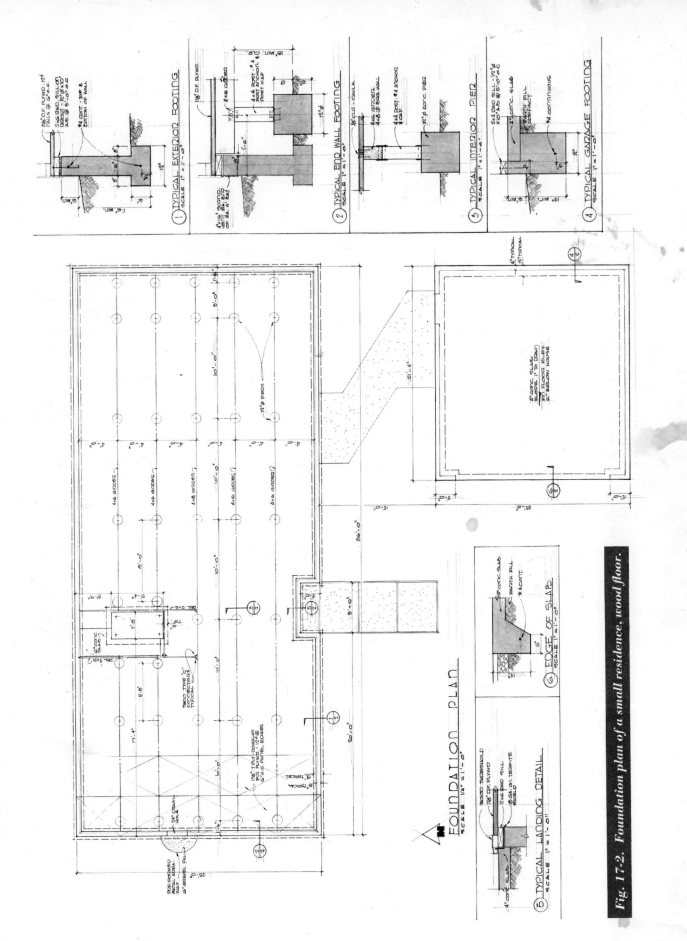

Fig. 17-2. Foundation plan of a small residence, wood floor.

117

Locate the inside of basement walls, planters, fireplaces, below-grade pits or above-grade slabs, and underground piping and ductwork in the same way. It is important to do this in order to avoid having concrete poured in the wrong places. These lines will determine the extent and location of foundation work.

Remove the floor plan from beneath the tracing to avoid possible damage, and then proceed with the foundation plan. It is assumed at this point that the student knows the sizes of all footings, walls, and flatwork; the locations and spacing of all girders and beams, etc. This information is derived from local building codes and the design data in the Appendix (see A-6 and A-7). As a general rule, all foundation walls are drawn as visible lines and footings as hidden lines. The edges of flatwork and any breaks or changes in elevation of concrete are shown in visible lines. Any feature underneath the concrete is shown as a hidden line. In visualizing the plan view of any part, refer to the cross-sectional detail involved.

Though there are many other types of construction, only the procedures for drawing the foundation plan of a wood-floored structure and a concrete-floored structure will be explained here. In each case it is assumed that the construction lines showing the outside walls, interior bearing walls, entrances, columns, inside of basement walls, masonry planters or fireplaces, below-grade pits or above-grade slabs, and underground piping are already placed.

Drafting the Foundation Plan for a Wood Floor

The procedure in drawing the foundation plan for a wood-floored structure follows (Fig. 17-3):

1. Size all concrete and wood structural parts (see A-6 to A-10).
2. Mark all breaks in the outside foundation walls (crawl holes, doors, windows), and locate porches.
3. Draw the outline of the foundation wall (usually 6 in. thick).
4. Draw the footings for the outside walls.
5. Draw the interior bearing walls or piers.
6. Draw the porches to the desired size in line with the entrances.
7. Draw in the locations of all columns, piers, and isolated footings.
8. Draw the basement walls and concrete steps if used.

9. Draw the fireplace and other masonry footings.
10. Draw any below-grade pits or above-grade slabs.
11. Draw in any under-floor ducts.
12. Show size and spacing of all floor joists with a double-pointed arrow.
13. Show the location of bearing walls as center lines. If parallel to joists, indicate doubled joists; if perpendicular to joists, indicate solid blocking between joists.
14. Place all section-keying symbols.
15. Draw in dimension lines.
16. Draw all sections indicated by keying symbols. Show all typical constructions (wall, interior bearing wall, etc.) plus the places where different constructions come together (such as porch to foundation wall). Place the appropriate keying symbol under each section along with the scale.
17. Place all lettering, notes, title, and scale.

Drafting the Foundation Plan for a Concrete Floor

The procedure in drawing the foundation plan for a concrete-floored structure follows (Fig. 17-4):

1. Size all concrete structural parts (see A-6 and A-7).
2. Locate all porches.
3. Draw the outline of the foundation wall showing wall breaks and centers of foundation bolts.
4. Draw the footings for the outside walls.
5. Draw the interior footings.
6. Draw porches on line with the desired openings.
7. Draw in the positions of all columns, piers, and isolated footings.
8. Draw the basement walls and concrete steps.
9. Draw the fireplace or other masonry footings.
10. Draw any below-grade pits.
11. Draw in under-floor ducts.
12. Place all section-keying symbols.
13. Draw in dimension lines.
14. Draw all sections indicated by keying symbols (see wood-floor construction).
15. Place all lettering, notes, title, and scale.

Dimensioning

Dimensioning of foundation plans is similar to the dimensioning of floor plans (Figs. 17-1 and 17-2). The outside line shows the overall size of the foundation. The second line shows all breaks, cen-

(continued on page 123)

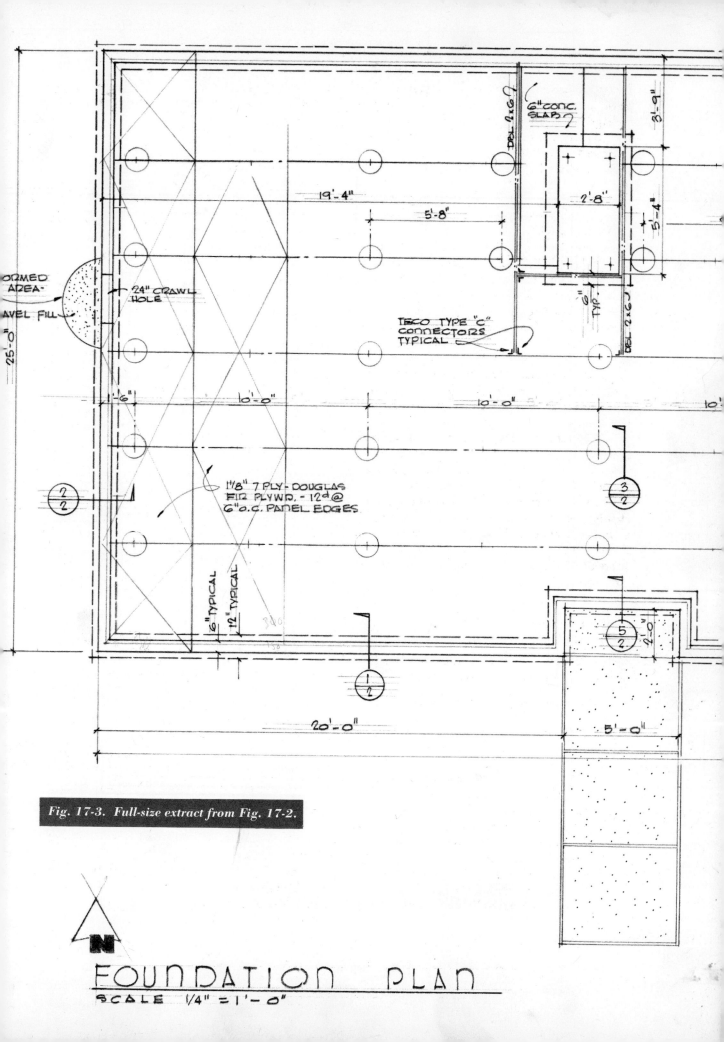

Fig. 17-3. Full-size extract from Fig. 17-2.

FOUNDATION PLAN

SCALE 1/4" = 1'-0"

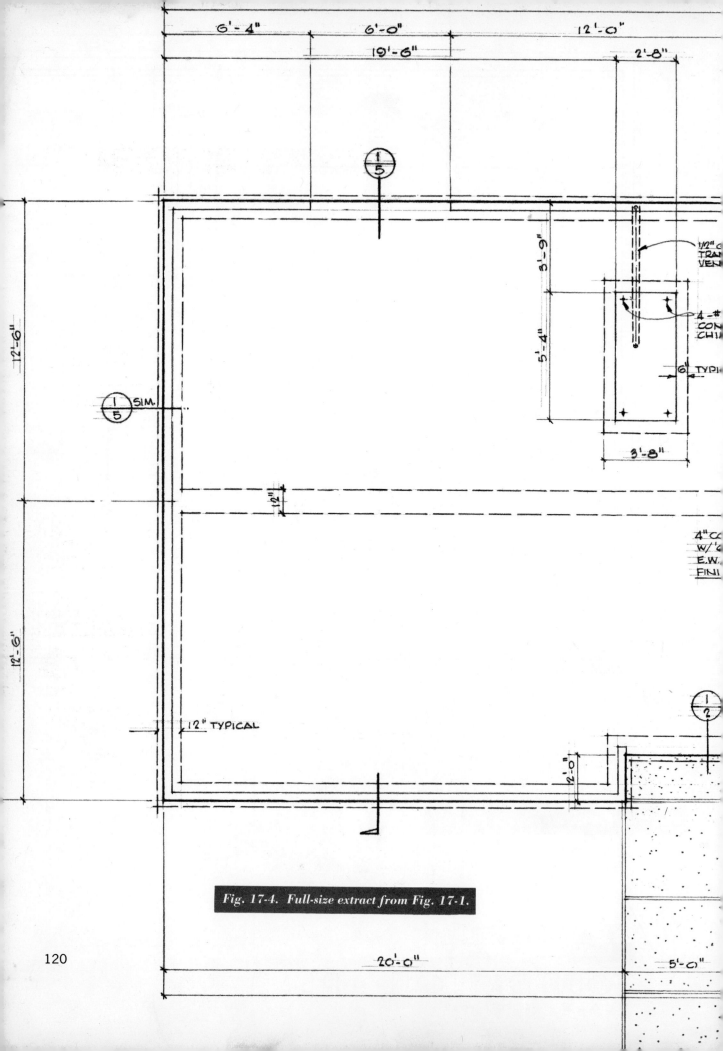

Fig. 17-4. Full-size extract from Fig. 17-1.

120

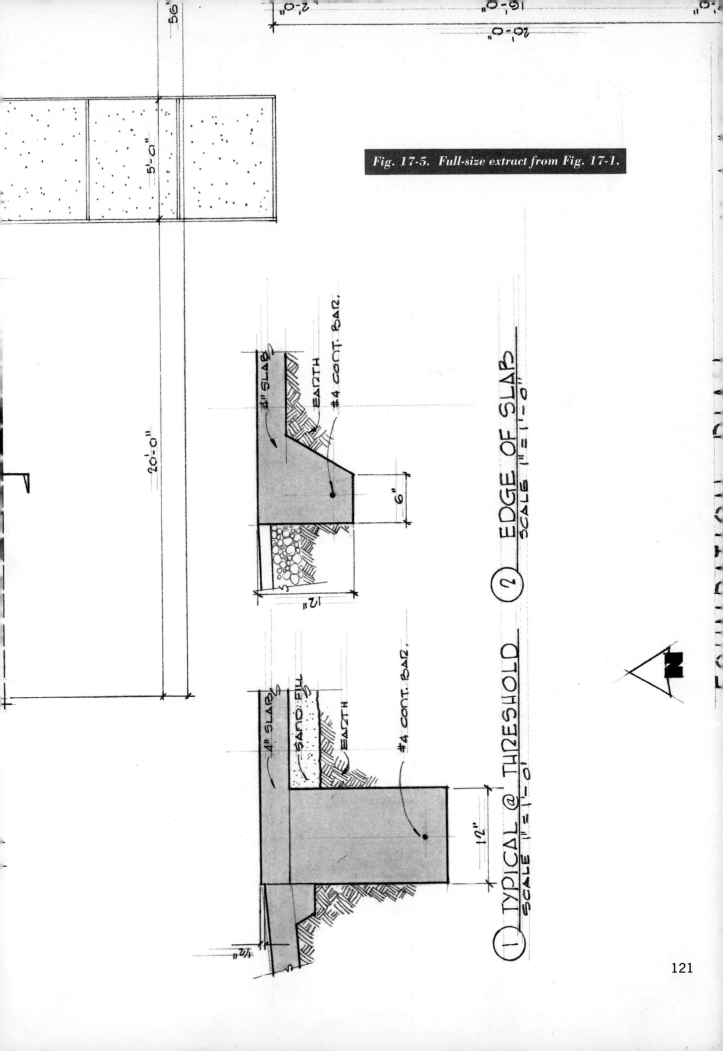

Fig. 17-5. Full-size extract from Fig. 17-1.

5'-0"

20'-0"

FOUNDATION PLAN

N

4" SLAB

EARTH

#4 CONT. BAR.

6"

12"

② EDGE OF SLAB
SCALE 1"=1'-0"

4" SLAB

SAND FILL

EARTH

#4 CONT. BAR.

12"

1/2"

① TYPICAL @ THRESHOLD
SCALE 1"=1'-0"

121

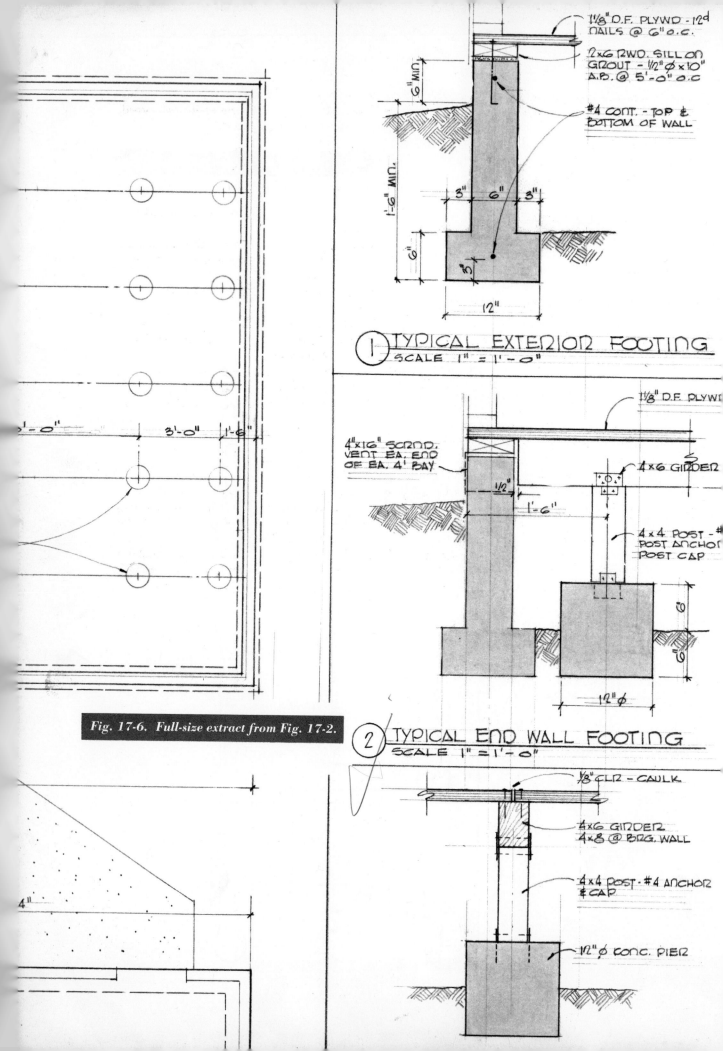

1⅛" D.F. PLYWD - 12d NAILS @ 6" O.C.

2×6 RWD. SILL ON GROUT - ½" ⌀ ×10" A.B. @ 5'-0" O.C

#4 CONT. - TOP & BOTTOM OF WALL

6" MIN.

1'-6" MIN.

6"

3" 6" 3"

5"

12"

① TYPICAL EXTERIOR FOOTING
SCALE 1" = 1'-0"

1⅛" D.F. PLYW

4"×16" SCRND. VENT EA. END OF EA. 4' BAY

4×6 GIRDER

½"

1'-6"

4×4 POST - # POST ANCHOR POST CAP

6"

6"

12" ⌀

② TYPICAL END WALL FOOTING
SCALE 1" = 1'-0"

⅛" CLR - CAULK

4×6 GIRDER
4×8 @ BRG. WALL

4×4 POST - #4 ANCHOR & CAP

12" ⌀ CONC. PIER

3'-0" 1'-6"

4"

Fig. 17-6. Full-size extract from Fig. 17-2.

ters of interior footings or dwarf walls, centers of isolated footings, etc. A third line is not needed. Locations and sizes of areas inside the building are dimensioned close to that area. The size of the foundation must jibe with the stud-to-stud size of the floor plan.

Sectional Details

The cross-sectional details shown here are sized to satisfy minimum requirements in a frost-free area assuming stable soil conditions (Figs. 17-5 and 17-6). The figures will have to be increased in areas of frost, earthquakes, hurricanes, or unstable soil. This information is available through local building departments. Some areas also demand insulation at the perimeter of slab floors. If the details shown conflict with local practice, follow the local practice.

Keying Symbols

The keying symbols used on foundation plans generally provide for two reference numbers (Figs. 17-1 and 17-2). The circle is about $\frac{1}{2}$ in. in diameter, and the simplified cutting-plane line, or *flag*, touches the circle in line with the center; it is drawn long enough to go through the plan view of the detail. No matter what the position of the flag is, the circle is always divided into two equal parts horizontally. The top space has a number or letter representing the desired detail. The lower space refers to the sheet number on which the section view of the detail can be found. Other types of keying symbols may be used as long as they are easily understood. Form is considered unimportant.

REVIEW QUESTIONS

1. What is the main purpose of the foundation system?
2. What is the most common foundation material?
3. What are the two most commonly used types of floor construction?
4. What other drawing is the basis for drawing the foundation plan?
5. State the most important advantage of wood floor.
6. How are interior bearing walls supported in a wood-floored house?
7. Which cross-sectional details are needed as a minimum on a typical foundation plan?
8. Draw and explain a foundation keying symbol.

STUDY SUGGESTIONS

1. Visit a residential building site, and compare the working drawings with the actual construction.
2. Visit your building department, and check typical foundation details.
3. Check out a book from the library on the subject of elementary structural design; read about the design of foundations.

Chapter

18

Roof and Floor Framing Plans

Definition and Purpose

The floor or roof framing plan shows the top view of the floor or roof construction. All structural members are shown in their proper relationships based on the floor plan, structural sections, and elevations. The scale of floor and roof framing plans is usually the same as that of the floor plan (Fig. 18-1).

Though all types of construction require framing drawings to complete a set, the problem of describing all systems—wood, metal, and concrete—is too large to be taken up here. A simple wood-frame system is shown complete in the following pages, while portions of other systems will be extracted. Framing systems, however, should be drawn in the order of their construction for logical reasons. Before starting any drawing, the student must learn the functions and symbols for all structural parts used in the plan (Fig. 18-2).

A separate floor framing plan is needed only above the ground floor. In this book, the foundation plan and first-floor framing plan are labeled "Foundation Plan."

Drafting the Floor Framing Plan

The procedure for drawing a wood-floor framing plan follows (Fig. 17-2):

1. Size all joists, beams, etc. (see A-8 to A-10).
2. In light lines draw the outline of the structure and the locations of all bearing walls and structures which rest on or pass through the floor.

3. Locate the members which support the floor structure, e.g., beams, girders, dwarf walls, as solid lines.
4. Locate all posts or piers which support beams, etc., according to their size and shape.
5. Draw in, as solid lines at the proper spacing, the individual joists or beams which support the subfloor.
6. Where bearing walls are parallel to joists, show doubled joists as center lines; where they are at an angle to joists, show solid blocking as solid lines.
7. Locate with solid lines all headers around stairwells, fireplaces, or other structures which pass through the floor.
8. Dimension where required.
9. Call out all structural members by note. Show size and spacing of all members, use of joist hangers, etc. Key plan to structural sections.
10. Letter in general notes, title, and scale.

Drafting the Roof Framing Plan

The procedure for drawing a wood-frame roof framing plan follows (Fig. 18-3):

1. Size all rafters, beams, etc. (see A-10 and A-12 to A-14).
2. In dashed lines draw the outline of the structure, the location of all bearing walls, structures which pass through the roof, and the extent of the roof overhang.
3. Locate any members, such as beams, which support the roof structure as object or center lines.

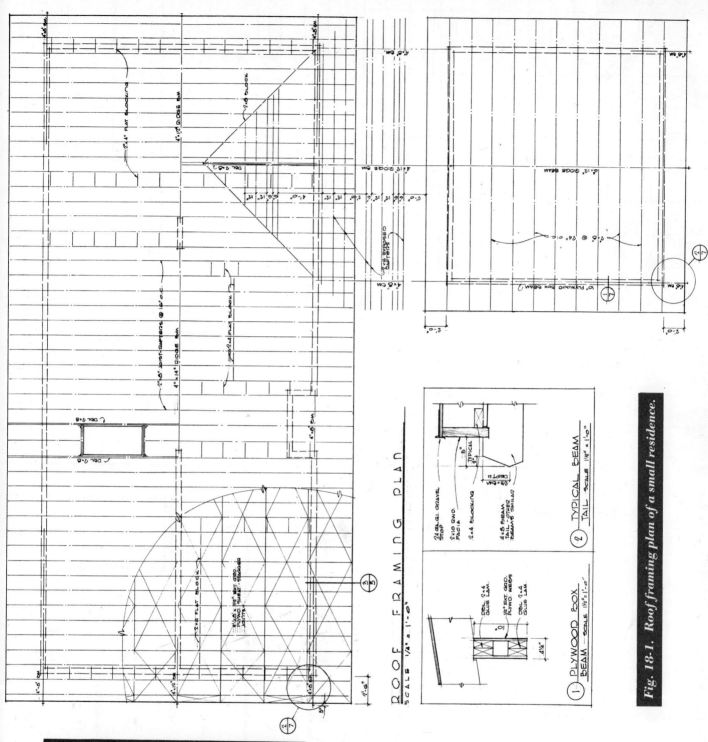

ROOF FRAMING PLAN
SCALE 1/4" = 1'-0"

① PLYWOOD BOX BEAM — SCALE 1½"=1'-0"

② TYPICAL BEAM TAIL — SCALE 1½"=1'-0"

Fig. 18-1. Roof framing plan of a small residence.

Fig. 18-2. Plan symbols for floor framing.

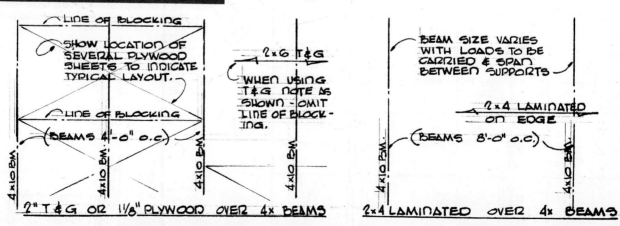

LINE OF BLOCKING

SHOW LOCATION OF SEVERAL PLYWOOD SHEETS TO INDICATE TYPICAL LAYOUT.

LINE OF BLOCKING

(BEAMS 4'-0" O.C.)

2×6 T&G

WHEN USING T&G NOTE AS SHOWN - OMIT LINE OF BLOCK-ING.

4×10 BM.

2" T&G OR 1⅛" PLYWOOD OVER 4x BEAMS

BEAM SIZE VARIES WITH LOADS TO BE CARRIED & SPAN BETWEEN SUPPORTS

2×4 LAMINATED ON EDGE

(BEAMS 8'-0" O.C.)

4×10 BM.

2×4 LAMINATED OVER 4x BEAMS

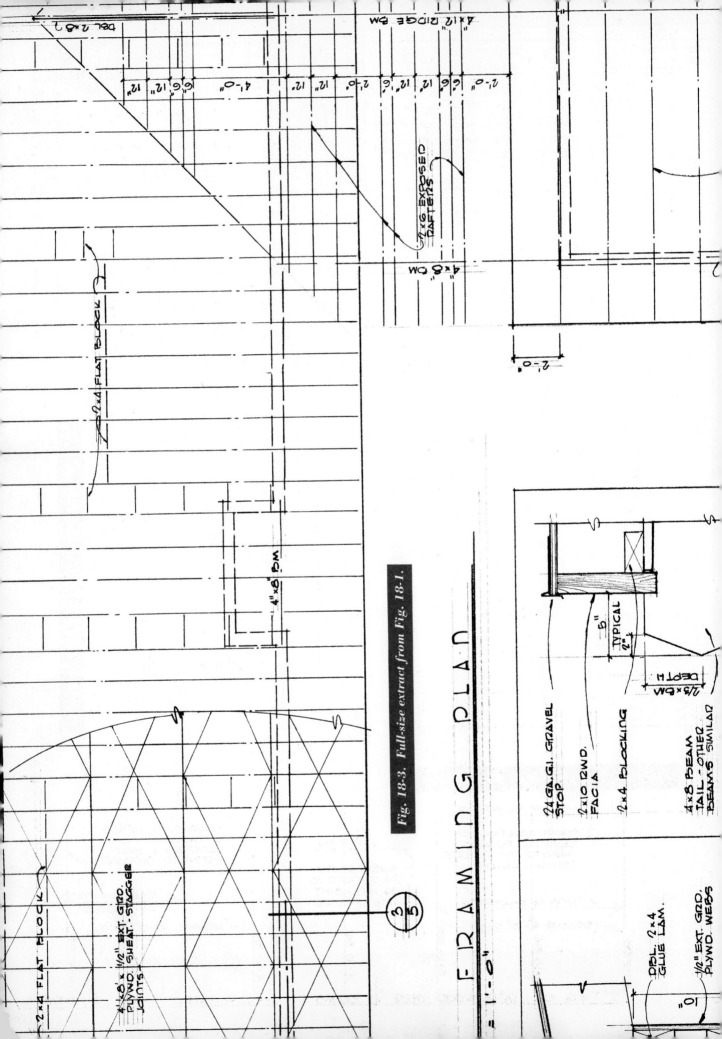

Fig. 18-3. Full-size extract from Fig. 18-1.

FRAMING PLAN

SCALE = 1'-0"

4. Draw any posts or columns which support the beams according to their size and shape.

5. Draw in as light lines the breaks of the roof surface, such as ridges, hips, and valleys.

6. Draw in as object lines all ridges, hips, valleys, etc.

7. Draw in with solid lines the individual rafters at the proper spacing.

8. Locate as object lines all headers around structures which pass through the roof.

9. Draw in the fascia board, if required, as an object line.

10. Dimension where required.

11. Call out the structural members by note; show size and spacing of all members, and use of hangers, clips, plates, rings, etc. Key the plan to the structural sections.

12. Letter in general notes, title, and scale.

REVIEW QUESTIONS

1. Define the terms: joist, rafter, beam, header, solid blocking, column.
2. Draw a plan view of the construction used to frame an opening through a floor.
3. Define the terms: ridge, hip, valley, cricket, fascia, gravel stop, soffit.

STUDY SUGGESTIONS

1. Visit a building under construction, and compare the floor and roof structure with the symbols on the drawing.
2. Compare a trussed-roof system with a joist-rafter system. Consider such things as type of labor used in building, speed of erection, and size of spans.
3. Study the design of simple braced and trussed roof structures in a book on elementary design.

Chapter

19

Electrical Plan

Definition and Purpose

The electrical drawing is a plan view of the building traced from the floor plan showing the service entrance and meter, all the electric outlets and controls in the house, and a description of all the symbols used on the drawing (Fig. 19-1).

Electrical Service

The point at which the electric power enters the building from the utility company's lines is called the service entrance. Current may enter the service entrance switchgear from overhead or through an underground conduit. This must be checked with the power company before starting the wiring layout (see A-16).

In most residential and light-commercial construction today, three wires are run in to provide 120/240-volt single-phase 60-cycle alternating current. Sometimes only two wires are run in, but then only 120-volt single-phase 60-cycle alternating current will be available. It is better to call for a three-wire service, because 240 volts is much more efficient for heavy loads or long runs of wire.

An electric meter is wired in ahead of everything else; its purpose is to measure the total amount of electric energy used in that building. Next in line is the service entrance switch, or disconnect, which is used to turn off all power to the building. Behind the disconnect are the branch circuit switches which control the individual power and lighting circuits. Most main and branch circuits at present are protected by circuit breakers rather than fuses (Fig. 19-2), since they are safer and more con-

venient. When a circuit is broken because of an overload or short circuit, it may be reset after the trouble is corrected merely by pushing the switch to the "reset" position. A residence of about 1,200 sq ft should have a three-wire entrance switch of 100 amp capacity minimum and 12 branch circuits to provide an adequate number of 120- and 240-volt circuits. Commercial buildings vary greatly in electrical requirements, and they often require three-phase power at 220 volts or more.

Types of Wiring

Structures are wired in many ways depending on local building codes. Following are descriptions of the most common types:

1. Line-voltage systems (120-volt). Switches and outlets handle line voltage.
   a. Conduit and insulated wire is most durable and most expensive. Wiring can easily be repaired or changed at a later date.
   b. BX or metallic sheathed cable has a coiled metal covering over insulated wire. It is flexible and can be placed easily in difficult places.
   c. Nonmetallic sheathed cable has a paper and fiber covering over insulated wire. It is most economical and easy to install.
2. Low-voltage switching systems (6 to 24 volts). Only fixture outlets handle line voltage.
   a. Auxiliary-bell system is in limited use in practically every building.
   b. Low-voltage switching through relays can be used in place of any line-voltage system.

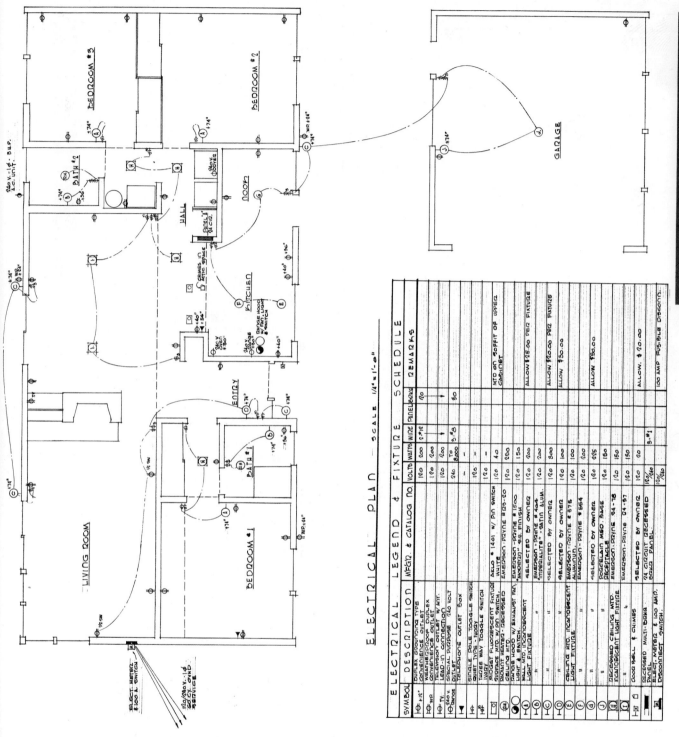

Fig. 19-1. Electrical plan of a small residence.

Electric Outlets

All systems use the same kinds of line-voltage outlets; the differences lie in the switches and relays.

The term *outlet* means floor, wall, and ceiling boxes of any type, including switch boxes, line voltage, or low voltage. Types of outlets and installations requiring outlets are listed below (see A-17).

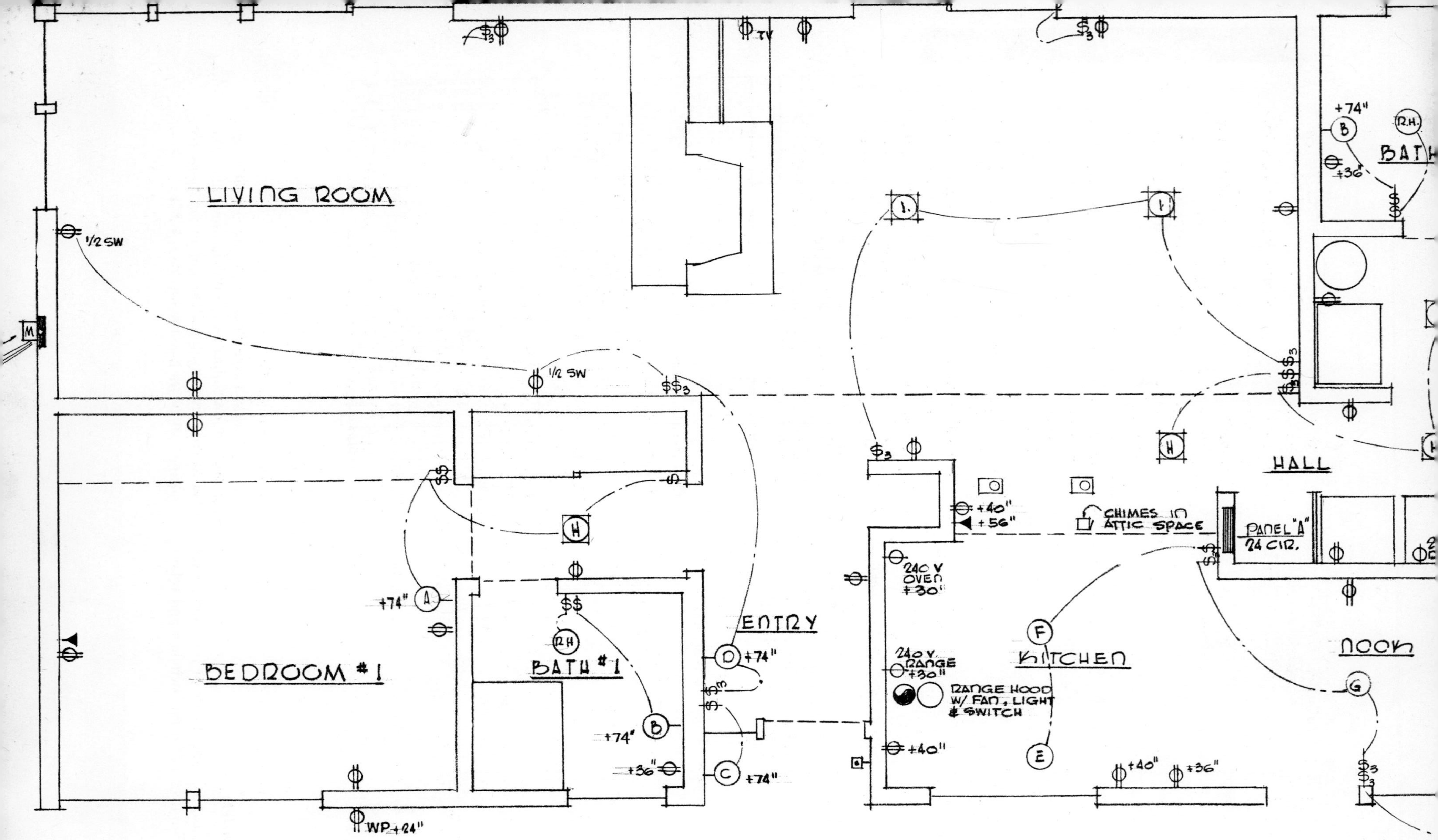

Fig. 19-2. Full-size extract from Fig. 19-1.

1. Duplex convenience outlets are used more often than any other type. They provide two 120-volt receptacles for lights and appliances. They are usually mounted 12 in. above the floor or at any convenient height above work surfaces, but they may be mounted at any place they are needed (ten or less per circuit).
2. Television or radio outlets provide a convenience outlet plus an aerial.
3. Clock outlets are built into a recessed plate so that the clock can mount flush with the wall.
4. Single three-wire 240-volt outlets are used for ranges, ovens, clothes dryers, or other appliances drawing heavy current. There are many different types available.
5. Bracket or wall lights are used in halls, near entrances, etc.
6. Telephone outlets are wired by the telephone company, but the draftsman locates them.
7. Radio-intercom panels and speakers are often installed in residences and light-commercial buildings.
8. Ceiling-fixture outlets are most often used. They accept any surface-mounted fixture and can use incandescent or fluorescent lamps.
9. Flush-mounted ceiling fixtures do not extend into the room. They require careful planning and must be built into the structure before the ceiling finish is applied. Either incandescent or fluorescent lamps may be used with them.
10. Luminous ceiling systems combine the functions of ceiling and lighting fixtures. Their use demands careful planning. They may employ incandescent or fluorescent lamps.
11. Convenience outlets on the floor are used often in commercial, but seldom in residential, construction.
12. Telephone jacks on the floor are used in offices where desks must be moved around.
13. Electric heaters, radiant or convection, are used for spot heating. They may be on a wall or ceiling.
14. Fans are used in kitchens, laboratories, bathrooms, etc.
15. Light-fan-heater combinations are used in bathrooms.
16. Range hoods, combining fan and light, are used in kitchens.
17. Floor lights or spotlights are used at entrances and also for decorative illumination.
18. Speakers are connected to the radio or intercom system.
19. Push buttons for doorbells are placed at front and back doors of residences or light-commercial buildings.
20. Chimes or bells are usually placed in a central part of the building.
21. Single-pole switches are used to control any one or a group of 120-volt outlets.
22. Three-way switches are used when it is desired to switch one or a group of outlets from two places.
23. Four-way switches are used to provide the third, fourth, etc., position from which to switch one or a group of outlets.
24. Two-pole switches must be used to switch 240-volt outlets or devices.

Switch legs are the wires run from the outlet to the switch box.

The outlets listed are those most often used in the design of a residence or light-commercial structure. Many others are used for special jobs. Information regarding them is available through various catalogs and manufacturers' publications. Their use is too technical to be described here.

The foregoing information concerns a line-voltage system only. Though the doorbell, chimes, speakers, and telephone are low-voltage devices, they are shown on almost every job and hence were included with the line-voltage devices.

Electrical Schedules

When many special fixtures are used in a building, an electrical-fixture schedule may be needed. This schedule describes the actual fixtures to be used at the various outlets (Fig. 19-3).

The headings used are:

1. *Symbol:* Identifying mark
2. *Description*
3. *Watts:* Number and size of lamps
4. *Volts:* Rated voltage
5. *Manufacturer and catalog number*
6. *Wire:* Wire gauge
7. *Panel:* Location of circuit switch
8. *Circuit:* Number of circuit switch
9. *Remarks:* Any further explanation

Planning

Before starting the actual electrical plan it is necessary to plan the type, number, and location of outlets. Naturally all decisions in this area are based upon lighting requirements and the locations of electric appliances. Tables in the reference section

ELECTRICAL PLAN SCALE 1/4"=1'-0"

ELECTRICAL LEGEND & FIXTURE SCHEDULE

SYMBOL	DESCRIPTION	MFGR. & CATALOG NO.	VOLTS	WATTS	WIRE	PANEL/BD	REMARKS
±12"	DUPLEX GROUNDING TYPE CONVENIENCE OUTLET		120	200		20	
WP	WEATHERPROOF DUPLEX CONVENIENCE OUTLET		120	200			
TV	TELEVISION OUTLET W/ ANT. LEAD-IN CONNECTION		120	200	→	▼	
240v RANGE	SPECIAL PURPOSE 240 VOLT OUTLET		240	TO 8,000	3-#8	30	
▼	TELEPHONE OUTLET BOX		−	−			
S	SINGLE POLE TOGGLE SWITCH QUIET TYPE - IVORY		120	−			
S₃	THREE WAY TOGGLE SWITCH IVORY		120	−			
▢	MIDGET FLUORESCENT FIXTURE SURFACE MTD. W/PIN SWITCH	AKLO # 1401 W/ PIN SWITCH WHITE	120	40			MTD ON SOFFIT OF UPPER CABINET
R.H.	RADIANT HEATER - RECESSED CEILING MTD.	EMERSON - PRYNE #R23-20	120	250			
◐	RANGE HOOD W/ EXHAUST FAN, LIGHT & SWITCH	EMERSON - PRYNE #1500 "MODERN" S.S. FINISH	120	150			
A	WALL MTD. INCANDESCENT LIGHT FIXTURE	SELECTED BY OWNER	120	200			ALLOW $25.00 PER FIXTURE
B	"	EMERSON - PRYNE # 464 "IMPERIALITE" - SATIN ALUM.	120	200			
C	"	SELECTED BY OWNER	120	300			ALLOW $20.00 PER FIXTURE
D	"	SELECTED BY OWNER	120	100			ALLOW $30.00
E	CEILING MTD. INCANDESCENT LIGHT FIXTURE	EMERSON - PRYNE # 375 ALUMINUM	120	100			
F	"	EMERSON - PRYNE # 554	120	200			
G	"	SELECTED BY OWNER	120	225			ALLOW $50.00
J	"	PORCELAIN MED BASE RECEPTACLE	120	150			
H	RECESSED CEILING MTD. INCANDESCENT LIGHT FIXTURE	EMERSON - PRYNE 64 - 78	120	150			
I	"	EMERSON - PRYNE 24 - 57	120	150			
□	DOOR BELL & CHIMES	SELECTED BY OWNER	120	20			ALLOW $20.00
▬	RECESSED MULTI-BRKR PANEL	24-CIRCUIT RECESSED BRKR PANEL	120/240		3-#1		
M	ELECT. METER & 100 AMP. DISCONNECT SWITCH.		100/240				100 AMP FUSIBLE DISCONN.

Fig. 19.3. Full-size extract from Fig. 19.1.

provide a basis for planning which will be adequate for student use (see A-17 to A-19). When placing outlets it is better to put in too many rather than too few. They are fairly inexpensive to install while the building is being constructed, but are very expensive to add to the completed structure. Use only weather-proof outlets out of doors.

Built-in Lighting

Several effective arrangements for lighting can be built into the structure and require only the simplest and cheapest fixtures. Soffit lights, cornice lights, cove lights, and others are illustrated in Fig. 19-4. Incandescent or fluorescent lamps, white or colored, may be used in special fixtures for very effective results. Weatherproof outdoor-lighting fixtures are available which can be used to advantage in the design of a residence or commercial building.

Drafting the Electrical Plan

The procedure for drawing the electrical plan follows (Figs. 19-1 and 19-2):

1. Select fixture types and locations based on lighting requirements, and locate all fixtures and outlets.
2. Trace the floor plan on the back of the paper (Fig. 10-4).
3. Place the service entrance as required by local codes and the serving utility company.
4. Place all convenience outlets.
5. Place all 240-volt three-wire outlets near the proper equipment—stove, oven, dryer, air conditioner, meat case, or other high-current device.
6. Place all ceiling fixtures and outlets.
7. Place all floor outlets.
8. Place all special outlets and fixtures.
9. Place all switches, and connect switch legs to proper fixtures or outlets.
10. Draw the electrical-outlet schedule and also the electrical-fixture schedule if needed.
11. Letter in all notes, title, and scale.

Low-voltage Switching Systems

A low-voltage switching system differs from a line-voltage system in several respects.

1. Line-voltage wires run to the outlet or main control panel only.
2. All switches operate at low voltage (6 to 24 volts).
3. Each switched outlet is controlled by the switch through a relay. In some systems the relay is mounted on the outlet, while in others it is mounted in a master control panel.
4. Any number of switches can control any number of outlets. There are no three- or four-way switches.
5. Any or all of the switches may easily be controlled by a centrally located master switch.
6. Light bell wire may be used to wire in switch circuits, and the wires can be stapled directly to the structure without protection.

Fig. 19-4. *Examples of different types of lighting.*

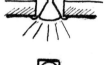

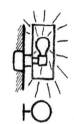

CEILING FIXTURE - MOST COMMON, MANY KINDS -INCANDESCENT.

FLUSH TYPE - UNOBTRUSIVE - INCANDESCENT.

FLUSH SPOT-LIGHT -USED OVER WORK AREAS

EXTERIOR SPOT-LIGHT OR FLOOD CAN BE MOUNTED IN ANY POSITION

BRACKET OR WALL TYPE - HALLWAYS, ENTRANCE

EXTERIOR IN-DIRECT - USED FOR LANDSCAPE LIGHTING.

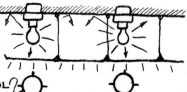

COVE LIGHT - SOFT INDIRECT, FLUORESCENT

LUMINOUS CEILING - ENTIRE CEILING IS THE FIXTURE LENS. EXCELLENT IN BATH & KITCHEN FLUORESCENT MORE EFFICIENT BUT INCANDESCENT MAY BE USED

CORNICE LIGHT - OVER DRAPED WINDOWS, FLUORESCENT.

CONCEALED SPOT-DRAMATIC EFFECT ON PAINTINGS, ETC.

7. There is no danger of electric shock at the switches.

Procedure for drawing a low-voltage switching system is similar to that used for a line-voltage system. Because of differences in the several low-voltage systems, it is necessary to refer to the manufacturer's brochure on the particular system used to get complete information needed for drawing.

Other electrical systems using d-c (direct-current) large motor controllers, electronic control devices, etc., are designed and drawn by electrical engineering firms and need not be described here.

REVIEW QUESTIONS

1. What type of current is used for most wiring in the United States, alternating or direct?
2. Which is most desirable, a two- or three-wire service? Why?
3. What types of wiring materials are called for by code for your own project?
4. What is the difference between a line-voltage system and a low-voltage switching system?
5. Sketch sections through a surface-mounted and a flush-mounted light fixture to show how they differ.
6. From the standpoint of safety, why is a low-voltage system desirable?
7. For a residence of 1,400 sq ft in area, estimate the following (use A-16 as a reference):
   a. Wire size of the service
   b. Size of main switch in amperes
   c. Size of fuses in main switch
   d. Number of general-purpose circuits
   e. Size of wires (3) to a small electric range
   f. Size of wires (3) to an electric dryer
   g. Minimum number of appliance circuits
   h. Size of wire to carry 40 amp
   i. Wattage of a $\frac{1}{4}$-hp motor.
8. What level of illumination in footcandles is required for sewing on dark cloth?
9. State the formula for finding the number of lamp lumens required to light a certain room to a given level of illumination.
10. How many lumens per watt does the average incandescent lamp produce?
11. Compute the number of 100-watt incandescent lamps required to light a 10- by 10-ft room to a level suitable for sewing on dark cloth.
12. How many 48-in. fluorescent lamps would be needed for the above conditions?

STUDY SUGGESTIONS

1. Visit an electric-supply warehouse, and inspect the different types of boxes, conductors, outlets, and fixtures available.
2. Visit two buildings under construction, one with a line-voltage and the other with a low-voltage switching system. Note the differences in construction. Compare the hardware with the drawing symbols.
3. Many books are available on basic electricity, wiring, and lighting; study these.

Chapter

20

Heating, Ventilating, and Air-conditioning Plan

Definition and Purpose

This drawing is a plan view of the building traced from the floor plan and showing all heating, ventilating, and air-conditioning equipment above and below ground (Fig. 20-1). Sizes and types of all lines, ducts, and equipment are called out by note. Dimensioning is occasionally required in critical areas, particularly the equipment room.

The heating, ventilating, and air-conditioning plan is most closely coordinated with the structural sections and the floor, foundation, plumbing, and electrical plans. Scale is the same as the floor plan. In some cases, elevations and isometric drawings are used to clarify certain details of construction.

Design

The computations involved in the design of a heating or cooling system, regardless of type, are as follows:

1. The heat loss or gain of the structure under the most severe conditions expected must be determined.
2. The most effective system for producing and distributing the heating or cooling must be chosen. The size of the heating or cooling equipment is based on the above figures.
3. Sizes of all conductors (pipes, ducts, wires, etc.) to each room must be sized to provide the proportional amount of air, water, steam, or electric current required in each room.
4. Heat exchange devices must be located throughout the structure in relation to the demands of

each area. These devices may be registers, radiators, coils, resistance elements, etc. Sizes are based on the volume of air or amount of heat energy needed at each point.
5. Thermostats must be located where they will be exposed to the average temperature of the room.
6. Provision must be made for all fuel, electric, water, steam, and other lines running to the heat machines—furnace, refrigeration equipment, etc.
7. Essential elements in the operation of the system must be provided, such as fuel storage bins or tanks, condensing coils, water-cooling towers, and dry wells.

The process of exactly determining the heating and cooling requirements of a building, choosing and sizing the equipment, and planning the distribution system involves considerable experience and many computations. The interested student should study one of the references cited in the bibliography. Abbreviated computation forms, or "short forms," are available which shorten and simplify the process. Because these forms are widely used and are reasonably accurate, the heating and cooling loads for the student project will be based on the use of a short form.

Types of Systems

Considering the fact that there are many possible combinations of equipment and means of exchanging heat, one system has been chosen to demonstrate the use of the short form (Figs. 20-2 and 20-3). The

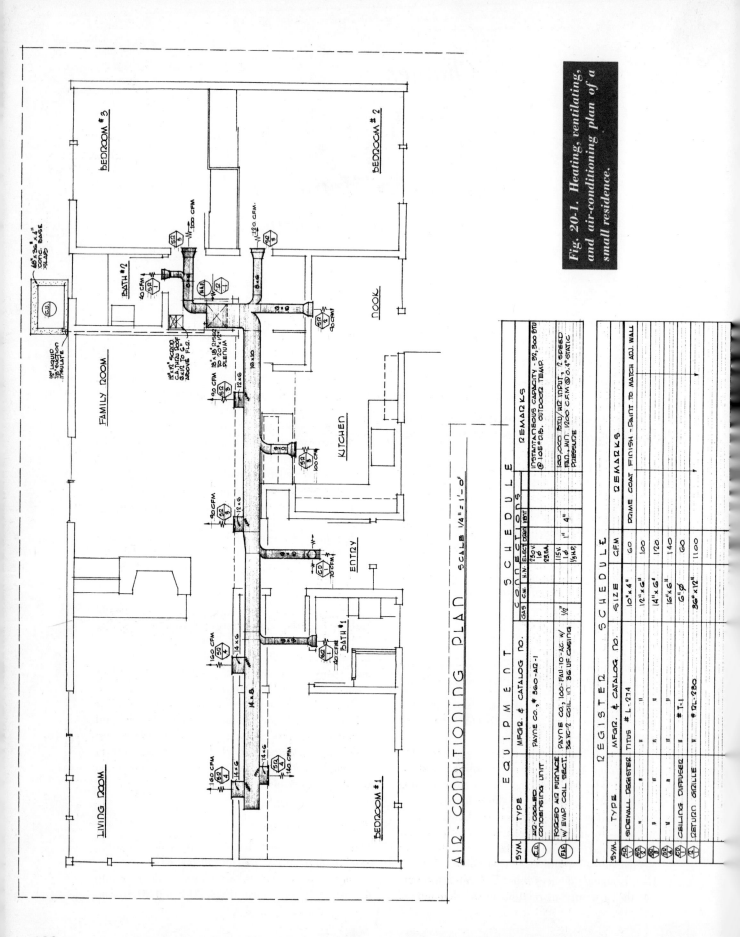

Fig. 20-1. Heating, ventilating, and air-conditioning plan of a small residence.

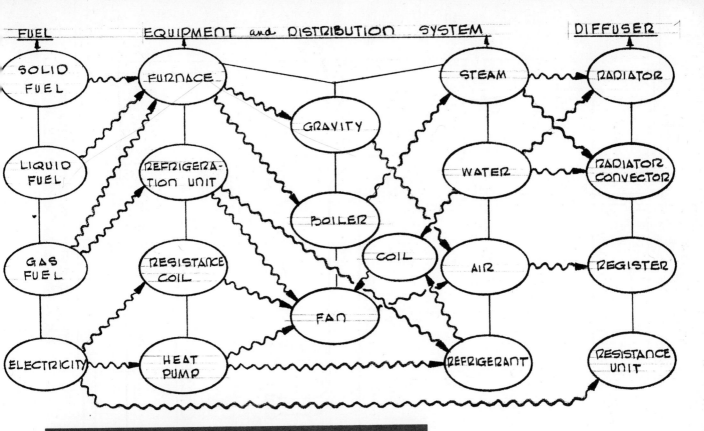

Fig. 20-2. *Methods of producing and distributing heat energy.*

short form in the Appendix provides heating and cooling load estimates for forced-air heating and cooling (see A-23, pages 200 to 211). Short forms are available for use with other systems and are obtainable from most heating-equipment manufacturers. Evaporative coolers, which have been found to work well only in areas of low humidity, are sized according to local practice.

Drafting the Heating, Ventilating, and Air-conditioning Plan

The procedure for drawing the heating and ventilating plan follows (Figs. 20-1 and 20-4):

1. Select and compute the size of the heating and/or cooling unit required; size ducts, pipes, radiators, etc. (see A-20 to A-26).

Fig. 20-3. *Cross sections of two typical furnaces.*

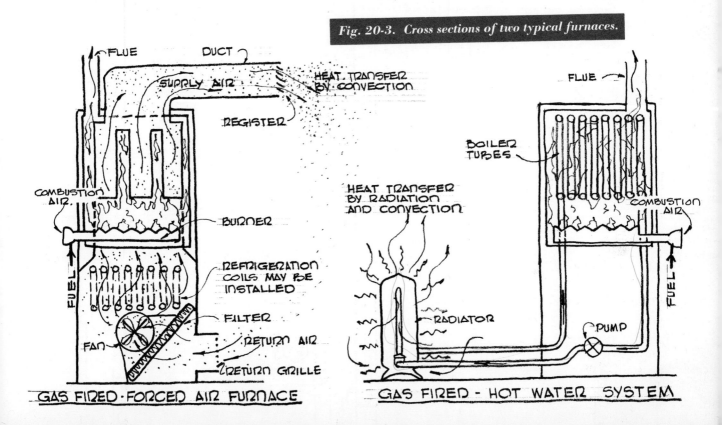

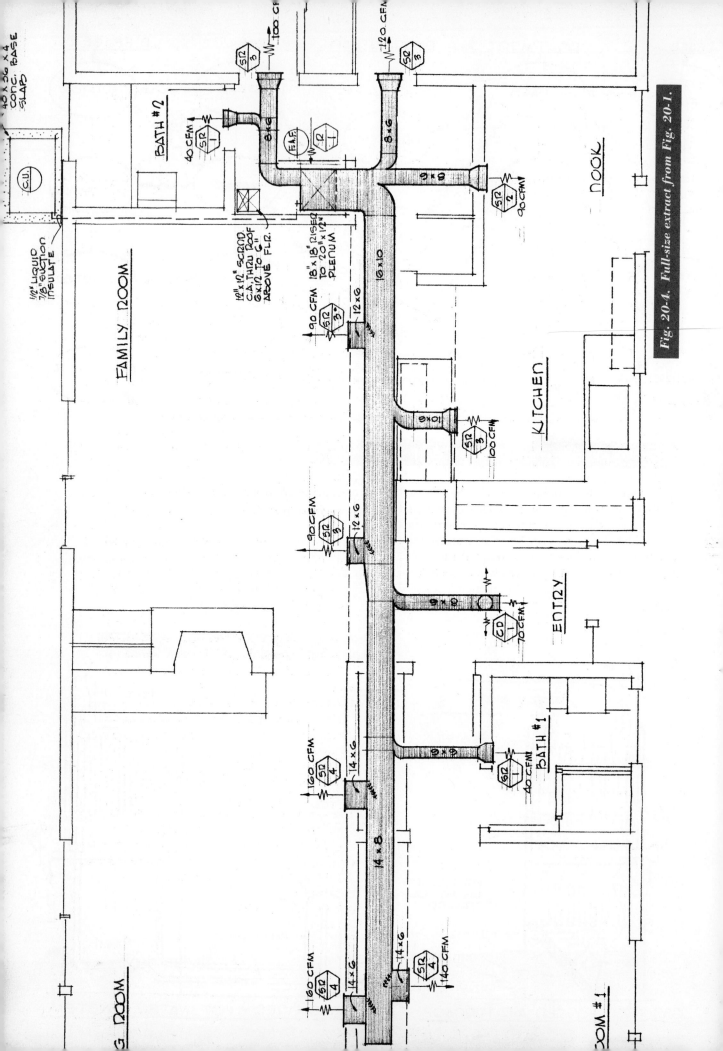

Fig. 20-4. Full-size extract from Fig. 20-1.

2. Trace the floor plan on the back of the tracing paper (Fig. 10-4).
3. Place the heating and/or cooling equipment. If the job calls for a simple floor or wall heater, placing of the unit and thermostat completes the drawing. In this case, however, no separate drawing would be needed. All the information could easily be put on the floor plan. Following are the items of equipment required for each type of job:
   a. Heating alone: Furnace, boiler, or other heating device
   b. Heating and evaporative cooling: Furnace and evaporative cooler
   c. Heating and refrigerated cooling: Furnace, cooling coils, compressor, and condenser and/or dry well
   d. Heat-pump heating and cooling: Compressor and inside and outside coils
4. Locate the radiators, coils, registers, air returns, or other means of exchanging heat and/or air (Fig. 20-4).
5. Run the water, electric, gas, or oil lines to the heating equipment. Indicate fuel tanks or storage if required.
6. Run the distribution lines between the heating equipment and the radiators, registers, radiant panels, or returns. Heating ducts are drawn to scale. Steam and water pipes are drawn as single lines, and sizes are called out.
7. Place thermostats and other controls.
8. Draw the equipment schedule.
9. Key the equipment to the equipment schedule.
10. Letter all notes including title and scale.

Further information concerning distribution systems may be found in the Appendix.

Schedules

Schedules are used with heating, ventilating, and air-conditioning plans to identify the symbols used on the drawing. The following headings and items of information should be shown (Fig. 20-5):

1. The indoor and outdoor design conditions for summer and winter are usually placed at the top.
2. *Symbol:* Mark identifying each part, e.g., register, diffuser, condenser, furnace, heat pump, and thermostat.
3. *Number:* Quantity of each unit required
4. *Manufacturer:* Trade name
5. *Model:* Catalog number

6. *Connections:* Electrical and horsepower rating, vent, drain, suction, liquid, gas, etc.
7. *Output* in Btu/hr: For cooling and heating
8. *Equipment Finish*
9. *Remarks:* Any further explanation

Other classifications may be included. These symbols are supplemented by additional notes on the drawing.

REVIEW QUESTIONS

1. Name three heating systems. How and by what medium is heat transferred in each case?
2. Why are certain objects drawn to scale and others drawn as symbols on the air-conditioning plan?
3. Assuming the following data for heating—inside design temp. = 75°F, outside design temp. = 25°F, design temp. diff. = 70°F—and using the short forms shown in A-23, pages 200 to 205, determine the following values.
   a. Heat loss in Btu/hr for 35 sq ft of double-hung window in 40 lin ft of exposed light-masonry wall.
   b. Heat loss through a 15- by 20-ft ceiling with $3\frac{5}{8}$-in. insulation.
   c. Heat loss through slab on grade floor 15 by 20 ft.
   d. Correct the heat-loss figure of 8,000 Btu/hr at 70°F to the design temperature difference of 40°F.
   e. Determine the room cfm for 9,000 Btu/hr and a register temperature of 140°F.
4. Assuming the following data for cooling—outside design temp. = 100°F, daily temp. range = 20°F—and using the short forms shown in A-23, pages 206 to 211, determine the following values.
   a. Solar transmission heat gain through windows and doors with a 24-in. overhang, eastern exposure, and 30 sq ft of sash area.
   b. Heat gain through a sunlit light-masonry wall 20 ft long with no overhang.
   c. Heat gain through a sunlit 2-in. insulated frame wall 20 ft long with a 48-in. overhang.
   d. Heat gain through a pitched roof with 2-in. ceiling insulation, no attic ventilation, and 12 by 30 ft in size.
   e. Using a correction factor of 1.17 and a value of 4,000 Btu/hr before correction, what is the corrected value?
5. With the help of A-24 to A-26, determine the following:

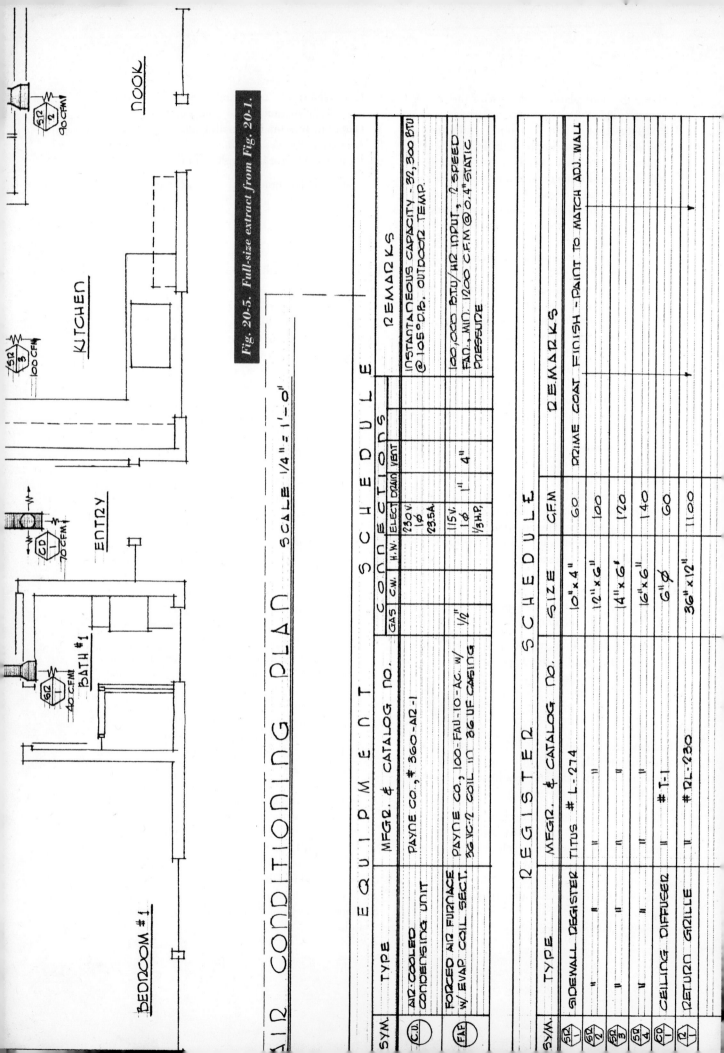

AIR CONDITIONING PLAN — SCALE 1/4" = 1'-0"

NOOK

KITCHEN

ENTRY

BATH #1

BEDROOM #1

Fig. 20-5. Full-size extract from Fig. 20-1.

EQUIPMENT SCHEDULE

SYM.	TYPE	MFGR. & CATALOG NO.	GAS	C.W.	H.W.	ELECT	DRAIN	VENT	REMARKS
C.U.	AIR-COOLED CONDENSING UNIT	PAYNE CO., #360-AR2-1				230V. 1∅ 23.5A.			INSTANTANEOUS CAPACITY - 32,300 BTU @ 105°D.B. OUTDOOR TEMP.
FAF	FORCED AIR FURNACE W/ EVAP. COIL SECT.	PAYNE CO., 100-FAU-10-AC W/ 36 VC-2 COIL IN 36 UF CASING	1/2"			115V. 1∅ 1/3 H.P.	1"	4"	100,000 BTU/HR INPUT, 2-SPEED FAN, MIN. 1200 C.F.M. @ 0.4" STATIC PRESSURE

REGISTER SCHEDULE

SYM.	TYPE	MFGR. & CATALOG NO.	SIZE	C.F.M.	REMARKS
SR/1	SIDEWALL REGISTER	TITUS #L-274	10"x4"	60	PRIME COAT FINISH - PAINT TO MATCH ADJ. WALL
SR/2	"	"	12"x6"	100	
SR/3	"	"	14"x6"	120	
SR/4	"	"	16"x6"	140	
CD/1	CEILING DIFFUSER	" #T-1	6"∅	60	
R/2	RETURN GRILLE	" #RL-230	36"x12"	1100	

a. Using a 20- by 6-in. register with a single deflection damper, what is the throw in feet at 200 cfm?

b. Using a 40- by 10-in. floor outlet, what is the spread in feet at 120 cfm?

c. What diameter ceiling outlet should be used for a discharge of 220 cfm?

d. What size sidewall return grille would be used to handle 900 cfm of return air?

e. What sizes of rectangular supply ducts will handle 2,500 cfm in a residential application?

f. What sizes of rectangular supply ducts will handle 2,500 cfm in a commercial application?

6. What is the inside design temperature recommended for a store in summer? (Use A-20).

STUDY SUGGESTIONS

1. Go to an air-conditioning-supply warehouse, inspect the many types of furnaces, air-conditioning units, registers, radiators, etc., and note how they are used in a building.

2. Visit a building under construction, and compare the air-conditioning system with the drawings.

3. Compute the heat loss of your own house in winter, using the reference tables and formula. You may have to make an educated guess as to the wall insulation.

4. Study the basic principles of air conditioning in a text such as "Modern Air Conditioning Practice." Compare the results of the computation of heating loads with the results obtained by the use of short forms.

Chapter

21

Plumbing Plan

Definition and Purpose

The plumbing plan is a plan view of the building, traced from the floor plan, which shows all plumbing lines and fixtures above and below the ground. Soil and waste lines, gas lines, hot- and cold-water lines, steam, air and gas lines, vents, and all fixtures and appliances (connected or proposed) are described. The sizes and types of all lines and fittings are described by note (Fig. 21-1). Extensions of lines and appliances beyond the lines of the floor plan are often shown on the plot plan.

Dimensioning is used for safety in critical areas, especially in locating fixtures. The lengths of pipelines are seldom given. The plumbing plan is closely coordinated with the floor plan, foundation plan, electrical plan, and heating and ventilating plans. In some cases isometric drawings are used to clarify certain details of construction.

When drawing the plumbing plan, refer to the plan views of plumbing symbols and lines (see A-27). Consult the Appendix for pipe, waste, and vent sizes, etc. (see A-28 to A-37).

Definitions

Waste and soil lines are gravity-flow drains which connect to all toilets, tubs, and other fixtures and carry solid and liquid waste matter to the house drain. The house drain becomes the house sewer or house trap when it passes beyond the foundation line. The house sewer is connected to the sewer main which is located in the street, alley, or sewer easement.

All fixtures require a trap or water seal ahead of the waste line to prevent gases and vermin from entering the house through the drain. In addition, each fixture or group of fixtures must have a vent. The vent permits air to enter the drains as wastes are drained away (Fig. 21-2).

Design

Before the working drawing can be started, many decisions and computations must be made.

1. The locations, types, and sizes of all fixtures must be determined. Many of these decisions are based on practical experience.
2. Locate all serving utilities—gas, steam, sewer, water, etc.—and decide how and where they will be connected to the building.
3. Compute the sizes of all lines to all fixtures. This includes the lines which serve heating and refrigeration machinery, elevators, hoists, etc. Start computing the load at the most remote fixture, and work toward the serving utility, the meter, shutoff valve, etc.
4. Locate all traps, cleanouts, vents, check valves, pressure reducers, etc. These are always called for in the plumbing code or the fixture manufacturer's literature.
5. Locate and size all fittings: tees, ells, wyes, etc.
6. Prepare a list of fixtures, and list all connections serving each. For instance, a kitchen sink requires hot-water, cold-water, drain, and convenience-outlet connections. This information should all be placed in the plumbing schedule.

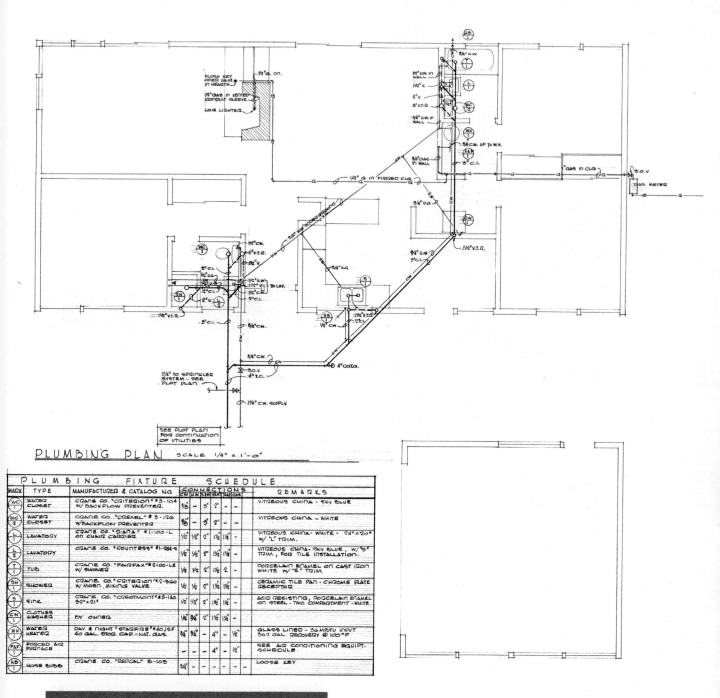

PLUMBING PLAN SCALE 1/4" = 1'-0"

MARK	TYPE	MANUFACTURER & CATALOG No.	CW	HW	S/W	VENT	TRAP	GAS	REMARKS
WC/1	WATER CLOSET	CRANE CO. "CRITERION" #3-104 W/ BACKFLOW PREVENTER	5/8		5"	2"	-	-	VITREOUS CHINA - SKY BLUE
WC/2	WATER CLOSET	CRANE CO. "DREXEL" #3-126 W/BACKFLOW PREVENTER	5/8		5"	2"	-	-	VITREOUS CHINA - WHITE
L/1	LAVATORY	CRANE CO. "DIANA" #1-100-L ON CHAIR CARRIER	1/2	1/2	2"	1½	1¼	-	VITREOUS CHINA - WHITE - 24"X20" W/ "L" TRIM
L/2	LAVATORY	CRANE CO. "COUNTESS" #1-284-S	1/2	1/2	2"	1½	1¼	-	VITREOUS CHINA - SKY BLUE, W/"S" TRIM, FOR TILE INSTALLATION.
T/1	TUB	CRANE CO. "FAIRFAX" #2-100-LE W/ SHOWER	1/2	1/2	2"	1½	2	-	PORCELAIN ENAMEL ON CAST IRON WHITE W/ "E" TRIM
SH/1	SHOWER	CRANE CO. "CRITERION" #2-360 W/MOEN, MIXING VALVE	1/2	1/2	2"	1½	1½	-	CERAMIC TILE PAN - CHROME PLATE RECEPTOR
S/1	SINK	CRANE CO. "CRESTMONT" #5-180 32"x21"	1/2	1/2	2"	1½	1½	-	ACID RESISTING, PORCELAIN ENAMEL ON STEEL - TWO COMPARTMENT - WHITE
CW/1	CLOTHES WASHER	BY OWNER	1/2	3/4	2"	1½	1½	-	
WH/1	WATER HEATER	DAY & NIGHT "STARFIRE" #40JSF 40 GAL. STOR. CAP.-NAT. GAS	3/4	3/4	-	4"	-	1/2	GLASS LINED - 36 MBTU INPUT 30.2 GAL. RECOVERY @ 100°F
FAF/1	FORCED AIR FURNACE		-	-	-	4"	-	1/2	SEE AIR CONDITIONING EQUIPT. SCHEDULE
HB	HOSE BIBB	CRANE CO. "REDCAL" B-105	3/4	-	-	-	-	-	LOOSE KEY

Fig. 21-1. Plumbing plan of a small residence.

Drafting the Soil and Waste Lines

The procedure in drawing the soil and waste lines follows (Fig. 21-3):

1. Choose the fixtures, toilets, sinks, tubs, showers, etc., and size the lines (see A-28 and A-29).

2. Trace the floor plan on the back of the paper. See "Working Drawings" (Fig. 10-4).

3. Draw construction lines from each fixture to the house drain. Check the local code for the number of fixtures to each line. Draw the house drain to a point which will be convenient to the sewer

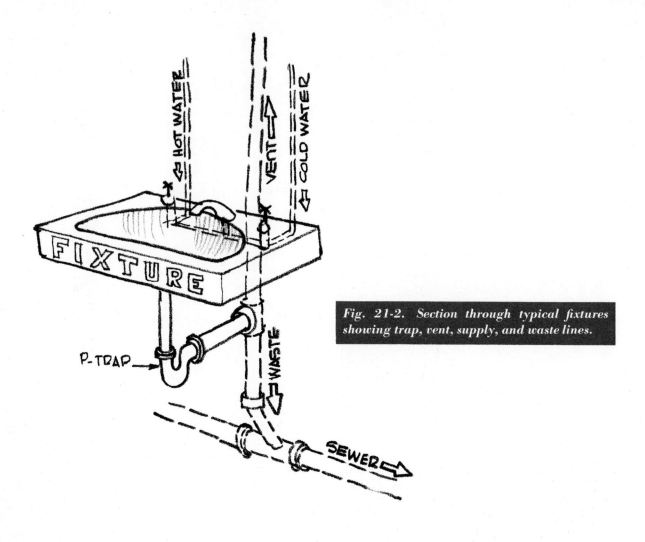

Fig. 21-2. Section through typical fixtures showing trap, vent, supply, and waste lines.

main or septic tank. Locate all plumbing vents according to code. Draw in taps and fittings.

4. Darken all lines. The exact location of taps, fittings, etc., is left to the judgement of the plumber.

5. Call out the size and material of all piping.

Drafting the Water Lines

Hot- and cold-water lines provide water under pressure ($\pm$ 45 psi) to all fixtures. The procedure in drawing the hot- and cold-water lines follows:

1. Choose the fixtures, hot-water tank, water softener, etc., and size the lines (see A-30 and A-31).

2. Draw construction lines from the main shutoff valve to all fixtures which require cold water. Consult the local building code. Next, run lines to the water heater from all fixtures which re-

quire hot water. Parallel the hot- and cold-water lines where possible.

3. Darken all lines.

4. Call out the size and material of all pipes. The type of fittings to be used is often left to the plumber.

Drafting the Gas Lines

The gas lines supply natural or bottled gas to all required fixtures. The procedure in drawing the gas lines follows:

1. Size supply lines based on the capacity of heating units. Use the manufacturer's recommendations (see A-32 and A-33).

2. Using construction lines, run lines from all fixtures to the gas meter or point of entrance.

3. Darken all lines.

4. Call out the size and material of all pipes.

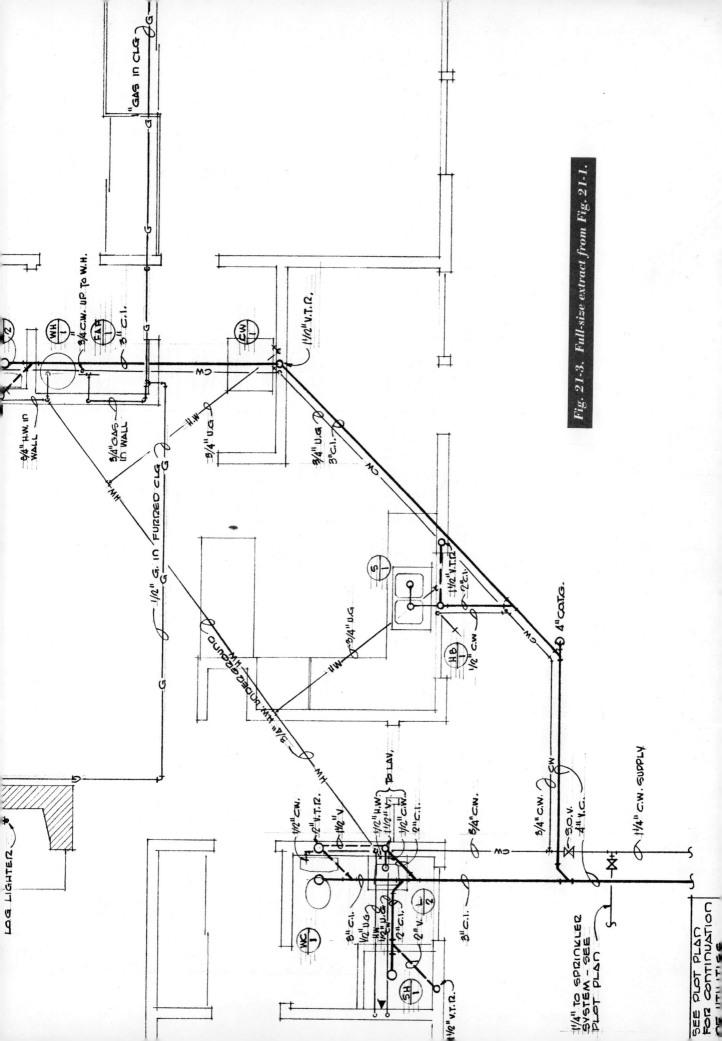

Fig. 21-3. Full-size extract from Fig. 21-1.

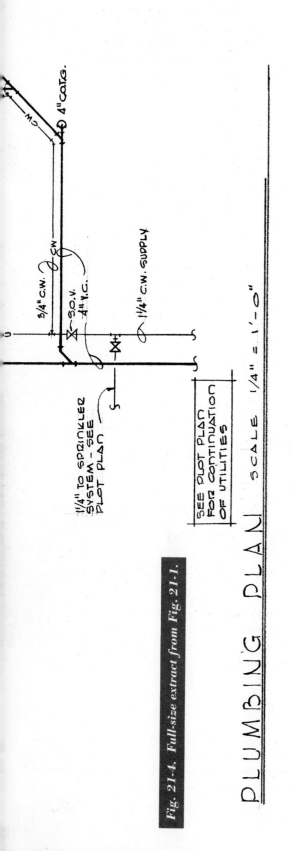

Fig. 21-4. Full-size extract from Fig. 21-1.

PLUMBING PLAN SCALE 1/4" = 1'-0"

Diagram labels: 4" C.O.T.G. · C.W. · C.O. · 3/4" C.W. · S.O.V. 4" V.C. · 1 1/4" TO SPRINKLER SYSTEM - SEE PLOT PLAN · 1 1/4" C.W. SUPPLY · SEE PLOT PLAN FOR CONTINUATION OF UTILITIES

PLUMBING FIXTURE SCHEDULE

MARK	TYPE	MANUFACTURER & CATALOG NO.	CW	HW	S&W	VENT	TRAP	GAS	REMARKS
WC 1	WATER CLOSET	CRANE CO. "CRITERION" #3-104 W/ BACKFLOW PREVENTER	3/8	-	3"	2"	-	-	VITREOUS CHINA - SKY BLUE
WC 2	WATER CLOSET	CRANE CO. "DREXEL" #3-126 W/ BACKFLOW PREVENTER	3/8	-	3"	2"	-	-	VITREOUS CHINA - WHITE
L 1	LAVATORY	CRANE CO. "DIANA" #1-100-L ON CHAIR CARRIER	1/2	1/2	2"	1 1/2"	1 1/2"	-	VITREOUS CHINA - WHITE - 24"x20" W/ "L" TRIM.
L 2	LAVATORY	CRANE CO. "COUNTESS" #1-084-5	1/2	1/2	2"	1 1/2"	1 1/2"	-	VITREOUS CHINA - SKY BLUE, W/ "S" TRIM, FOR TILE INSTALLATION.
T 1	TUB	CRANE CO. "FAIRFAX" #2-100-LE W/ SHOWER	1/2	1/2	2"	1 1/2"	2	-	PORCELAIN ENAMEL ON CAST IRON WHITE W/ "E" TRIM
SH 1	SHOWER	CRANE CO. "CRITERION" #2-360 W/ MOEN MIXING VALVE	1/2	1/2	2"	1 1/2"	1 1/2"	-	CERAMIC TILE PAN - CHROME PLATE RECEPTOR
S 1	SINK	CRANE CO. "CRESTMONT" #5-140 32"x21"	1/2	1/2	2"	1 1/2"	1 1/2"	-	ACID RESISTING, PORCELAIN ENAMEL ON STEEL, TWO COMPARTMENT - WHITE
CW 1	CLOTHES WASHER	BY OWNER	1/2	3/4	2"	1 1/2"	1 1/2"	-	
WH 1	WATER HEATER	DAY & NIGHT "STARFIRE" #40JSF 40 GAL. STOR. CAP - NAT. GAS.	3/4	3/4	-	4"	-	1/2"	GLASS LINED - 36 MBTU INPUT 30.2 GAL. RECOVERY @ 100°F
FAF 1	FORCED AIR FURNACE		-	-	-	4"	-	1/2"	SEE AIR CONDITIONING EQUIPT. SCHEDULE
HB 1	HOSE BIBB	CRANE CO. "REDCAL" #5-103	3/4	-	-	-	-	-	LOOSE KEY

146

Other plumbing lines, which are used mostly in commercial occupancies, are steam lines, air, oxygen, and other gas lines. The procedure in drawing is identical to the above.

Schedules

The plumbing plan includes a tabular schedule which has the following headings (Fig. 21-4):

1. *Symbol:* Shape of the fixture as shown on the drawing
2. *Type:* Name of the fixture
3. *Location:* Fixture symbol, such as WC 2, sink 3, etc.
4. *Manufacturer and Number:* Taken from the catalog
5. *Connections:* For instance, a kitchen sink would show HW, hot water; CW, cold water; T, trap; V, vent; S & W, soil and waste; Elec, electrical, if there is a garbage disposal

Septic Tanks

In areas where sewers are not available, septic tanks are required for the sanitary disposal of waste (Figs. 21-5 to 21-7). The size of tank and the length of leaching lines are controlled by local codes. The septic tank and leaching field are not usually drawn on the plumbing plan but are placed on the plot plan. Sizes of septic tanks and leaching fields are based upon the number of fixtures, rate of use, and soil conditions (see A-34 to A-37).

REVIEW QUESTIONS

1. Why are toilets, sinks, etc., drawn to scale and convenience outlets, switches, etc., drawn as symbols?
2. What is the function of a trap?
3. What is the function of a vent?
4. Draw a cross section of a sink, its trap, its vent, and the drain. What would happen if the vent were to become stopped up while the sink was draining?
5. Why are vents and traps used on waste and soil lines but not on hot- and cold-water lines?
6. Using the table A-28, determine the following:
   a. What is the trap size for a bathtub?
   b. A toilet is equivalent to how many fixture units?

c. A toilet, bathtub, floor drain, clothes washer, shower, residential sink, three washbasins, and a drinking fountain together are equivalent to how many fixture units?

7. Using the table A-29, determine the following:
   a. As drainage piping, how many fixture units can a 6-in. pipe carry horizontally?
   b. As drainage piping, how many fixture units can a 4-in. pipe carry vertically?
   c. As drainage piping, how many feet can a 4-in. pipe run vertically?
   d. As vent piping, how many fixture units can a 3-in. pipe carry?
8. Using the table A-30, determine the following:
   a. For public use, a toilet is equivalent to how many fixture units of water demand?
   b. For private use, a hose bibb is equivalent to how many fixture units of water demand?
9. Using the table A-31, determine the following in a flush-tank system at 40 psi.:
   a. What is the maximum number of fixture units which can be handled through a 1-in. meter and a $1\frac{1}{4}$-in. building-supply pipe over a maximum distance of 80 ft?
   b. What size meter would be required to handle 445 fixture units up to a distance of 40 ft?
10. Using the table A-32, determine the following:
   a. What is the demand in cubic feet per hour of a domestic gas range?
   b. What is the total demand of a 50-gal storage water heater plus a clothes dryer and a barbeque?
11. Using the table A-33, determine the following:
   a. In a system with a length of 70 ft, what size pipe would be required to handle the total load in problem 10b?
   b. If the length were 300 ft for the same demand, would a 1-in. pipe be large enough?
12. Using the table A-34, determine the following:
   a. What is the minimum distance from a stream that a cesspool may be located?
   b. What is the minimum distance between two disposal fields using 3-ft-wide trenches?
13. Using the table A-35, determine the following:
   a. How many gallons of water per day are required per machine in a self-service laundry?
   b. How many gallons of water per day are required by a 30-seat restaurant?
14. Using the table A-36, determine the following:
   a. What is the minimum capacity of a septic

(continued on page 150)

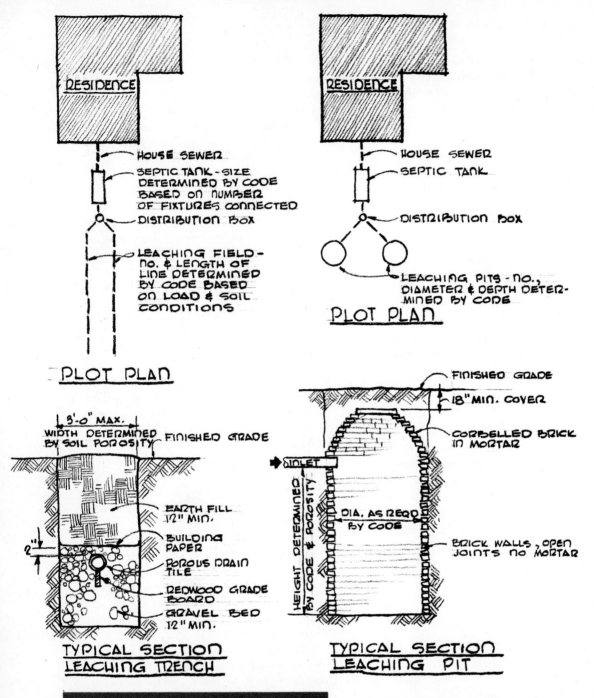

RESIDENCE

HOUSE SEWER

SEPTIC TANK - SIZE DETERMINED BY CODE BASED ON NUMBER OF FIXTURES CONNECTED

DISTRIBUTION BOX

LEACHING FIELD - NO. & LENGTH OF LINE DETERMINED BY CODE BASED ON LOAD & SOIL CONDITIONS

PLOT PLAN

RESIDENCE

HOUSE SEWER

SEPTIC TANK

DISTRIBUTION BOX

LEACHING PITS - NO., DIAMETER & DEPTH DETERMINED BY CODE

PLOT PLAN

3'-0" MAX.
WIDTH DETERMINED BY SOIL POROSITY   FINISHED GRADE

EARTH FILL 12" MIN.

BUILDING PAPER

POROUS DRAIN TILE

REDWOOD GRADE BOARD

GRAVEL BED 12" MIN.

2"

TYPICAL SECTION LEACHING TRENCH

FINISHED GRADE

18" MIN. COVER

CORBELLED BRICK IN MORTAR

INLET

HEIGHT DETERMINED BY CODE & POROSITY

DIA. AS REQD BY CODE

BRICK WALLS, OPEN JOINTS NO MORTAR

TYPICAL SECTION LEACHING PIT

Fig. 21-5. Typical septic-tank installations.

Fig. 21-6. Section through typical septic tank.

GROUND LINE

2'-0" MIN.

16"x16" MANHOLE

16"x16" MANHOLE

6"

INLET

2"

FLOW LINE

WOOD BAFFLE

WOOD BAFFLE

4" SLOT

(L-4") 2/3

(L-4") 1/3

2"

12"

OUTLET

5'-0"

4"

LENGTH "L"

4"

148

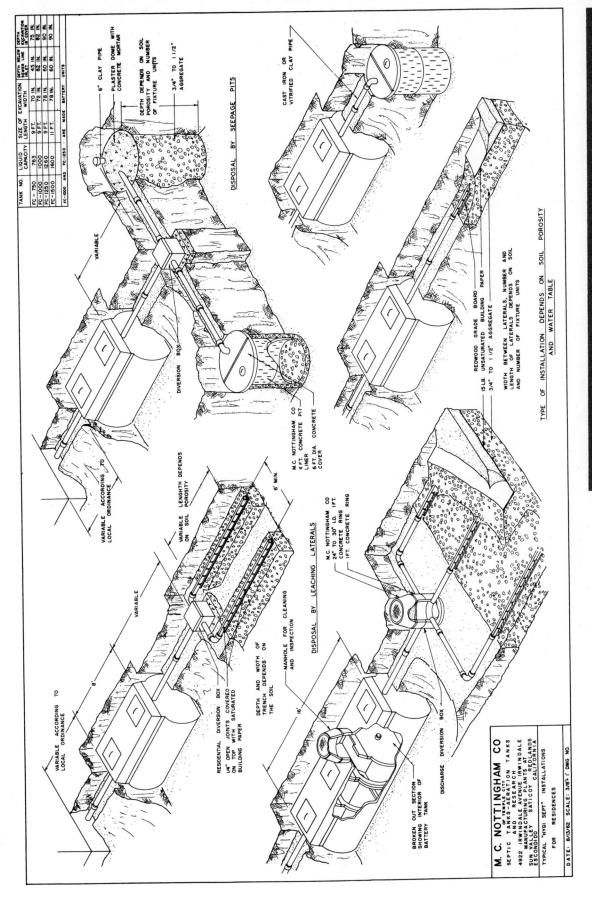

TANK NO.	LIQUID CAPACITY	SIZE OF EXCAVATION		DEPTH BELOW SEWER LINE	DEPTH EXCAVATION BELOW COVER
		LENGTH	WIDTH		
FC-750	763	9 FT.	70 IN.	45 IN.	75 IN.
FC-1000	1000	9 FT.	72 IN.	52 IN.	82 IN.
FC-1250	1260	9 FT.	78 IN.	60 IN.	90 IN.
FC-1500	1600	11 FT.	78 IN.	60 IN.	90 IN.

FC-1000 AND FC-1250 ARE MADE BATTERY UNITS

6" CLAY PIPE

PLASTER DOME WITH CONCRETE MORTAR

DEPTH DEPENDS ON SOIL POROSITY AND NUMBER OF FIXTURE UNITS

3/4" TO 1 1/2" AGGREGATE

DISPOSAL BY SEEPAGE PITS

CAST IRON OR VITRIFIED CLAY PIPE

VARIABLE

DIVERSION BOX

M.C. NOTTINGHAM CO 4 FT. CONCRETE PIT LINER
6 FT. DIA. CONCRETE COVER

VARIABLE ACCORDING TO LOCAL ORDINANCE

VARIABLE ACCORDING TO LOCAL ORDINANCE

VARIABLE

VARIABLE

VARIABLE LENGHTH DEPENDS ON SOIL POROSITY

6' MIN.

RESIDENTIAL DIVERSION BOX

1/4" OPEN JOINTS COVERED ON TOP WITH SATURATED BUILDING PAPER

DEPTH AND WIDTH OF TRENCH DEPENDS ON THE SOIL

MANHOLE FOR CLEANING AND INSPECTION

8'

16'

DISPOSAL BY LEACHING LATERALS

M.C. NOTTINGHAM CO 24" TO 30" I.D. 1FT. CONCRETE RING
1 FT. CONCRETE RING

BROKEN OUT SECTION SHOWING INTERIOR OF BATTERY TANK

DISCHARGE DIVERSION BOX

REDWOOD GRADE BOARD

15 LB. UNSATURATED BUILDING PAPER

3/4" TO 1 1/2" AGGREGATE

WIDTH BETWEEN LATERALS, NUMBER AND LENGTH OF LATERALS DEPENDS ON SOIL AND NUMBER OF FIXTURE UNITS

TYPE OF INSTALLATION DEPENDS ON SOIL POROSITY AND WATER TABLE

M. C. NOTTINGHAM CO
SEPTIC TANKS-AERATION TANKS
AND RESEARCH
4922 IRWINDALE AVENUE IRWINDALE
MANUFACTURING PLANTS AT REDLANDS
SUN VALLEY SATICOY CALIFORNIA
ESCONDIDO

TYPICAL "HYGI SEPT" INSTALLATIONS
FOR RESIDENCES

DATE: 8/13/62   SCALE: 3/8"-1'   DWG NO.

Fig. 21-7. Typical septic-tank installation (from M. C. Nottingham Company).

149

tank for a four-bedroom single dwelling?

b. What is the minimum capacity of a septic tank for a six-unit apartment building with one-bedroom apartments?

c. What is the minimum capacity of a septic tank for any occupancy using 90 fixture units per day?

d. In a single dwelling, how many bedrooms would be permitted if the septic tank were of 2,000-gal capacity?

15. Using the table A-37, how many square feet of absorption area are needed in fine sand for a septic tank of 1,200-gal capacity?

STUDY SUGGESTIONS

1. Visit a plumbing-supply house; look at the various fixtures, piping, fittings, etc., and note how they are put together.

2. Go to a building under construction, and compare the plumbing fixtures and fittings with the symbols on the plumbing plan.

Chapter

22

Plot and Landscaping Plans

Definition and Purpose

The plot plan is a plan view of the site, the building, and all outside work in connection with the job. The outside work includes all concrete and paving work, locations of utilities, and smaller structures, such as covered walks or arbors (Fig. 22-1). Landscaping can be shown on the plot plan but is usually on a separate drawing to avoid confusion. Scale varies considerably depending on the size of the project and sheet size. Typical scale is $\frac{1}{16}$ in. = 1 ft 0 in.

Plot Plan

Before starting the plot plan, however, the student should be familiar with the use of contour lines and polar coordinates and the problem of setbacks and easements. These subjects are not usually encountered in a first-year drafting course.

CONTOUR LINES

A contour line is a conventional means to show height on the flat surface of a drawing (Fig. 22-2). It is simply a line on a map which represents the intersection of an imaginary horizontal plane with the surface of the ground. The uniform vertical distance between contour lines is called the contour interval. The contour interval used on a small map may be as small as a fraction of a foot or, on a large map, 100 ft. The usual contour interval used on small maps is 1 or 2 ft. Contours are labeled according to their height above mean sea level or any other convenient base plane. A simple way of visualizing contours follows: If one were to draw lines at the varying water levels of a lake as the water level dropped, each line, when viewed from above, would represent a contour line, and all of them together would represent a contour map of the shore around the lake. With a little practice, a draftsman can easily visualize the shape of the land through the use of contour lines.

LOT LINES

Lots are usually laid out by surveyors by the use of polar coordinates; that is, each line around a lot is described by its length plus its angle in relation to true north or south, i.e., *distance* and *bearing* (Fig. 22-3). The distance is laid off in feet and hundredths of a foot, rather than feet and inches. For example, 150 ft 9 in. would equal 150.75 ft. Angles, or bearings, are measured in relation to true north or true south. North and south are both read as 0°; east and west are both read as 90°. To avoid ambiguity, the compass is divided into four quadrants of 90°—NW, NE, SE, and SW. Angles are labeled thus: N14°53'11"W; this reads "north fourteen degrees, fifty-three minutes, eleven seconds west." As there are sixty minutes to a degree and sixty seconds to a minute, the student may safely round this figure off to N15°W, because the ordinary protractor cannot be used to measure such small increments as minutes and seconds. For plot plans, $\frac{1}{2}$° accuracy is sufficient. When copying a lot from a map to a plot plan, start at the point of beginning (pob) which will permit each line to be laid out in order, head to tail, without using a reverse heading (Fig. 22-3). Lay off the bearing first, then the distance.

Other methods of expressing angular relation-

(continued on page 154)

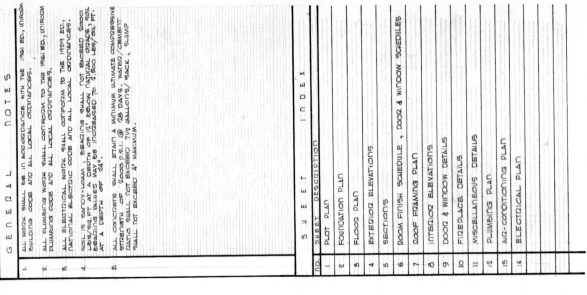

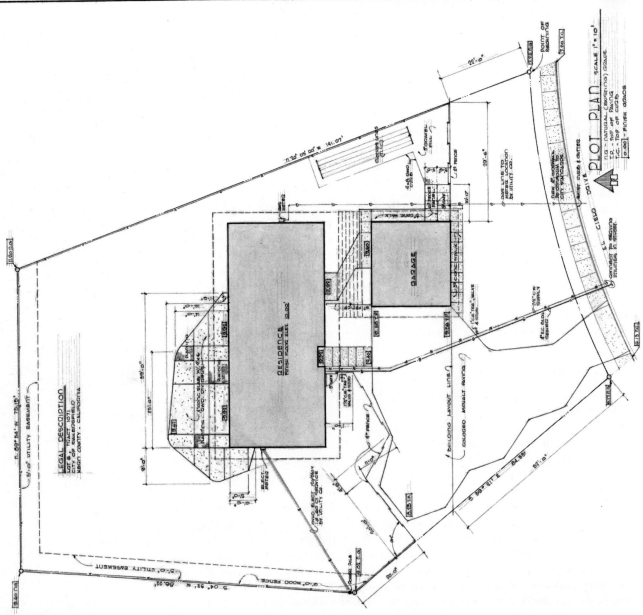

Fig. 22-1. *Plot plan of a small residence.*

152

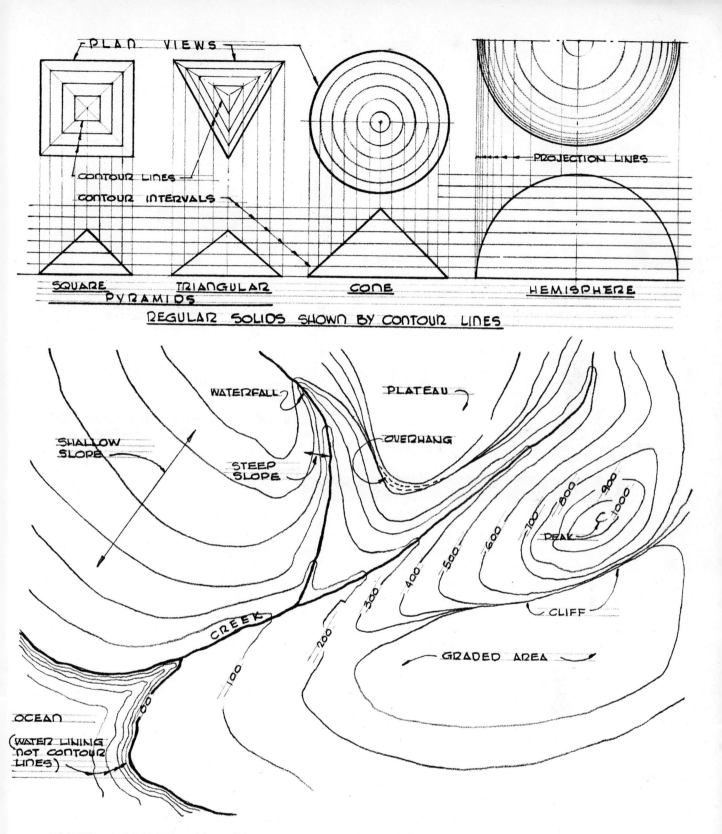

PLAN VIEWS

CONTOUR LINES

CONTOUR INTERVALS

PROJECTION LINES

SQUARE PYRAMIDS · TRIANGULAR · CONE · HEMISPHERE

REGULAR SOLIDS SHOWN BY CONTOUR LINES

WATERFALL · PLATEAU

OVERHANG

SHALLOW SLOPE

STEEP SLOPE

PEAK

100 · 800 · 900 · 1000

700 · 600

500

400

CLIFF

300

GRADED AREA

CREEK

200

100

60

OCEAN

(WATER LINING NOT CONTOUR LINES)

NATURAL FEATURES OF THE EARTHS SURFACE SHOWN BY CONTOUR LINES

Fig. 22-2. Contour lines of regular and irregular surfaces.

153

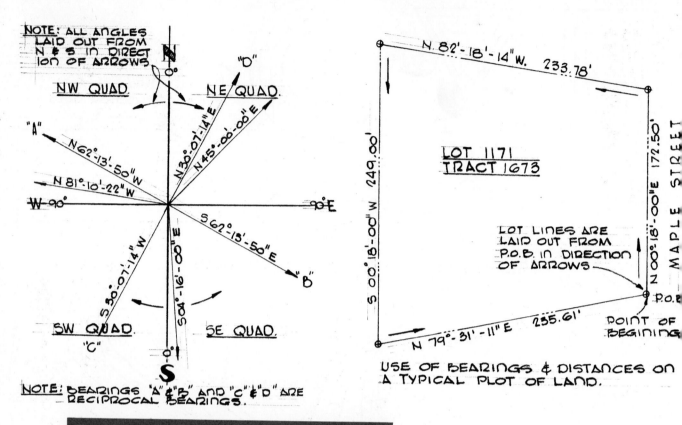

Fig. 22-3. Use of bearings in describing a plot of land.

ships are used, but all are based on a circle divided into 360°. The included angle between two lines or the included angle between a line and a base line may be indicated by an arc. The angle between a line and either north or south as 0° may be shown. A special case is the sun table used in this book. North is considered to be 0° and south 180°. No angle is larger than 180°. Angles to the east, or morning, read clockwise from north; angles to the west, or afternoon, read counterclockwise. It is easy to determine the method by which any angle is expressed by comparing the line with a north-south line or noting the arc used to dimension the angle.

SETBACKS AND EASEMENTS

Setbacks and easements limit the space on the lot within which buildings may be placed. Setbacks are found in the building codes and zoning ordinances. They establish the distances from the front, rear, and sides of the lot beyond which the building may not be placed. They vary greatly, depending upon the part of the country and type of building

involved. The city and county building departments keep these restrictions on file for all areas under their jurisdiction (see A-38 and A-39). Easements are other areas within the lot over which construction may not be placed. Permission to use these areas at any time has been deeded to certain agencies for access to the facilities which they maintain. Easements are provided for power lines, sewer lines, etc. The location and extent of easements are found on the subdivision maps (Fig. 22-4).

DRAFTING THE PLOT PLAN

When drawing a plot plan, it is good practice to draw the project in the order of its construction, as follows (Figs. 22-1 and 22-4):

1. Lay out the lot and show contour if needed; flat lots do not have or need contour lines. Place the north arrow.
2. Indicate the streets and alleys.
3. Show locations of all utilities: electrical, gas, and water service; sewer lines; steam-heating lines; etc.

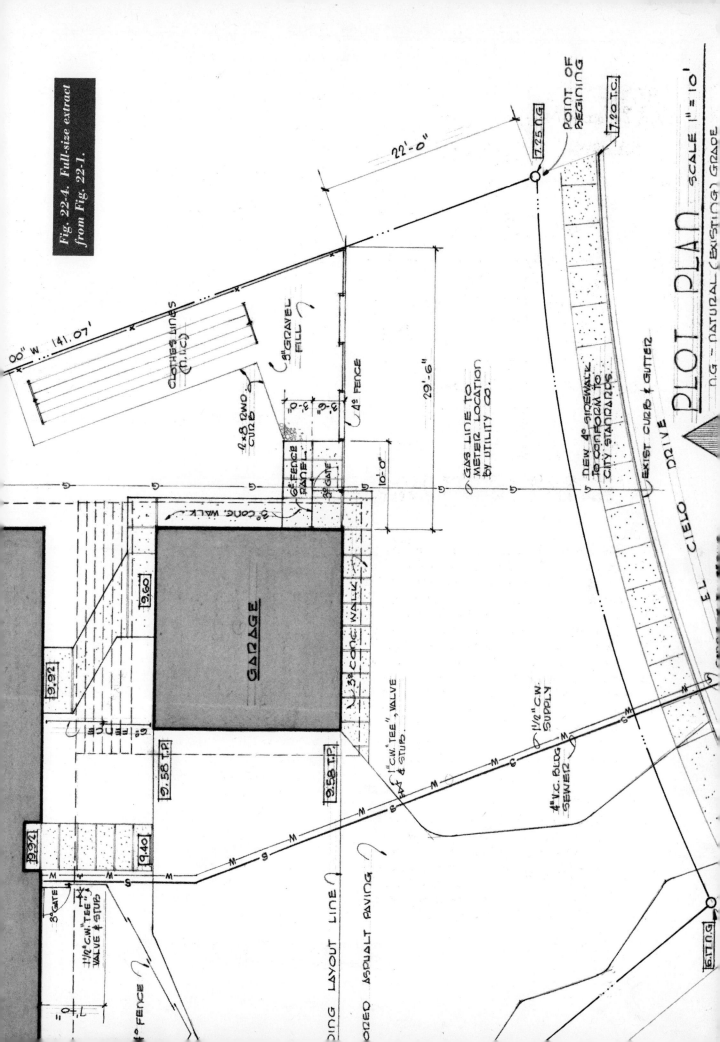

Fig. 22-4. Full-size extract from Fig. 22-1.

PLOT PLAN — SCALE 1" = 10'

N.G. = NATURAL (EXISTING) GRADE

POINT OF BEGINING

7.25 N.G.

7.20 T.C.

22'-0"

29'-6"

EL CIELO DRIVE

EXIST CURB & GUTTER

NEW 4" SIDEWALK TO CONFORM TO CITY STANDARDS

GAS LINE TO METER LOCATION BY UTILITY CO.

8° W   141.07'

CLOTHES LINES (T.L.C.)

3" GRAVEL FILL

2×8 RWD CURB

6" FENCE PANEL

4" FENCE

3'-0"

8'-9"

3° GATE

10'-0"

3" CONC. WALK

GARAGE

3" CONC. WALK

1"C.W. "TEE", VALVE & STUB

1½" C.W. SUPPLY

4" V.C. BLDG SEWER

9.60

9.92

6" FENCE

9.58 T.P.

9.58 T.P.

9.94

9.40

3° GATE

1½"C.W. "TEE", VALVE & STUB

4° FENCE

BUILDING LAYOUT LINE

SCORED ASPHALT PAVING

6.17 N.G.

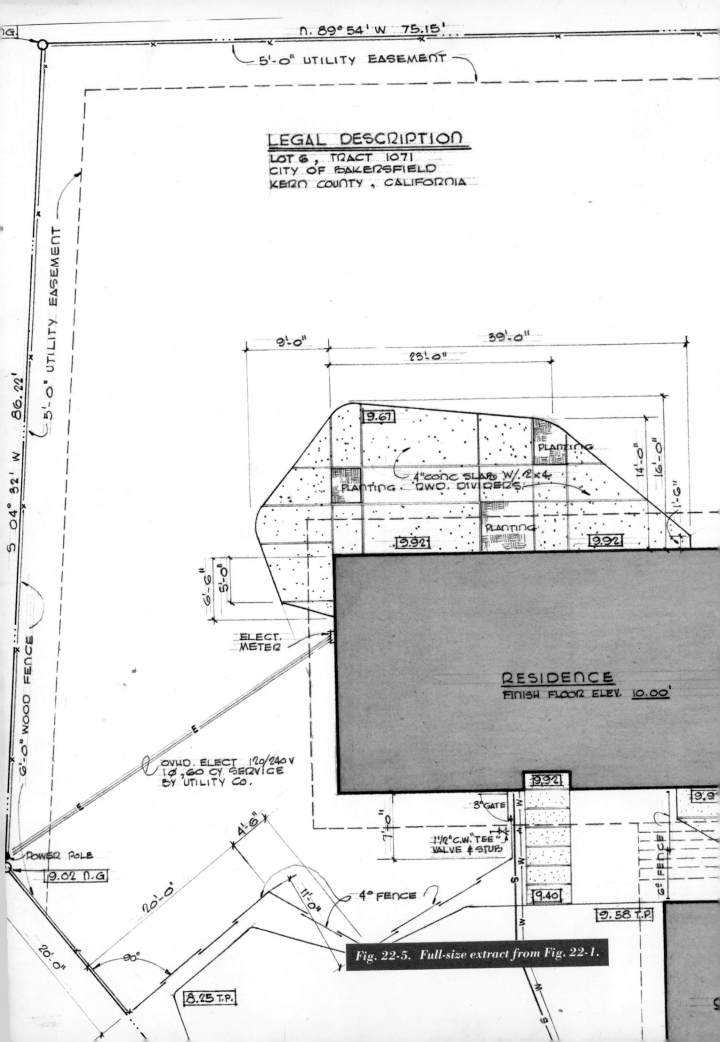

n. 89° 54' W 75.15'

5'-0" UTILITY EASEMENT

5'-0" UTILITY EASEMENT

S 04° 32' W 86.22'

6'-0" WOOD FENCE

LEGAL DESCRIPTION
LOT 6, TRACT 1071
CITY OF BAKERSFIELD
KERN COUNTY, CALIFORNIA

9'-0"

39'-0"

23'-0"

9.61

PLANTING

14'-0"

16'-0"

1'-6"

4"CONC SLAB W/ 2x4
RWD. DIVIDERS

PLANTING

PLANTING

9.92

9.92

6'-6"

5'-0"

ELECT.
METER

E

OVHD. ELECT 120/240 V
1Ø, 60 CY. SERVICE
BY UTILITY CO.

E

POWER POLE

9.02 N.G

20'-0"

20'-0"

90°

8.25 T.P.

4'-6"

11'-0"

4° FENCE

RESIDENCE
FINISH FLOOR ELEV. 10.00'

9.92

3' GATE

1½"C.W. TEE
VALVE & STUB

7'-0"

W

W

6° FENCE

9.9

9.40

9.58 T.P.

Fig. 22-5. Full-size extract from Fig. 22-1.

4. Draw in any existing construction which will be left in place after construction starts.
5. In dashed lines draw any existing construction which will be removed before construction. Indicate by a general note which construction is to be removed and by whom.
6. Lay off light lines representing the front, rear, and side setbacks allowed by ordinance. Construction is not permitted beyond these lines, except for walks, drives, etc. Lay off any easements which cross the site; no construction should be placed in these areas.
7. Lay out the outlines of all buildings and roof overhangs.
8. Locate miscellaneous details, such as plumbing vents, advertising signs, fences, gates, etc.
9. Draw in all concrete work, plant-mix surfacing, and areas of rock or gravel.
10. Dimension the building in relation to the lot lines. If the lot lines are at 90° to each other and the building is parallel to one of them, two dimensions are needed. If the building is not parallel to a lot line, locate one important corner of the building in relation to a corner of the lot with two dimensions. Show the distance from a lot line to another corner, on a wall common to the first corner. Dimension lines are always perpendicular or parallel to the lot lines.
11. Dimension concrete or paved areas by location and/or size, whichever is clearer.
12. Place all notes; all areas should be identified. The thickness of concrete and paving should be noted, and all utilities should be identified. Show elevations of the ground at the building and property corners. Show the elevation of each floor level of the structure.

Landscaping Plan

The landscaping plan is closely related to the plot plan. It shows the type and location of all trees, plants, lawn, ground cover, etc., on the building site. Sometimes fences, lath houses, benches, etc., are placed on the landscaping plan (Fig. 22-1).

DRAFTING THE LANDSCAPING PLAN

Following is a logical order of work:

1. Trace the plot plan omitting utilities and dimensioning.
2. Place all large trees and shrubs; draw them as mature plants, even though they may be quite small when planted. Mark the locations of the trunks as small circles.
3. Outline all planters and areas of lawn and ground cover.
4. Place small plants and hedges.
5. Identify all plants and planting areas by note. The common names for trees and shrubs are usually used by students.
6. Sprinkler systems are placed on the landscape plan (Fig. 22-5). Start from the water source and place the valves or automatic timing device. Run the water lines where needed, and identify all sprinkler heads. The information concerning pipes, valves, area covered by various sprinkler heads, etc., may be found in the manufacturers' catalogs.

TREES AND SHRUBS

The methods of drawing trees, shrubs, ground cover, etc., vary considerably, but the lines should usually be the weight of dimension lines (see A-40). In a plot plan that is part of a presentation drawing, trees and foliage are drawn in great detail, primarily to create an artistic effect. On a working drawing, circles drawn with a template or a compass are suitable for trees and shrubs. Some draftsmen devise their own symbols and lines for landscape features. In addition, landscape templates are available which increase speed in drafting. The type of rendition is a matter of taste or office practice.

REVIEW QUESTIONS

1. Round off the figure 37°21′37″ to $\frac{1}{2}$°. Why is this done?
2. What is the angular difference between:
   a. N31°18′57″W and N18°01′32″W?
   b. N31°18′57″W and S18°01′32″E?
   c. N31°18′57″W and S31°18′57″E?
   Draw a rough sketch to avoid confusion.
3. Draw a contour map, at any convenient contour interval, of:
   a. A hemisphere resting on flat side
   b. A cone resting on the flat side
   c. A square pyramid
   d. Any irregular object you desire
4. On your own landscape plan, why have you drawn the trees as you have? Appearance? Economy of time?
5. Using the diagram A-38, determine the following for an interior lot:

a. The minimum front yard setback for a residence.

b. The minimum side yard setback for a residence.

c. The minimum rear yard setback for a residence.

6. Using the diagram A-38, determine the following for a corner lot:

a. The minimum front yard setback for a residence.

b. The minimum distance from the garage or carport to the property line for a residence.

c. The minimum side yard setback on the street side for a residence.

d. The minimum side yard setback on the side opposite the street for a residence.

e. The minimum rear yard setback for a residence.

STUDY SUGGESTIONS

1. Visit the assessor's office or a building-tract office, and check the map of a certain area against the land itself. Note the contour, locations of curbs and gutters, utilities, easements, etc.

2. Check a finished building against the original plot and landscaping plans.

Chapter
23
Interior Elevations

Definition and Purpose

The interior elevations describe the interior walls of each room in the building. Each elevation is an orthographic projection based on the floor plan of the particular wall and the structural section at that point (Fig. 23-1). Other drawings used to determine height are the fireplace section, cabinet sections, planter sections, and manufacturers' illustrations showing special equipment. All walls should be shown and identified in a complete set of drawings. However, on a minimum set of drawings, only the important walls are shown, such as the kitchen, fireplace, and special cabinet work. The scale of interior elevations is usually $\frac{1}{4}$ or $\frac{3}{8}$ in. = 1 ft 0 in. but can be made larger to show more detail.

The procedure used in laying out accurate interior elevations is practically the same as that used for exterior elevations; the only difference is that the inside, rather than the outside, walls are projected (Fig. 23-2).

Drafting the Interior Elevations

Many features are common to the interior walls of any structure, and the following procedure is used for drawing all interior walls (Fig. 23-3):

1. Project or measure the true width of the wall, and locate all windows, doors, stairs, etc., from the floor plan. The space remaining is available for cabinet work, appliances, display cases, etc.
2. Project or measure the height of all features of the wall from a section, or get the information from one of the schedules. In a room with a sloping ceiling show the ceiling area, beams, etc., above the plate line.
3. Draw in the light outlines of all cabinets, shelves, wardrobes, and plumbing fixtures which are to be built in. Locate with light lines all stoves, refrigerators, and other appliances which must have space reserved for them and label NIC.
4. Wherever cabinets, soffits, shelves, etc., return on a wall toward the observer, they should be drawn in heavy outline. Omit the lines of the wall and floor behind the cabinet, because these areas are not part of the wall being drawn. Also, this procedure makes the drawing easier to read.
5. Draw the outlines of varying wall materials, such as tile, stainless steel, and wood wainscoting.
6. Mark off the doors, drawers, shelves, toe spaces, soffits, etc., of all cabinet work, display cases, and wardrobes.
7. Draw in all base molding, door and window trim, etc., where needed.

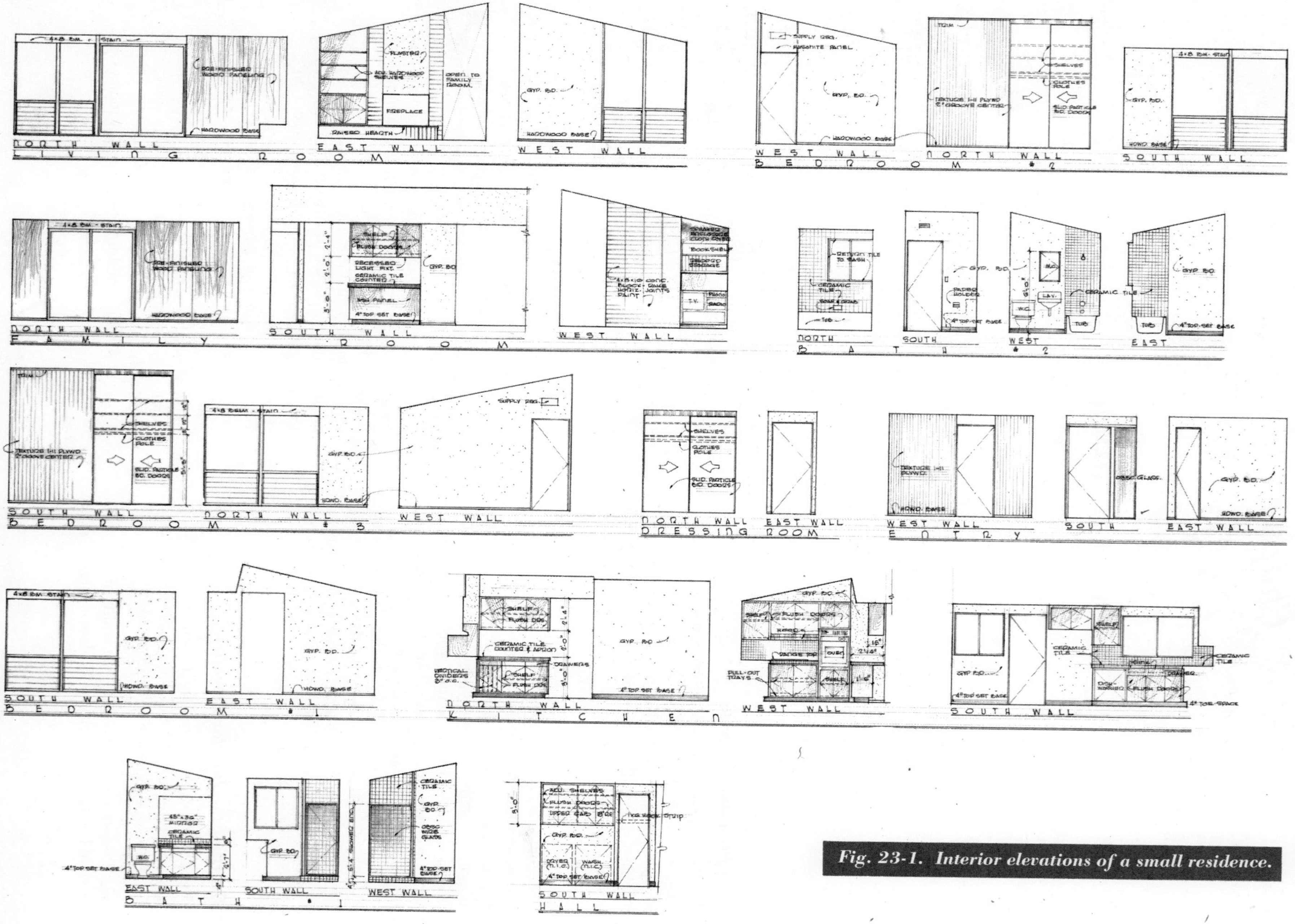

Fig. 23-1. Interior elevations of a small residence.

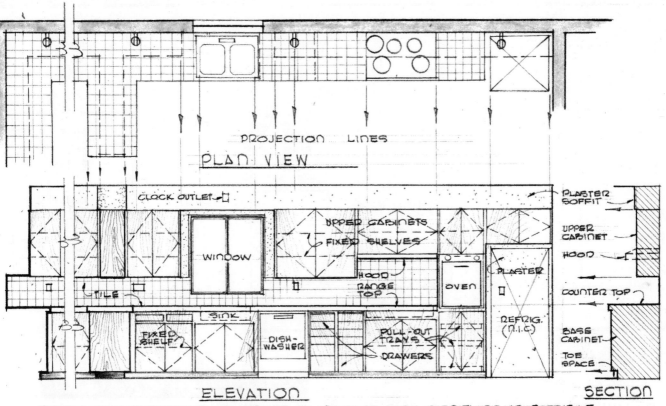

PROJECTION LINES
PLAN VIEW

CLOCK OUTLET

PLASTER SOFFIT

UPPER CABINETS
FIXED SHELVES

UPPER CABINET

WINDOW

HOOD

HOOD
RANGE TOP

OVEN

PLASTER

COUNTER TOP

TILE

SINK

REFRIG. (N.I.C.)

BASE CABINET

FIXED SHELF

DISH-WASHER

PULL-OUT TRAYS

DRAWERS

TOE SPACE

ELEVATION

SECTION

NOTE: THIS ELEVATION CONTRIVED TO SHOW AS MANY CONDITIONS AS POSSIBLE

Fig. 23-2. Method of direct projection of interior elevations.

8. Place all electric outlets, such as convenience outlets, wall switches, and wall fixtures, in the proper places.
9. Letter in all notes concerning surface materials and equipment.
10. Letter in all notes, titles, and scale.
11. Draw in the textures of all surface materials lightly.

Refer to the appropriate chapters of the book for specific information on drawing cabinets, stairs, fireplaces, trim, tile, plumbing and electric fixtures, etc.

Keying Symbols

Each drawing must be keyed to the others in the set (Fig. 23-3). Cabinet elevations must be keyed to the appropriate cabinet section. Door- and window-head jamb and sill conditions must be related to the correct sections. Store fronts and display cases should be keyed to their sections.

REVIEW QUESTIONS

1. What good reason is there for showing all the walls of all rooms of a building, even though some of them are practically blank?
2. Is it possible to draw an interior elevation from the floor plan of the wall without the cross section? Why?
3. In a frame and plaster structure, what is the main purpose of door trim?

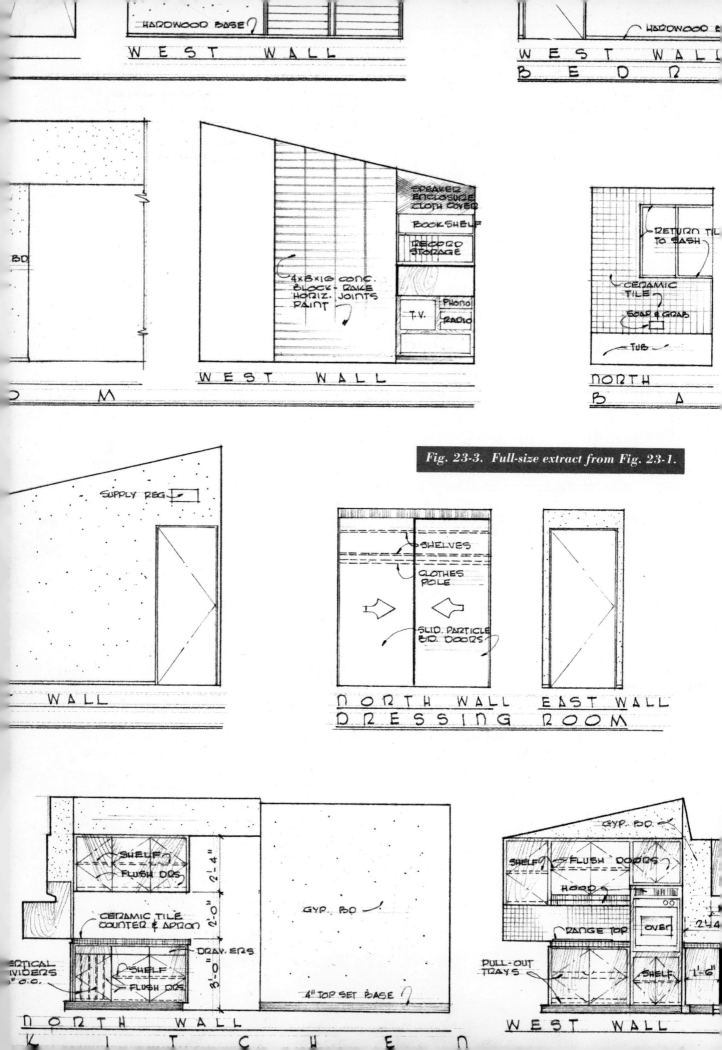

HARDWOOD BASE

W E S T   W A L L

HARDWOOD B

W E S T   W A L L
B E D R

SPEAKER
ENCLOSURE
CLOTH COVER

BOOKSHELF

RECORD
STORAGE

4×8×16 CONC.
BLOCK - RAKE
HORIZ. JOINTS
PAINT

T.V.

PHONO
RADIO

W E S T   W A L L

BD

O M

RETURN TILE
TO SASH

CERAMIC
TILE

SOAP & GRAB

TUB

N O R T H

B A

SUPPLY REG.

Fig. 23-3.   Full-size extract from Fig. 23-1.

SHELVES

CLOTHES
POLE

SLID. PARTICLE
BD. DOORS

W A L L

N O R T H   W A L L   E A S T   W A L L
D R E S S I N G   R O O M

SHELF
FLUSH DRS

CERAMIC TILE
COUNTER & APRON

2'-4"

2'-0"

DRAWERS

VERTICAL
DIVIDERS
" O.C.

SHELF
FLUSH DRS.

3'-0"

4" TOP SET BASE

N O R T H   W A L L
K I T C H E N

GYP. BD.

SHELF   FLUSH DOORS

HOOD

GYP. BD.

RANGE TOP   OVEN

PULL-OUT
TRAYS

SHELF

2'-4"

1'-6"

W E S T   W A L L

STUDY SUGGESTIONS

1. Visit two buildings under construction, a typical frame residence and a high-quality commercial building. Compare construction features, such as windows, doors, hardware, and trim. Compare the drawings with the actual construction.

2. Inspect specific interior details, such as fireplaces, planters, room dividers, or cabinet work, in an architectural magazine. You may be able to use similar details on a future project.

Chapter
24
Door and Window Details

Definition and Purpose

Though much information regarding windows and doors is shown on the floor plan, elevations, and schedules, additional details are required to make installation and construction clear to the builder. These details usually include sections through each window and door as well as plan or elevation views where needed (Figs. 24-1 and 24-2). All parts used in construction are called out by note. Heights, clearances, openings, and sizes of special millwork are dimensioned. Parts furnished by certain manufacturers are described by note. Door and window details are drawn at large scale for ease of reading, $1\frac{1}{2}$ or 3 in. = 1 ft 0 in. Where large numbers of standard windows or doors are used, a typical detail is drawn to show the method of their installation (Figs. 24-3 and 24-4).

It is a simple job to show the method of connecting windows or doors to the building, but the design of a custom-built opening demands much knowledge of construction and millwork. The procedure shown here is typical of the type of work expected of a beginning draftsman. The design of millwork will not be discussed.

The sections required, in the order of their importance, are head, jamb, and sill or threshold (required in all cases); and transom, post, muntin, and mullion (where required). For reasons of logic and clarity, the sections should be arranged in order vertically, head or transom above, threshold or sill below, and from side to side, jamb to post to mullion to muntin to jamb.

Drafting the Window and Door Details

The same procedure is used in drawing a window or door detail (Figs. 24-3 and 24-4).

1. Draw a section through the wall showing the structure of the wall around the rough opening.
2. Copy the correct section from the manufacturer's literature in its proper relation to the opening.
3. Place weatherproofing and flashing as recommended.
4. Draw in exterior and interior finish materials.
5. Draw in blocking if required.
6. Draw in the trim if required.
7. Letter in all notes, title, and scale.

Check as the work progresses to be certain that the construction of all sections is consistent all around the frame. Coordinate the sections with the exterior and interior elevations and the door and window schedules. Use the correct keying symbol to relate the sections to the elevations.

Some special types of doors and windows are detailed in Fig. 24-4, such as store fronts, pass-throughs, overhead doors, and rolling doors. The required information is found in the manufacturers' catalogs.

(continued on page 169)

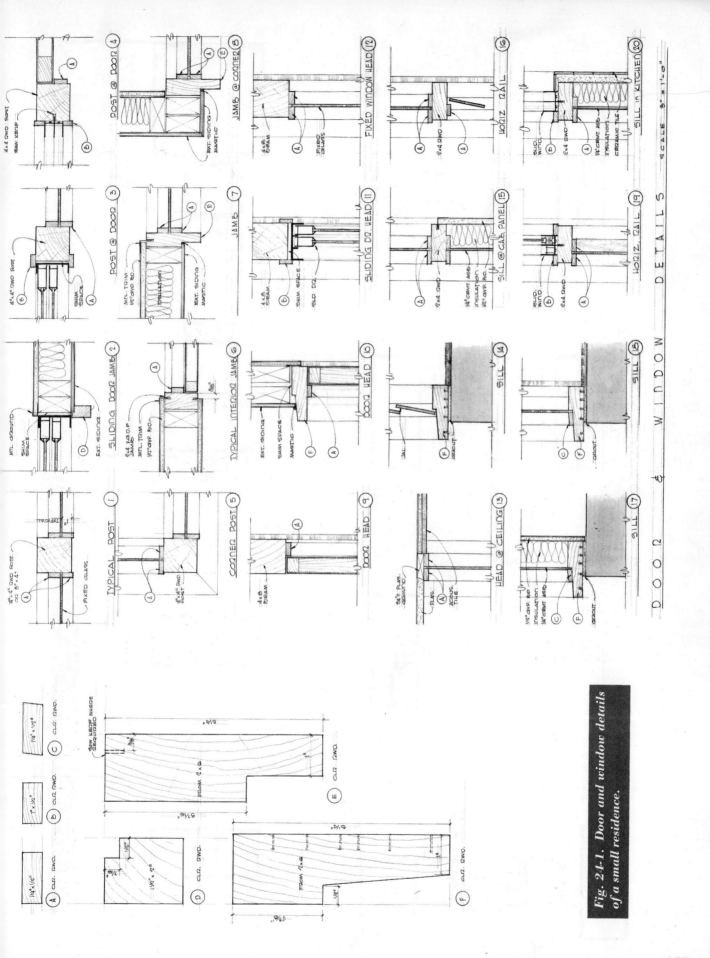

Fig. 24-1. Door and window details of a small residence.

165

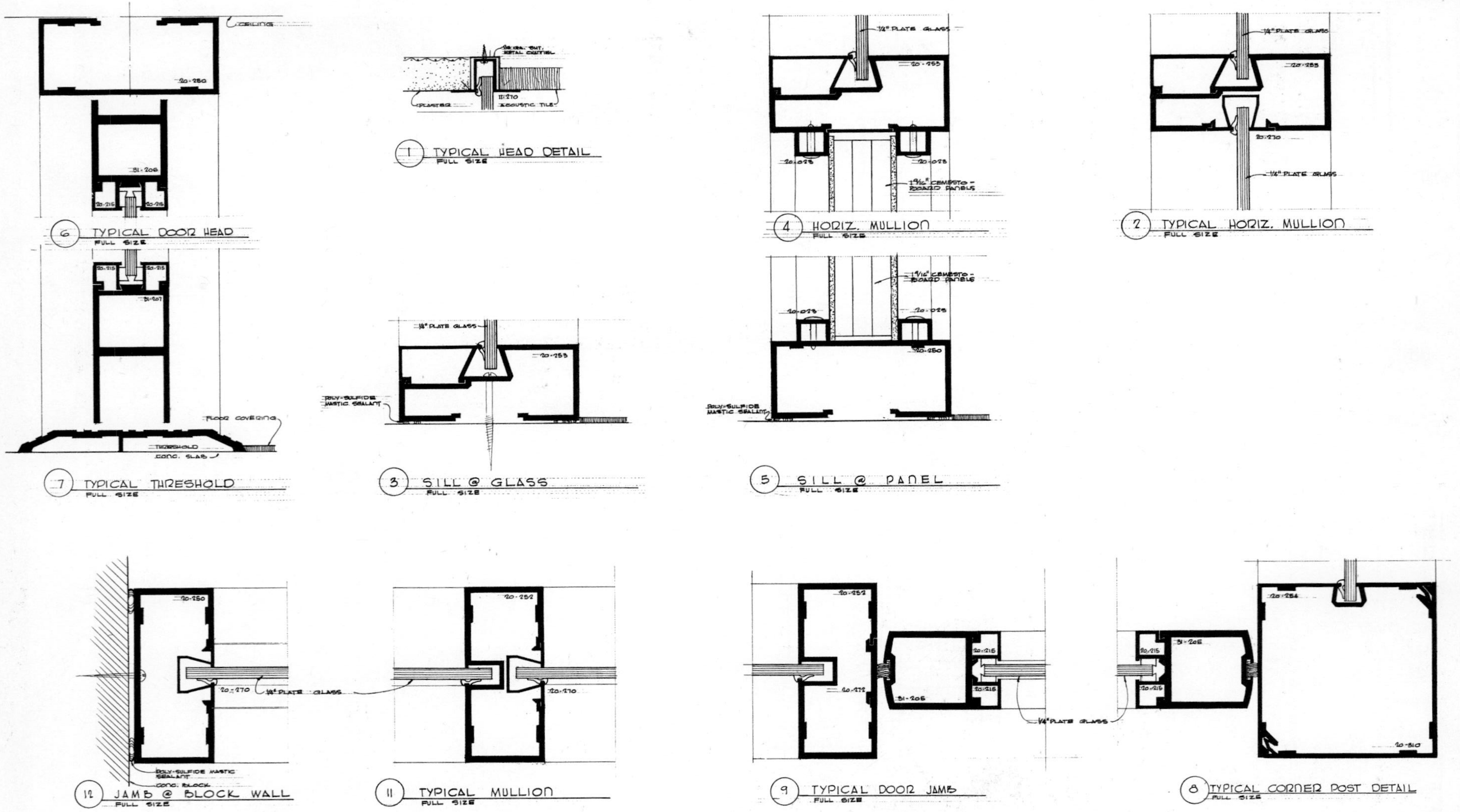

166

Fig. 24-2. *Door and window details of a small restaurant.*

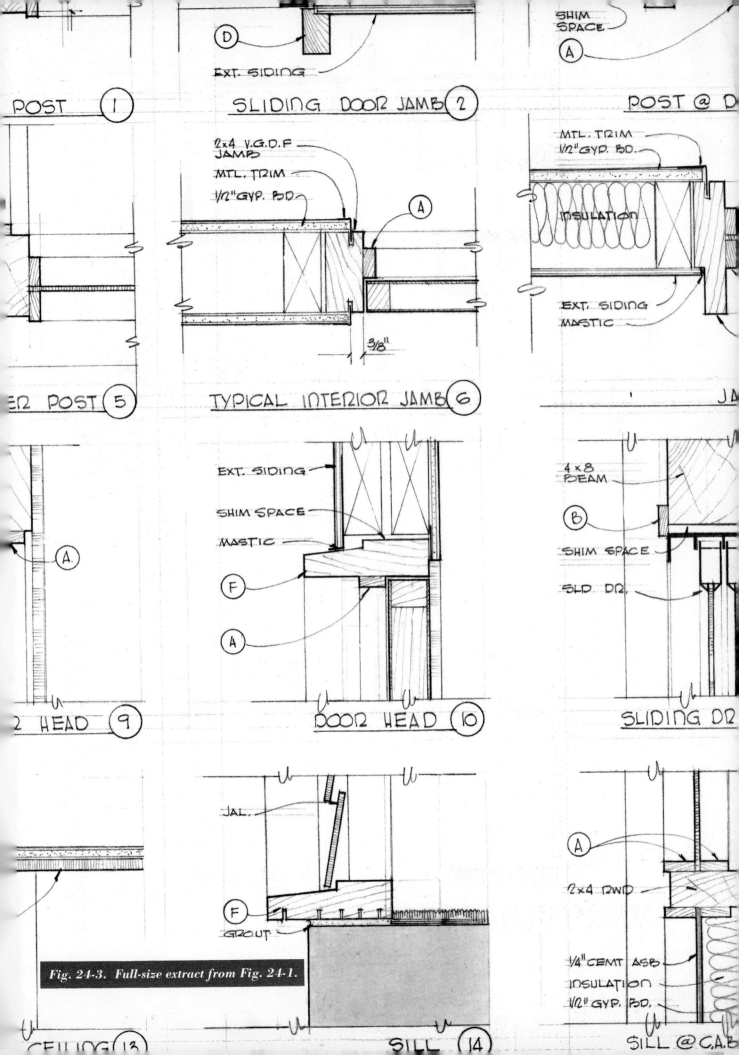

POST (1)

SLIDING DOOR JAMB (2)

D
EXT. SIDING

SHIM
SPACE
(A)

POST @ D

MTL. TRIM
1/2" GYP. BD.

ER POST (5)

2×4 V.G.D.F
JAMB
MTL. TRIM
1/2" GYP. BD.

(A)

TYPICAL INTERIOR JAMB (6)

3/8"

INSULATION

EXT. SIDING
MASTIC

JA

2 HEAD (9)

EXT. SIDING
SHIM SPACE
MASTIC
(F)
(A)

DOOR HEAD (10)

(A.)

4×8
BEAM
(B)
SHIM SPACE
SLD. DR.

SLIDING DR

SILL (14)

JAL.
(F)
GROUT.

(A)
2×4 RWD
1/4" CEMT. ASB
INSULATION
1/2" GYP. BD.

SILL @ C.A.B

CEILING (13)

Fig. 24-3. Full-size extract from Fig. 24-1.

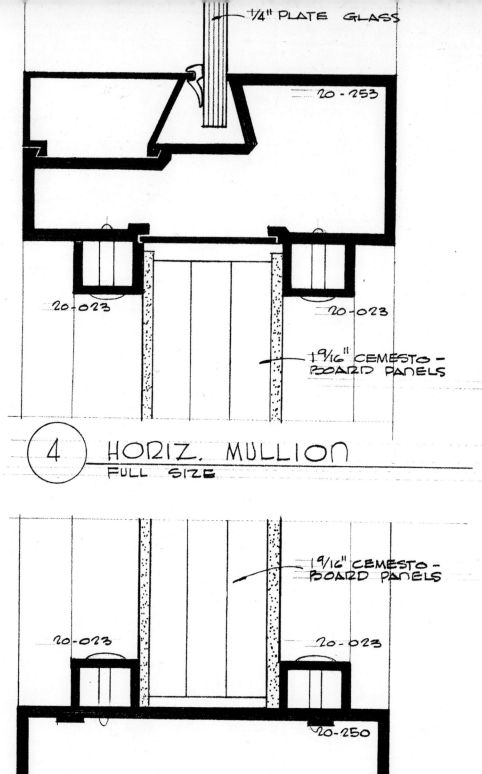

¼" PLATE GLASS

20-253

20-023

20-023

19/16" CEMESTO-
BOARD PANELS

4 HORIZ. MULLION
FULL SIZE

19/16" CEMESTO-
BOARD PANELS

20-023

20-023

20-250

POLY-SULFIDE
MASTIC SEALANT

Fig. 24-4. Full-size extract from Fig. 24-2.

5 SILL @ PANEL
FULL SIZE

REVIEW QUESTIONS

1. Define the following terms: stud, header, trimmer, stool, head, jamb, sill, threshold, mullion, post, muntin. Illustrate them in sketches.
2. In your locality, what are the advantages and disadvantages of casement, double-hung, awning, jalousie, or horizontal-sliding windows?
3. What advantages and disadvantages are inherent in the design of flush doors?

STUDY SUGGESTIONS

1. Visit a building-supply house, and inspect the various types of windows and doors.
2. Visit two buildings under construction, one of frame and the other of masonry construction. Compare the methods of framing windows and doors in both structures.

Chapter
25
Miscellaneous Details

Definition and Purpose

All small details difficult to classify elsewhere are placed on this drawing. In case the draftsman feels that some detail might be misinterpreted by the builder, it should be clarified by additional drawings and notes (Fig. 25-1). Notes and dimensioning should be quite complete. Sometimes isometric drawings are used to clarify details of construction. The scale of these drawings varies widely but is usually large, $1\frac{1}{2}$ in. = 1 ft 0 in. to full size.

The list of details shown below is by no means complete. It is intended merely to demonstrate the wide range of information found in the miscellaneous details. Procedures in drawing several of the most commonly used details are demonstrated. Much information is derived from catalogs, brochures, and technical literature regarding particular items of equipment.

Types of Miscellaneous Details

Some types of construction found in the miscellaneous details follows (Figs. 25-2 and 25-3):

1. All cabinet work
2. Range hoods
3. Planters
4. Screens and room dividers
5. Shower stalls
6. Ceramic-tile, metal, and plastic surfacing
7. Attic louvers
8. Access panels
9. Suspended ceilings
10. Sun screens, patio covers
11. Signs and displays
12. Fences
13. Special equipment
    a. Overhead tracks
    b. Restaurant equipment
    c. Conveyors
    d. Letter slots, etc.

Cabinet Work

The term *cabinet work* or *case work* covers all storage spaces not considered as an integral part of the structure. Cabinet work may be job-built, shop-built, or manufactured, and it may be of wood or metal. There are three grades of wood cabinet work: standard, custom, and premium. Manufactured storage units may be purchased in a wide variety of sizes, materials, and finishes. Catalogs furnished by the manufacturers make planning for these units quite simple.

Because of the wide variety of cabinet constructions and local building practices, this description must be in general terms. See "Time-Saver Standards" or "Architectural Graphic Standards."

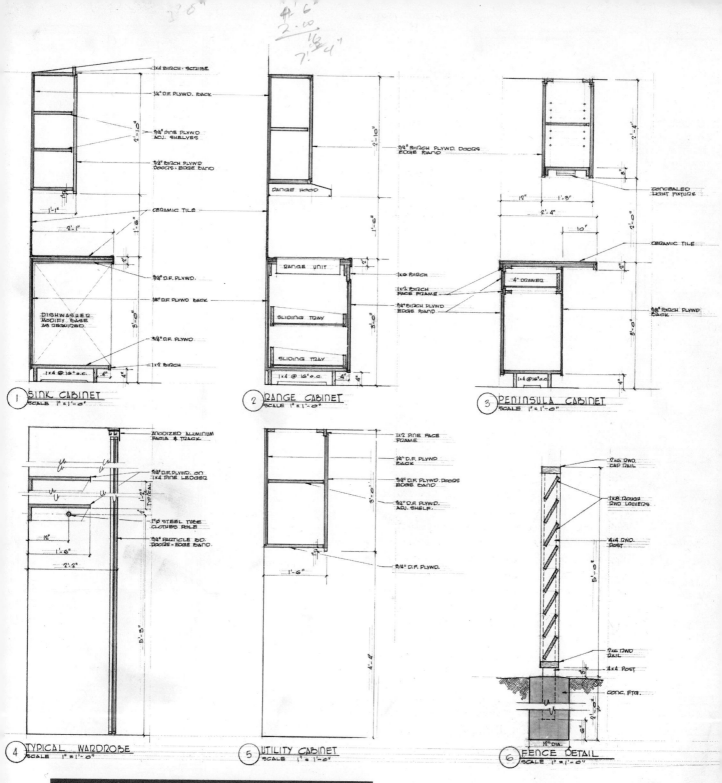

Fig. 25-1. Miscellaneous details of a small residence.

Drafting the Cabinet Details

The procedure in drawing the vertical sections for cabinet work, built-in furniture, wardrobes, etc., follows (Fig. 25-4):

1. Draw the floor, wall, and ceiling in light lines.
2. Check all heights and widths of cabinet work and sizes of component parts. Draw outlines as light lines.

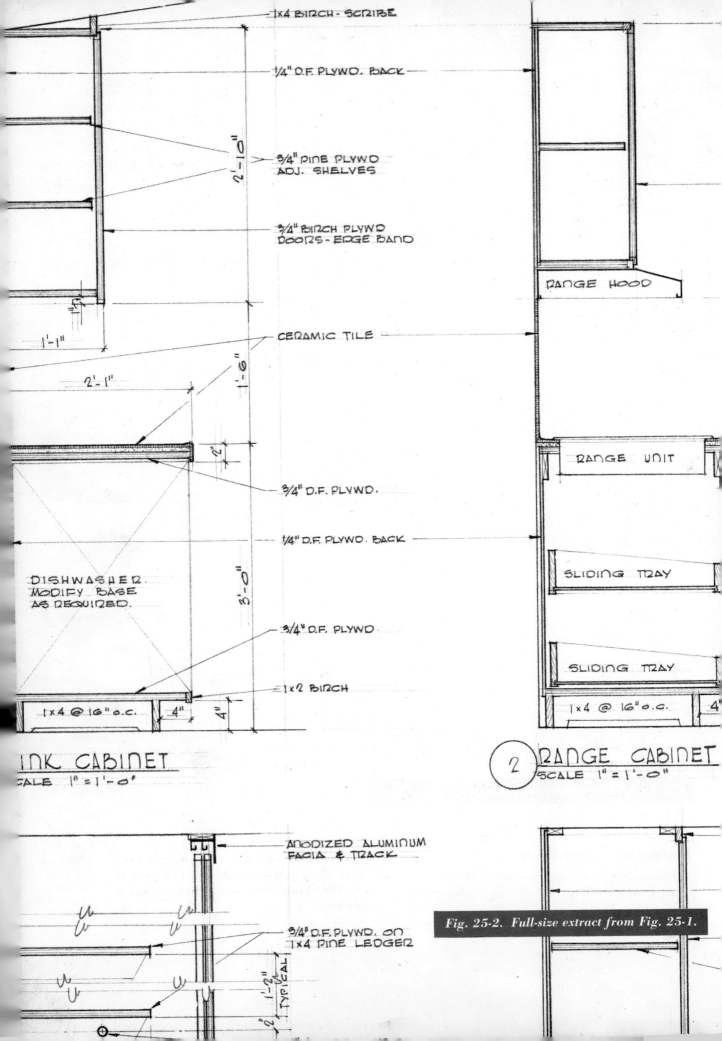

1×4 BIRCH - SCRIBE

1/4" D.F. PLYWD. BACK

3/4" PINE PLYWD
ADJ. SHELVES

3/4" BIRCH PLYWD
DOORS - EDGE BAND

2'-10"

CERAMIC TILE

1'-6"

1'-1"

2'-1"

2"

3/4" D.F. PLYWD.

1/4" D.F. PLYWD. BACK

DISHWASHER
MODIFY BASE
AS REQUIRED.

3'-0"

3/4" D.F. PLYWD

1×2 BIRCH

1×4 @ 16" O.C.   4"   4"

INK CABINET
SCALE 1" = 1'-0"

RANGE HOOD

RANGE UNIT

SLIDING TRAY

SLIDING TRAY

1×4 @ 16" O.C.   4

(2) RANGE CABINET
SCALE 1" = 1'-0"

ANODIZED ALUMINUM
FACIA & TRACK

3/4" D.F. PLYWD. ON
1×4 PINE LEDGER

1'-2"
TYPICAL

2"

Fig. 25-2. Full-size extract from Fig. 25-1.

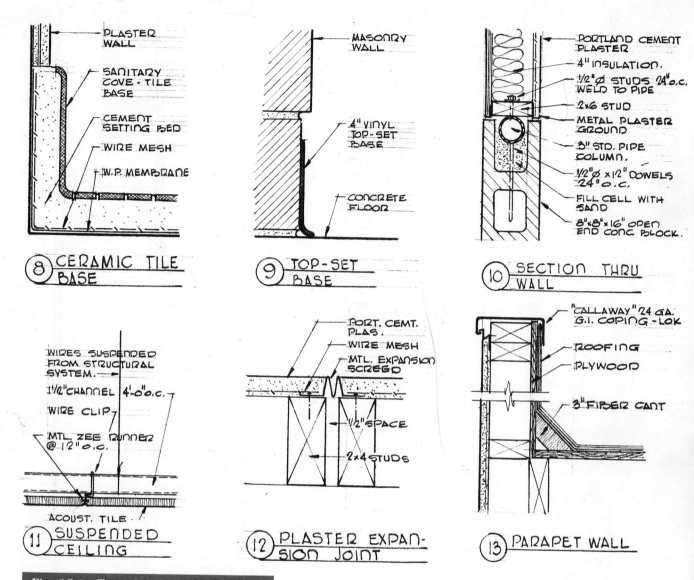

8 CERAMIC TILE BASE

- PLASTER WALL
- SANITARY COVE·TILE BASE
- CEMENT SETTING BED
- WIRE MESH
- W.P. MEMBRANE

9 TOP-SET BASE

- MASONRY WALL
- 4" VINYL TOP-SET BASE
- CONCRETE FLOOR

10 SECTION THRU WALL

- PORTLAND CEMENT PLASTER
- 4" INSULATION
- 1/2" Ø STUDS 24" o.c. WELD TO PIPE
- 2x6 STUD
- METAL PLASTER GROUND
- 3" STD. PIPE COLUMN
- 1/2" Ø x 12" DOWELS 24" o.c.
- FILL CELL WITH SAND
- 8"x8"x16" OPEN END CONC. BLOCK

11 SUSPENDED CEILING

- WIRES SUSPENDED FROM STRUCTURAL SYSTEM
- 1 1/2" CHANNEL 4'-0" o.c.
- WIRE CLIP
- MTL. ZEE RUNNER @ 12" o.c.
- ACOUST. TILE

12 PLASTER EXPANSION JOINT

- PORT. CEMT. PLAS.
- WIRE MESH
- MTL. EXPANSION SCREED
- 1/2" SPACE
- 2x4 STUDS

13 PARAPET WALL

- "CALLAWAY" 24 GA. G.I. COPING-LOK
- ROOFING
- PLYWOOD
- 3" FIBER CANT

Fig. 25-3. Typical miscellaneous details.

3. Place shelves, drawers, breadboards, clothespoles, special hardware, etc.
4. Draw in all finish materials.
5. Draw in drawer guides, forms or frames for finish materials, etc.
6. Dimension completely.
7. Place all lettering, notes, title, and scale.
8. Draw in textures where needed.

Partial horizontal sections are needed to show locations of structural parts, construction of face frame, etc. (Fig. 25-5). They are done in the same manner and must be in projection with the vertical sections. Vertical and horizontal sections must be made at all points where the construction changes.

When using manufactured cabinet work, it is only necessary to fit the desired units into the available space and show all soffits, furring, and methods of attachment to the building. All units must be identified by note and dimensions. Special louvers, sunscreens, gutters, and downspout details, etc., may be taken directly from "Time-Saver Standards," "Architectural Graphic Standards," or various manufacturers' catalogs.

Other miscellaneous details are designed by either the architect or the draftsman. The procedure in drawing is the same as the foregoing. It is im-

(continued on page 176)

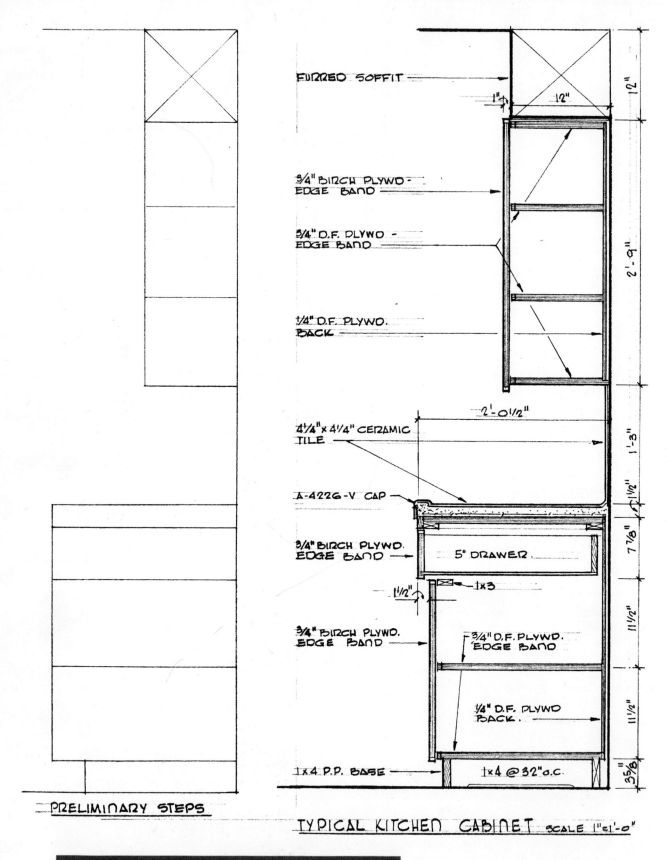

FURRED SOFFIT

3/4" BIRCH PLYWD - EDGE BAND

3/4" D.F. PLYWD - EDGE BAND

1/4" D.F. PLYWD. BACK

4 1/4" x 4 1/4" CERAMIC TILE

A-4226-V CAP

3/4" BIRCH PLYWD. EDGE BAND

3/4" BIRCH PLYWD. EDGE BAND

1" 12"

12"

2'-9"

2'-0 1/2"

1'-3"

1 1/2"

7 1/8"

5" DRAWER

1 1/2"

1x3

3/4" D.F. PLYWD. EDGE BAND

11 1/2"

1/4" D.F. PLYWD BACK.

11 1/2"

1x4 P.P. BASE

1x4 @ 32" o.c.

3 5/8"

PRELIMINARY STEPS

TYPICAL KITCHEN CABINET SCALE 1"=1'-0"

Fig. 25-4. Procedure in drawing a typical cabinet detail.

174

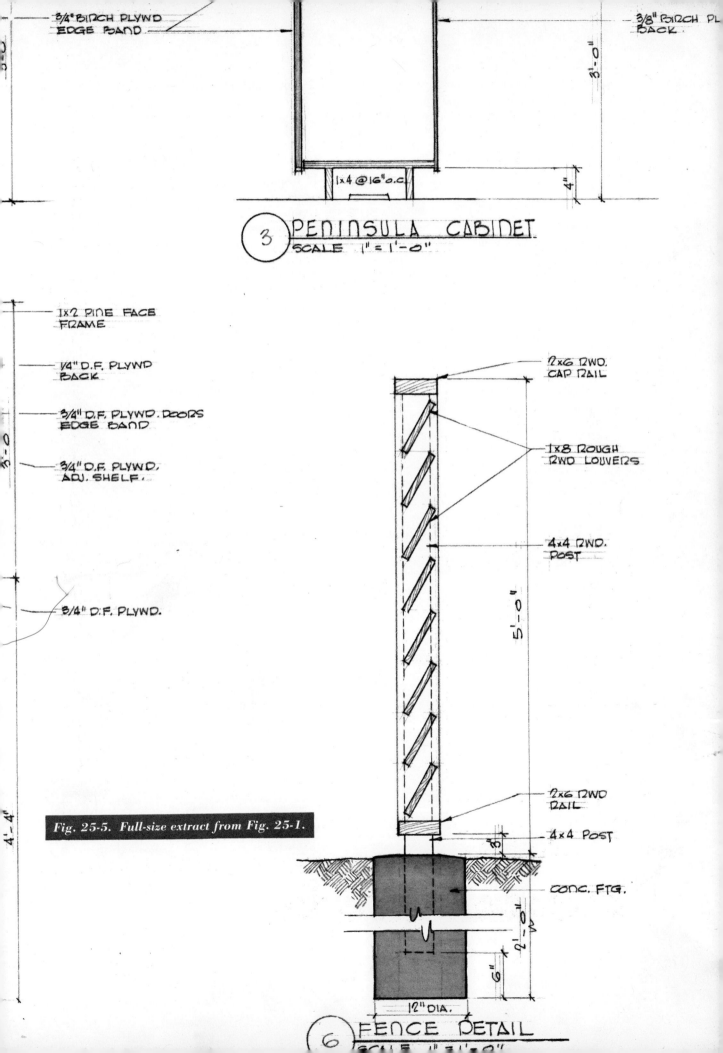

3/4" BIRCH PLYWD
EDGE BAND

3/8" BIRCH PL
BACK

3'-0"

4"

1x4 @ 16" O.C.

③ PENINSULA CABINET
SCALE 1" = 1'-0"

1x2 PINE FACE
FRAME

1/4" D.F. PLYWD
BACK

3/4" D.F. PLYWD. DOORS
EDGE BAND

3/4" D.F. PLYWD.
ADJ. SHELF.

3/4" D.F. PLYWD.

2x6 RWD.
CAP RAIL

1x8 ROUGH
RWD LOUVERS

4x4 RWD.
POST

5'-0"

2x6 RWD
RAIL

4x4 POST

3"

CONC. FTG.

2'-0"

6"

12" DIA.

Fig. 25-5. Full-size extract from Fig. 25-1.

3'-0"

4'-4"

⑥ FENCE DETAIL

portant to show enough sections, properly dimensioned, to make it possible for the builder to execute the drawings correctly. All sections must be related to the other drawings by the use of keying symbols (Fig. 25-5).

REVIEW QUESTIONS

1. Why is it impossible to describe completely such details as base and window trim and baluster on a $\frac{1}{8}$ in. = 1 ft 0 in. floor plan or elevation?
2. Pick out any special detail from a catalog, and sketch a sectional detail of it as it would be installed in your building.

3. How many drawings in the set are affected by a shower stall?

STUDY SUGGESTIONS

1. Inspect a completed building, and note the points which would require explanation in the miscellaneous details.
2. Using several details as examples, decide how many building trades would need to use the drawings of these details.
3. Check a magazine such as *Progressive Architecture* for construction details which you might use in your own project.

Chapter
26
Specifications

Definition and Purpose

As not all the information needed to construct a building can be placed on the drawings, much of the verbal information is in the form of specifications. The specifications are a bound volume of instructions, conditions, and descriptions which enable the builder to do the job properly and which also protect the interests of the architect, client, and builder.

Because of the nature and extent of the work involved, students are not required to furnish specifications with drawings. However, a good draftsman should know their uses and be able to read them intelligently.

Categories

The specifications are arranged in three general categories for ease of reference: legal documents; conditions, general and special; and technical descriptions.

1. Legal documents
   a. Advertisement for bids
   b. Invitation to bidders
   c. Instruction to bidders
   d. Owner-contractor contract agreement
   e. Bond forms
      (1) Labor and materials
      (2) Faithful performance
2. Conditions
   a. General: This section defines the rights and responsibilities of the architect, the client, the contractor, and the subcontractors concerned. These general conditions will vary only slightly from one set of specifications to another. The AIA has prepared a standardized form at nominal cost for the use of anyone who needs it.
   b. Special: These describe special requirements that are not a specific part of the technical section, such as the job office, sanitary facilities for workmen, barricades and scaffolding, and permits and licenses.
3. Technical descriptions of materials and methods to be incorporated into the project. For convenience, this section is divided into trade sections, e.g., electrical, plumbing. Each section is organized as follows:
   a. Scope of work
   b. Work included
   c. Work not included
   d. Materials
   e. General requirements
   f. Special requirements

If the drawings and specifications are accurate and complete, the finished structure will evolve as conceived by the client and the architect. Further, the rights of all parties will be protected, and all possible contingencies will be met. Any inaccuracy or omission will create serious problems for all concerned. A typical set of specifications may contain well over a hundred single-spaced typewritten pages.

REVIEW QUESTIONS

1. Using a tiled bathroom vanity as an example, list all the factors you can think of which must be covered by specifications in its construction.
2. Why are bond forms included in the specifications?
3. Why is there a distinction between general and special conditions in the specifications?

STUDY SUGGESTIONS

1. Read through a set of specifications, and notice the method of classification, type of language, and extent of coverage of the document.

Appendix

A-1   Simplified Residential Checklist for Clients   180

A-2   Final Residential Data Sheet   182

A-3   Sun Angle Tables   184

A-4   Format Suitable for Architectural Working Drawings   185

A-5   Architectural Symbols for Plans, Sections, and Elevations   186

A-6   Procedure for Designing Footings   187

A-7   Reinforcing Steel Foundation Table   188

A-8   Wood Floor and Ceiling Joist Table   189

A-9   Span Table for Tongue-and-Groove Wood Decking   189

A-10   (a) Wood Lintel Table (b) Concrete Lintel Table   190

A-11   Maximum Span of Masonry Wall between Supports   190

A-12   Wood Rafter Tables   190

A-13   Wood Ceiling Joist Tables   190

A-14   Wood Girder Tables   191

A-15   Fireplace Table   192

A-16   Residential Wiring Table   194

A-17   Electrical Symbols   195

A-18   Recommended Minimum Lighting Levels for Specific Areas   196

A-19   Recommended Spacing of Convenience Outlets   196

A-20   Inside Design Temperatures   196

A-21   Outside Design Temperatures for Winter   197

A-22   Outside Design Temperatures for Summer   198

A-23   Short Form Method for Computing Heating and Cooling Loads   200

A-24   Table for Sizing Registers, Outlets, and Grilles in an Air-distribution System   212

A-25   Table for Sizing Supply and Return Ducts in a Residential Air-distribution System   213

A-26   Table for Sizing Supply and Return Ducts in a Commercial Air-distribution System   214

A-27   Plumbing Symbols   215

A-28   Fixture Unit and Trap Table   219

A-29   Waste and Vent Sizing Table   219

A-30   Fixture Units for Hot and Cold Water   220

A-31   Pipe Sizes Based on Demand for Hot and Cold Water   220

A-32   Minimum Demands of Typical Gas Appliances   220

A-33   Pipe Sizes Based on Gas Demand   221

A-34   Location of Sewage-disposal System   221

A-35   Fixtures Needed for Commercial Usage   221

A-36   Sizes of Septic Tanks Based on Fixtures Needed   222

A-37   Required Absorption Areas for Leaching Systems   222

A-38   Typical Residential Yard Requirements for a Rectangular Interior Lot   223

A-39   Typical Residential Yard Requirements for a Corner Lot   224

A-40   Landscape Symbols   225

Check List, Architectural Working Drawings
(Attach Blank Sheet for Sketches & Additional Notes)

I. Room sizes, relationships
   A. Living room
      Approx. area **12 × 18**   Faces rear or front **rear**

      Walls **wood panel & plaster** floor **carpet (by owner)** ceiling **sloping - acoustic**

      Special features, fireplace, planters? Describe **Fireplace with raised hearth (Family room)**

   B. Kitchen
      Approx. area **8' × 11'**   breakfast nook? **7' × 9'**

      Type of cabinets **natural wood cabinets - ceramic tile counter tops**

      Walls **plaster - enamel** floor **vinyl - asb. tile** ceiling **plaster**

      List special equipment desired plus cat. nos. & brand **built-in elect. range oven, dishwasher — prefers G.E. equipment.**

   C. Bedrooms, including den

	Area	Walls	Floors	Ceilings	Type Closets
BR #1	10×15	plaster	carpet (n.i.c.)	acoustic	wardrobe
BR #2	10×13	"	"	"	"
BR #3	10×13	"	"	".	"
BR #4					
BR #5					

   D. Bathrooms

	Area	Walls	Floors	Ceilings	List Fixtures
Bath #1		cemt. plas.	cer. tile	plaster	shr, lav., w.c.
Bath #2		"	V. A. t.	"	tub, lav., w.c.
Bath #3					

   E. Family Room?
      Approx. area **12 × 20**   Opens to which room? **kitchen**

      Walls **wood panel** floor **vinyl - asb. tile** ceiling **acoustic**

      Special features, fireplace, planters? Describe **radio, t.v., record player cabinet, bookshelves**

   F. Dining Room or dinette
      Approx. area _____ walls _____ floor _____ ceiling

      Special features **eating bar**

   G. Utility room or porch
      Approx. area **minimum**   walls _____ floor

      Ceiling _____ list equipment in room plus size of each appliance

      washer, dryer — will iron in kitchen, family room or bedroom

H. Entry, if required
   Approx. area _make it friendly_ Opens to which room? _Living, Family,_
   and Bedroom Hall

I. Storage, service areas
   Linear ft. of linen closets _no opinions - use own judgement._

   Area of heater space, if used, plus brand & cat. nos. of equipment _____
   provide refrigeration

   Space provided for hot water heater? _yes, gas fired_
J. Carport, garage
   Approx. area _for two cars - if cost can be held down, prefer garage_

K. Approx total area of house, excluding garage _1,300ᵈ to 1400ᵈ_

II. Plot plan
   A. Size, shape of lot, sketch and description _Pie-shaped lot in Hillcrest_
      Area - possibly lot #6 or #7 tract 1071

   B. Largest window areas face (N., E., S., or W.) _No view - avoid west if possible_
   C. Location of patio _off Family Room_
   D. Location of utilities, gas _in street_ electricity _rear easement_
      Sewer _in street_ water _in street_
   E. Type of fences _wood - 6' in rear yard._
   F. Swimming pool? _not at present time_

III. Structure
   A. Floor
      Concrete ~~or wood?~~ _____

   B. Walls
      Stud, post and beam, brick veneer, concrete block, other _no preference - would_
      like some stone if not too expensive
   C. Roof
      ~~Flat, one pitch, hip or~~ gable, ~~other~~
      Clerestory, skylights? _no - do not like either_

IV. Elevations
   A. Walls-- ~~stucco, brick,~~ wood, ~~other~~ _____

   B. Roof-- ~~shingle, shale,~~ rock, ~~other~~ _gravel or slag - good 20 year._

   C. Windows-- ~~casement, awning, double-hung, other~~ _horiz. slid. alum._

   D. Doors-- ~~panel,~~ slab _____

   E. Planters? Describe _none inside_

   F. Fascia board? Describe _no requirements._

181

FINAL DATA SHEET

These drawings and notes have been done this semester by my client and myself.

(Signed) _____

_____ Floor Plan, Single Line, 1/8"=1'-0"

_____ Plot Plan and Landscaping, any scale

_____ Elevations (2), 1/8"=1'-0"

_____ Structural Section, Full Size of $8\frac{1}{2}$ x 11 sheet.

_____ Elevation and Section of Fireplace and/or Interior Planters

_____ Elevation of Kitchen and Bath Cabinets

_____ Elevation of Special Cabinets, Hi-Fi, Etc.

FIXTURES AND APPLIANCES

NAME	BRAND	CAT. #	H	W	D
Furnace					
Bath Heater					
Bath Fan					
Kitchen Fan					
Dishwasher					
Water Heater					
Built-in Stove					
Built-in Oven					
Washer					
Dryer					
Freezer					
Refrigerator					
Other					

NOTE: Cat. # needed only if appliance is installed when house is built.

WINDOW SCHEDULE

HOW MANY	MARK	TYPE SIZE	BRAND & CAT. #

DOOR SCHEDULE

HOW MANY	MARK	TYPE SIZE	BRAND & CAT. #

ROOM FINISH SCHEDULE

ROOM	FLOOR	WALLS	CEILING

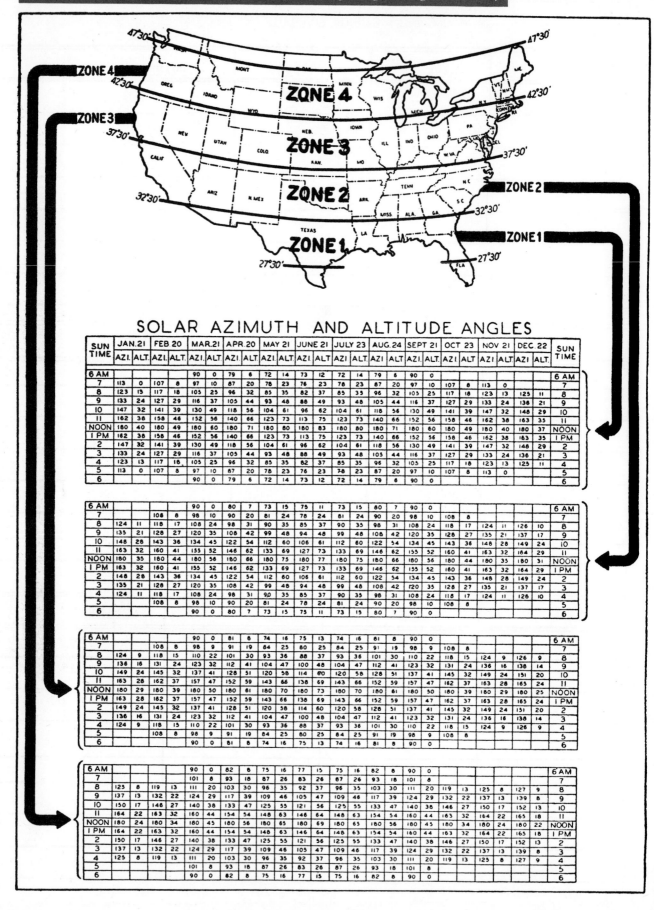

SOLAR AZIMUTH AND ALTITUDE ANGLES

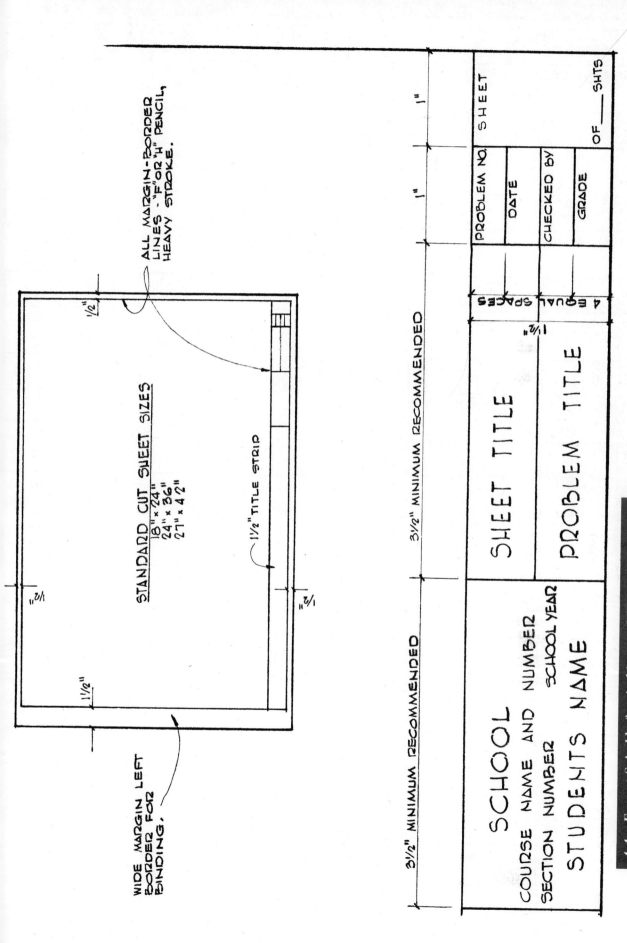

STANDARD CUT SHEET SIZES
18" × 24"
24" × 36"
27" × 42"

1/2" TITLE STRIP

ALL MARGIN-BORDER LINES "F" OR "H" PENCIL, HEAVY STROKE.

1/2"

1/2"

1 1/2"

1/2"

WIDE MARGIN LEFT BORDER FOR BINDING.

3 1/2" MINIMUM RECOMMENDED

3 1/2" MINIMUM RECOMMENDED

1"

1"

1 1/2"

4 EQUAL SPACES

PROBLEM NO.	SHEET
DATE	
CHECKED BY	
GRADE	OF ____ SHTS

SHEET TITLE

PROBLEM TITLE

SCHOOL

COURSE NAME AND NUMBER

SECTION NUMBER   SCHOOL YEAR

STUDENTS NAME

A-4 Format Suitable for Architectural Working Drawings

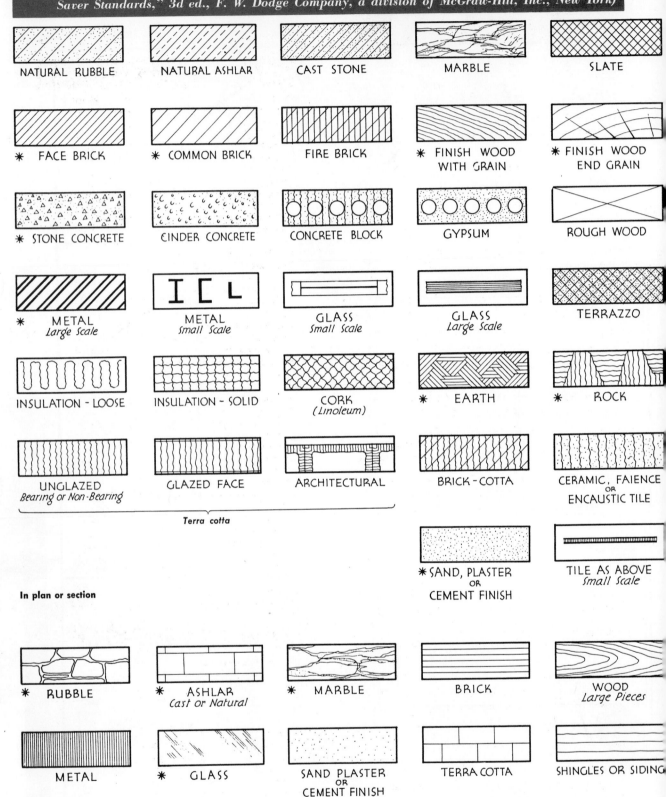

In plan or section

In elevation

GRAPHIC SYMBOLS

Graphic symbols shown above are for use on drawings in plan or section and in elevation. Symbols marked with an asterisk are American Standards (ASA Y14.2–1957). All others are recommended symbols that should be incorporated in a legend on each drawing when applicable. Specific kinds of metal, stone, and the like should not be indicated since they are the province of the specification.

The size of a footing is generally determined by two factors:

1. The load or weight of the structure it is to support, including the live load (anticipated movable load) as well as the dead weight of the construction.
2. The bearing capacity of the supporting soil.

The first step in the design of footings for residential or light structures is to determine the load-bearing capacity of the soil. This can be done by visual inspection of the site and by the use of the arbitrary tables established by the local building codes. Soil classifications are generally divided into five categories based on the relative size of soil particle and its crushing strength. The following table is shown for reference only, and all loading values should be checked with local codes.

A-6a Bearing Values of Common Soils

Soil classification	Min. depth below undisturbed soil	Bearing value of material, psf
ROCK	0'0"	5,000 or 20% of ultimate crushing value
SAND		
Coarse compact	1'0"	1,500
Fine compact	1'0"	1,000
Fine loose	2'0"	500
CLAY		
Hard	1'0"	3,000
Sandy	1'0"	2,000
Soft	2'0"	1,000
ADOBE	2'0"	1,000
SILT, DRY	2'0"	500

The values given in the right-hand column of the table are the allowable weights that may be supported by each square foot of footing area.

WEIGHTS OF BUILDING MATERIALS

When the soil-bearing values have been determined, the weight of the structure is calculated using A-6b. Multiply the weights of the materials by the surface area, total all the dead loads, and add the applicable live loads from A-6c.

A-6b Weights of Building Construction

Materials	Weight
ROOF COVERINGS	
Wood shingles	3 psf
¼" slate	10 psf
Spanish tile	15 psf
Copper sheet	2 psf
Corrugated iron	2 psf
Corrugated aluminum	1 psf
Asbestos shingle	5 psf
Composition shingle	1 psf
Tar and gravel	6 psf
ROOF STRUCTURES	
Wood joist and sheathing	3 psf
Wood truss and purlin	3 psf
2" plank and beam	5 psf
CEILINGS	
Wood joist and plaster	10 psf
Wood joist and ½" gypsum board	7 psf
Wood joist and acoustic tile	5 psf
Suspended metal lath and plaster	10 psf
WALLS	
2 x 4 stud—gypsum lath and plaster	20 psf
2 x 4 stud—½" gypsum board	12 psf
Metal stud and plaster	20 psf
4" clay tile and plaster	20 psf
8" brick, reinforced	85 psf
8" concrete block	70 psf
8" concrete, reinforced	100 psf
12" stone	140 psf
FLOORS	
Wood joist—¾" wood floor	6 psf
Wood joist—linoleum	5 psf
Wood joist—ceramic tile	16 psf
4" concrete	50 psf
FOOTINGS	
Concrete	150 pcf

A-6c Live Loads

Area under Consideration	Live Load, psf
ROOFS	20 plus snow load
FLOORS	
Residence	40
Apartment	40
Public corridor	100
Balconies	100
Fire escape	100
Garage	50
Hotel	40
Office	50
Restrooms	50
Stores	75

(continued on next page)

Divide the total load (live + dead) of the structure by the allowable soil-bearing value to determine the required footing area. All footings of a structure should be proportioned to provide uniform bearing on the soil. Unbalanced loadings have a tendency to cause settling and cracking of a structure. The footing under the heavy end of a structure must be proportionately wider than that under the lighter end.

Where soil values are 1,500 psf or greater and wood-frame construction is used, arbitrary footing sizes may be used from A-6d.

A-6d	Footing Sizes for One- and Two-story Structures			
Stories of height	Min. thickness of foundation wall	Min. width of footing	Min. thickness of footing	Min. d below na
1	6″	12″	6″	12
2	8″	15″	7″	18

A-7 Foundation Reinforcing Steel Table

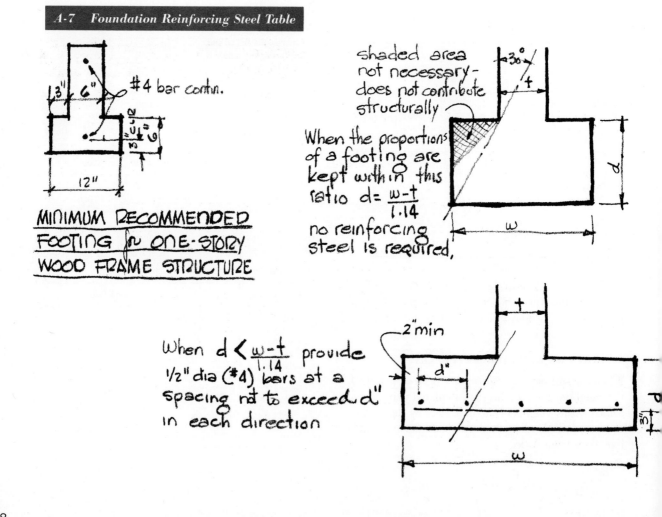

#4 bar contin.

12″

MINIMUM RECOMMENDED
FOOTING IN ONE-STORY
WOOD FRAME STRUCTURE

shaded area not necessary — does not contribute structurally

When the proportions of a footing are kept within this ratio $d = \frac{w-t}{1.14}$ no reinforcing steel is required,

When $d < \frac{w-t}{1.14}$ provide ½″ dia (#4) bars at a spacing not to exceed d″ in each direction

2″ min

188

This Table was calculated using fiber-stress of 1,200 lb. per sq. in. This is generally accepted as allowable on good common grades of yellow pine and fir. However, some ultra-conservative ordinances limit these grades to 1,000 lb. For 1,000 lb. fiber-stress, reduce the allowable spans 1/6. For 1,800 lb. "stress-graded" lumber, or for selected joists of clear heart fir or yellow pine, they may be increased over half. Be sure to check your local code for compliance.

Size of Joists	Distance c. to c.	40# S.F. Total Load	50# S.F. Total Load	60# S.F. Total Load	70# S.F. Total Load	80# S.F. Total Load	90# S.F. Total Load	100# S.F. Total Load
2 x 4	12"	8' 5"	7' 6"	6' 11"	6' 4"	6' 0"	5' 7"	5' 4"
2 x 4	16"	7' 1"	6' 6"	6' 0"	5' 6"	5' 2"	4' 10"	4' 8"
2 x 4	18"	6' 11"	6' 2"	5' 7"	5' 2"	4' 11"	4' 7"	4' 4"
2 x 4	24"	6' 0"	5' 4"	4' 11"	4' 6"	4' 3"	4' 0"	3' 9"
2 x 6	12"	13' 1"	11' 9"	10' 8"	9' 11"	9' 3"	8' 9"	8' 3"
2 x 6	16"	11' 4"	10' 1"	9' 3"	8' 7"	8' 0"	7' 7"	7' 2"
2 x 6	18"	10' 8"	9' 7"	8' 9"	8' 1"	7' 7"	7' 1"	6' 9"
2 x 6	24"	9' 9"	8' 3"	7' 7"	7' 0"	6' 6"	6' 2"	5' 10"
2 x 8	12"	17' 5"	15' 7"	14' 5"	13' 2"	12' 4"	11' 8"	11' 0"
2 x 8	16"	15' 2"	13' 5"	12' 4"	11' 5"	10' 8"	10' 1"	9' 7"
2 x 8	18"	14' 3"	12' 9"	11' 8"	10' 9"	10' 1"	9' 6"	9' 0"
2 x 8	24"	12' 4"	11' 0"	10' 1"	9' 4"	8' 9"	8' 3"	7' 10"
2 x 10	12"	22' 1"	19' 9"	18' 1"	16' 9"	15' 8"	14' 9"	14' 0"
2 x 10	16"	19' 3"	17' 1"	15' 8"	14' 6"	13' 6"	12' 9"	12' 1"
2 x 10	18"	18' 1"	16' 2"	14' 9"	13' 8"	12' 9"	12' 0"	11' 5"
2 x 10	24"	15' 8"	14' 0"	12' 9"	11' 10"	11' 1"	10' 5"	9' 11"
2 x 12	12"	26' 9"	23' 11"	21' 10"	20' 3"	18' 11"	17' 11"	16' 11"
2 x 12	16"	23' 3"	20' 2"	18' 11"	17' 7"	16' 4"	15' 5"	14' 8"
2 x 12	18"	21' 10"	19' 6"	17' 11"	16' 6"	15' 5"	14' 7"	13' 10"
2 x 12	24"	18' 11"	16' 11"	15' 5"	14' 4"	13' 5"	12' 7"	12' 0"

MAXIMUM SPANS / SELECTED and COMMERCIAL DECKING (6" and wider)

Spans based on uniform live load. Assumed 10psf dead load.
Random length spans. Deflection 1/240 of span.
Spans may be modified for other deflection limitations (.93 for 1/360, 1.10 for 1/180).

Western Pine Association Rules January 1, 1961

SPECIES	Nominal Thick.	Live Load						
		20psf	30psf	40psf	50psf	60psf	70psf	80psf
WHITE FIR	2"	9'1"	8'0"	7'2"	6'8"	6'4"	6'0"	5'8"
	3"	14'8"	12'10"	11'8"	10'9"	10'2"	9'11"	9'4"
	4"	19'7"	17'1"	15'7"	14'5"	13'7"	12'11"	12'4"
PONDEROSA PINE IDAHO WHITE PINE SUGAR PINE LODGEPOLE PINE INCENSE CEDAR RED CEDAR *ENGELMANN SPRUCE	2"	8'10"	7'8"	7'0"	6'6"	6'1"	5'10"	5'6"
	3"	14'2"	12'5"	11'5"	10'6"	9'11"	9'5"	9'0"
	4"	19'0"	16'7"	15'0"	14'0"	13'1"	12'6"	12'0"
DOUGLAS FIR AND/OR LARCH	2"	10'1"	9'0"	8'2"	7'7"	7'1"	6'10"	6'6"
	3"	16'8"	14'6"	13'2"	12'5"	11'6"	10'11"	10'6"
	4"	22'2"	19'5"	17'7"	16'4"	15'5"	14'7"	14'0"
†ENGELMANN SPRUCE	2"	8'10"	7'8"	7'0"	6'6"	6'1"	5'10"	5'6"
	3"	13'7"	11'9"	10'6"	9'8"	9'0"	8'5"	7'10"
	4"	18'1"	15'8"	14'0"	12'9"	11'11"	11'0"	10'5"

*Applies to Selected Decking only.
†Applies to Commercial Decking only.
 For 1-9/16" thickness reduce nominal 2" thickness spans 4%.
 For 1½" thickness reduce nominal 2" thickness spans 8%.

A-10a Wood Lintel Table

Arbitrary table for light frame single-story structures. Supporting roof structures whose span does not exceed 26 ft. Verify with local code requirements.

Spans to 3'6" = 4 x 4
3'6" to 5'6" = 4 x 6
5'6" to 7'6" = 4 x 8
7'6" to 9'6" = 4 x 10
9'6" to 11'0" = 4 x 12

A-10b Reinforced Concrete Lintels

Clear opening	Total load	Size	Wall thick.	Bars	Cu ft conc per ft	Lb steel per ft
3'	400	6" x 8"	6"	2—$\frac{1}{4}$"φ	.33	.33
	535	8" x 8"	8"	2—$\frac{1}{4}$"φ	.45	.33
	800	12" x 8"	12"	2—$\frac{1}{4}$"φ	.67	.33
4'	625	6" x 8"	6"	2—$\frac{1}{4}$"φ	.33	.33
	835	8" x 8"	8"	2—$\frac{1}{4}$"φ	.45	.33
	1250	12" x 8"	12"	2—$\frac{1}{4}$"φ	.67	.33
6'	1250	6" x 8"	6"	3—$\frac{1}{4}$"φ	.33	.50
	1670	8" x 8"	8"	3—$\frac{1}{4}$"φ	.45	.50
	2500	12" x 8"	12"	2—$\frac{3}{8}$"φ	.67	.75
8'	2000	6" x 8"	6"	1—$\frac{1}{2}$"φ 1—$\frac{3}{8}$"φ	.33	1.05
	2670	8" x 8"	8"	3—$\frac{3}{8}$"φ	.45	1.13
	4000	12" x 8"	12"	2—$\frac{1}{2}$"φ 1—$\frac{3}{8}$"φ	.67	1.71

All loads calculated on triangular loading at 45°.
No stirrups required.

A-11 Maximum Span of Masonry Walls between Supports

NONBEARING WALLS					BEARING WALLS
Exterior unreinforced 20t	Exterior reinforced 30t	Interior unreinforced 36t	Interior reinforced 48t	Wall thickness t	Reinforced 25t
6'8"	10'0"	12'0"	16'0"	4"	
10'0"	15'0"	18'0"	24'0"	6"	12'6"
13'4"	20'0"	24'0"	32'0"	8"	16'8"
20'0"	30'0"	36'0"	48'0"	12"	25'0"

A-12 Wood Rafter Table

Size of member	Spacing of member—center to center	MAXIMUM ALLOWABLE SPAN IN FEET AND INCHES					
		FLAT SLOPES 0 to 4/12			STEEP SLOPES 4/12 and GREATER		
		1,000 psi	1,200 psi	1,500 psi	1,000 psi	1,200 psi	1,500 psi
2 x 4	12"	6'6"	8'0"	9'6"	7'0"	9'0"	10'0"
	16"	5'6"	7'0"	8'0"	6'0"	7'6"	8'6"
	24"	4'6"	6'0"	6'6"	5'0"	6'0"	7'0"
	32"	4'0"	5'0"	5'6"	4'0"	5'6"	6'0"
2 x 6	12"	11'6"	14'0"	16'6"	12'6"	15'0"	17'6"
	16"	10'0"	12'0"	14'0"	11'0"	13'0"	15'6"
	24"	8'0"	10'0"	11'6"	9'0"	10'6"	12'6"
	32"	7'0"	8'6"	10'0"	7'6"	9'6"	11'0"
2 x 8	12"	16'0"	19'0"	22'0"	17'6"	21'0"	23'6"
	16"	14'0"	16'6"	19'0"	15'0"	18'0"	20'6"
	24"	11'6"	13'6"	15'6"	12'6"	14'6"	16'6"
	32"	8'0"	12'0"	13'6"	10'6"	12'6"	14'6"
2 x 10	12"	21'6"	26'0"	27'6"	23'0"	28'0"	30'0"
	16"	18'6"	22'6"	24'0"	20'0"	24'0"	26'0"
	24"	15'0"	18'6"	19'6"	16'0"	19'6"	21'0"
	32"	13'0"	16'0"	17'0"	14'0"	17'0"	18'0"
		20# LL + 8# DL			16# LL + 8# DL		

A-13 Wood Ceiling Joist Tables

A 1200 lb. per. sq. in. fiber stress is allowed upon the joists.

The following table of maximum joist spans may be used for ceiling joists where there is access to the attic, with the possibility that the attic may be used for light storage. It includes a plaster on rock lath ceiling under, but no flooring over, and a 20 lb. per sq. ft. live load allowance.

Size of Joists	12" CC	16" OC	24" OC
2" x 8"	20' 4"	17' 10"	14' 10"
2" x 6"	15' 6"	13' 7"	11' 3"
2" x 4"	10' 2"	8' 10"	7' 4"

The following table may be used for ceiling joists where there is no access to the attic. Plaster on rock lath is included, but no live loading. The lengths of spans and spacing given are adequate for practically all kinds of dry-wall ceilings, but the longer spans and wider spacings may give trouble from sagging in time, under the load of a plaster ceiling, though the timbers are theoretically adequate.

Size of Joists	12" OC	16" OC	24" OC
2" x 6"	28' 4"	25' 6"	21' 9"
2" x 4"	19' 4"	17' 3"	14'

FRAMING and STRUCTURAL WORK
Wood Joists & Girders: Spans & Loads

MAXIMUM SPAN FOR JOISTS
(Bending Strength Based on Dressed Size)

Lumber Size (Nominal)	Spacing Center to Center In Inches	1100# Fibre Stress 30#+D.L.	40#+D.L.	50#+D.L.	1250# Fibre Stress 30#+D.L.	40#+D.L.	50#+D.L.	1450# Fibre Stress 30#+D.L.	40#+D.L.	50#+D.L.	1700# Fibre Stress 30#+D.L.	40#+D.L.	50#+D.L.
2 x 6	12	12'11"	11' 5"	10' 5"	13' 9"	12' 2"	11' 1"	14' 9"	13' 2"	11'11"	16' 1"	14' 3"	12'11"
	16	11' 3"	10' 0"	9' 1"	11'10"	10' 8"	9' 8"	12'11"	11' 5"	10' 5"	14' 0"	12' 5"	11' 3"
2 x 8	12	17' 0"	15' 1"	13' 9"	18' 1"	16' 2"	14' 8"	19' 6"	17' 4"	15'10"	22' 0"	18'10"	17' 2"
	16	14'11"	13' 1"	12' 0"	15'11"	14' 0"	12'10"	17'1"	15' 1"	13' 9"	18' 4"	16' 4"	14'11"
2 x 10	12	21' 3"	19' 0"	17' 4"	22' 9"	20' 3"	18' 6"	24' 6"	21'10"	19'11"	26' 5"	23' 7"	21' 6"
	16	18' 9"	16' 7"	15' 2"	19'11"	17' 9"	16' 2"	21' 5"	19' 1"	17' 5"	23' 2"	20' 8"	18'10"
2 x 12	12	25' 6"	22'10"	20'10"	27' 2"	24' 4"	22' 2"	29' 3"	26' 2"	23'11"	31' 9"	28' 4"	25'11"
	16	22' 5"	20' 4"	18' 3"	23'11"	21' 4"	19' 5"	25' 9"	23' 0"	20'11"	27'11"	24'10"	22' 8"

D. L. (dead load) includes weight of joist, 1 in. subfloor and 1 in. finished floor. Where plastered ceiling under joists, use span for 10# heavier live load.

JOIST SPANS LIMITED BY DEFLECTION
(To 1/360 of Span; Modulus of Elasticity: 1,600,000)

Nom.	Actual	10# L.L.+D.L.① 12" o.c.	16" o.c.	20# L.L.+D.L.① 12" o.c.	16" o.c.	30# L.L.+D.L.② 12" o.c.	16" o.c.	40# L.L.+D.L.② 12" o.c.	16" o.c.	50# L.L. D.L.② 12" o.c.	16" o.c.
2 x 6	1⅝ x 5½	15' 6"	14' 4"	13' 1"	12' 0"	11' 5"	10' 6"	10 8"	9' 8"	10' 0"	9' 1"
2 x 8	1⅝ x 7½	19' 1"	18'10"	17' 4"	15' 1"	15' 2"	13'11"	14' 1"	12'11"	13' 3"	12' 1"
2 x 10	1⅝ x 9½	25' 4"	23' 6"	21' 8"	20' 0"	19' 1"	17' 6"	17' 9"	16' 3"	16' 8"	15' 3"
2 x 12	1⅝ x 11½	29'11"	28' 1"	26' 1"	24' 0"	22'11"	21' 0"	21' 4"	19' 7"	20' 1"	18' 5"

①D.L. includes joist & 1" single floor.   ②D.L. includes joist, 1" subfloor & 1" finish floor.

Use for floor joists with or without plaster ceiling load, weight of plaster is neglected in assumed loads for deflection computation as initial deflection from plaster load occurs before plaster sets.

ALLOWABLE LOADS ON BUILT-UP GIRDERS
(Uniform Normal Loading; Allowance for Weight of Dimension Only)
SPAN IN FEET

Grade	Nominal Size	9	10	11	12	13	14	15	16	17	18	19	20
1700# Fibre Stress	2 x 6	1079	971	883	809	747	694	647	607	571			
	2 x 8	1918	1726	1569	1438	1328	1233	1151	1079	1015	959	908	863
	2 x 10	3077	2770	2518	2309	2131	1978	1847	1731	1629	1539	1458	1385
	2 x 12			3690	3383	3123	2900	2706	2537	2388	2255	2137	2030
1450# Fibre Stress	2 x 6	921	829	753	691	637	592	552	518	487			
	2 x 8	1636	1472	1338	1227	1132	1052	982	920	866	818	775	736
	2 x 10		2348	2148	1969	1818	1688	1575	1477	1390	1313	1243	1181
	2 x 12				2886	2664	2474	2309	2164	2037	1924	1822	1732
1250# Fibre Stress	2 x 6	794	715	649	595	549	511	476	447	420			
	2 x 8	1411	1269	1154	1058	976	907	846	793	747	700*	688	635
	2 x 10		2037	1852	1697	1567	1455	1358	1273	1198	1132*	1072	1019
	2 x 12				2488	2296	2132	1990	1866	1756	1659	1571	1493
1100# Fibre Stress	2 x 6	698	628	571	524	483	449	419	393	370			
	2 x 8	1241	1117	1015	931	859	798	745	698	657	620	588	558
	2 x 10			1629	1493	1379	1280	1195	1120	1054	996	943	896
	2 x 12					2021	1876	1751	1642	1545	1459	1382	1313
Limited * by deflection 1/360 span applies to all grades.	2 x 6	705	571	472	397	338	291	254					
	2 x 8	1672	1354	1119	940	801	691	602	529	469			
	2 x 10	3397	2752	2274	1911	1628	1404	1223	1075	952	849	762	688
	2 x 12			4034	3390	2889	2491	2170	1907	1689	1507	1352	1220

* When load is limited by deflection, check allowable load for grade used.

Courtesy, Southern Pine Assn.

FIREPLACE DESIGN

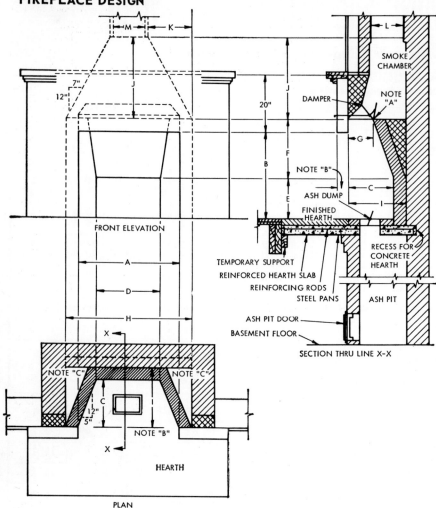

FRONT ELEVATION

TEMPORARY SUPPORT
REINFORCED HEARTH SLAB
REINFORCING RODS
STEEL PANS
ASH PIT DOOR
BASEMENT FLOOR

SMOKE CHAMBER

DAMPER

NOTE "A"

NOTE "B"

ASH DUMP
FINISHED HEARTH

RECESS FOR CONCRETE HEARTH

ASH PIT

SECTION THRU LINE X-X

NOTE "C"   NOTE "C"

NOTE "B"

HEARTH

PLAN

Fireplaces will give trouble-free service when properly proportioned and built, and when sufficient air for combustion is supplied. Shown on these two pages are basic designs that work — the style is a matter of preference. The drawings, left, and table below are for the usual or conventional fireplace which has one face exposed to the room.

Notes

A.—The back flange of the damper must be protected from intense heat by being fully supported by the back wall masonry. Damper should not be built in solidly at the ends. It should be left free to expand, as shown in the front elevation view.

B.—The drawing indicates thickness of brick fireplace front as 4 in. No definite dimension can be given for this because the various materials, such as marble, stone, tile, etc., have various thicknesses.

C.—These hollow spaces should be filled to form solid backing.

Standard Flue Linings

The custom of using flue linings has become universal, due to the recommendation of the National Fire Underwriters and building code requirements. Flue linings should be tightly cemented together. This is especially important where more than one flue occupies a single stack. Otherwise there may be suction of smoke down one flue while smoke ascends in the other. A minimum of 4 in. of masonry between parallel flues is likewise recommended.

Hearth Shape—Sides should go straight back for about 4 in., then toe-in at an angle of 5 in. to the foot.

Separate Flue—A separate flue should be provided for each fireplace. It should rise from the top center of the smoke chamber, and any change of direction from the vertical should be above this starting point and no slope of the flue should be greater than 7 inches per foot of rise.

Rear Wall—Should be plumb for 14 or 15 in., then slope forward to form smoke shelf and to support rear flange of damper. This shape deflects heat forward into room while smoke and gases pass through damper.

Smoke Chamber—Just above the damper is the smoke chamber. The sides should slope about 7 in. to each foot in height. Smooth, unobstructed walls are important.

APPROX. DIMENSIONS IN INCHES

A	B	C	D	E	F	G	H	I	J		K	L	M	Inside Area		Outside Dimension	Inside Area		Inside Dimension	Inside Area
											Rectangular					**Modular**			**Round**	
24	24	16	11	14	15	8¾	32	20	19		11¾	8½ ×	8½	52.56		8 × 12	57		8	50.26
26	24	16	13	14	15	8¾	34	20	21		12¾	8½ ×	8½			8 × 16	74			
28	24	16	15	14	15	8¾	36	20	21		11½	8½ ×	13	80.5		12 × 12	87		10	78.54
30	29	16	17	14	21	8¾	38	20	24		12½	8½ ×	13							
32	29	16	19	14	21	8¾	40	20	24		13½	8½ ×	13							
36	29	16	23	14	21	8¾	44	20	27		15½	13 ×	13	126.56		12 × 16	120		12	113
40	29	16	27	14	21	8¾	48	20	29		17½	13 ×	13							
42	32	16	29	14	23	8¾	50	20	32		18½	13 ×	13							
48	32	18	33	14	23	8¾	56	22	37		21½	13 ×	13			16 × 16	162		15	176
54	37	20	37	16	27	13	68	24	45		25	13 ×	18	182.84		16 × 20	208			
60	37	22	42	16	27	13	72	27	45		27	13 ×	18							
60	40	22	42	16	29	13	72	27	45		27	18 ×	18	248.06		20 × 20	262		18	254
72	40	22	54	16	29	13	84	27	56		33	18 ×	18							
84	40	24	64	20	26	13	96	29	61		36	20 ×	20	298.00		20 × 24	320		20	314.1
96	40	24	76	20	26	13	108	29	75		42	24 ×	24	441.00		24 × 24	385		22	380.13

DATA FOR MULTI-OPENING FIREPLACE DESIGN

The trend in contemporary houses toward open planning of rooms has resulted in many fireplaces being designed so they are open on two, three or even four sides, the latter being free-standing.

The chimney flue in a fireplace must be sized for the opening. A fireplace opened on two or more sides will require a larger flue than that for a fireplace of conventional design. *Each face of a fireplace must be included when computing flue size.*

For efficient operation of a corner, two-way or three-way fireplace, use a damper, or damper and smoke chamber designed for the particular fireplace style, and follow the manufacturer's details, including flue sizes.

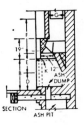

FIREPLACE OPEN TO THREE SIDES

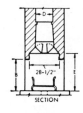

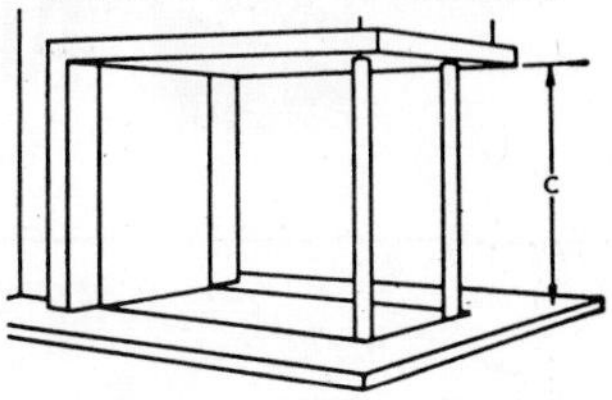

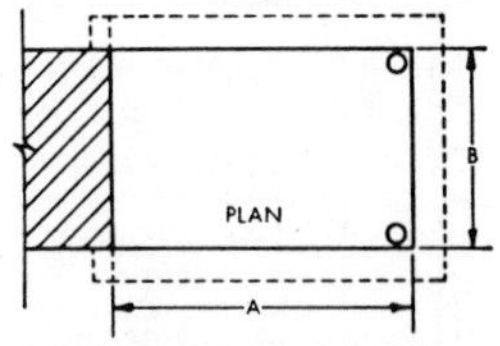

PLAN

MINIMUM AREA OF FLUE (AND DAMPER) = AREA OF OPEN FRONT + AREA OF OPEN SIDES / 12

CORNER FIREPLACE

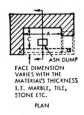

FACE DIMENSION VARIES WITH THE MATERIAL'S THICKNESS I.E. MARBLE, TILE, STONE ETC.

PLAN

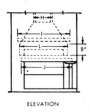

ELEVATION

SECTION   ASH PIT

A	B	C	D	E	F	Rectangular Flue G	Rectangular Flue H	Modular Flue G	Modular Flue H	L	Upper Angle I	Lower Angle J	Plate Lintel K	Corner Post
32"	29"	16"	14"	20"	32"	13"	13"	12"	16"	40"	42"	42"	11" x 16"	29"
36"	29"	16"	14"	20"	32"	13"	18"	16"	16"	44"	48"	48"	11" x 16"	29"
40"	29"	16"	14"	20"	35"	13"	18"	16"	20"	48"	54"	54"	11" x 16"	29"
48"	32"	20"	14"	24"	40"	13"	18"	16"	20"	56"	60"	60'	11" x 16"	32"

Hearth Size A	B	Maximum Opening Height For Standard Flue Tile (C) 13x13	13x18	18x18	18x24	24x24
30	34	21	27	35	38	—
37	41	—	—	21	27	32
34	24	20	26	34	—	—
38	28	—	22	30	36	—
42	28	—	—	29	35	—
46	28	—	—	28	34	40
58	32	—	—	24	30	36

FIREPLACE OPEN TO TWO SIDES

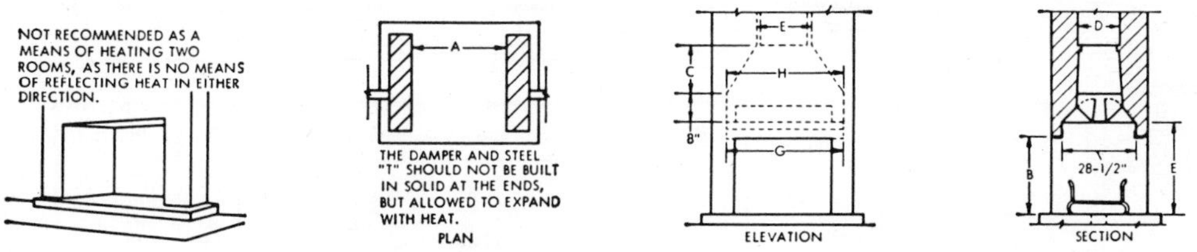

NOT RECOMMENDED AS A MEANS OF HEATING TWO ROOMS, AS THERE IS NO MEANS OF REFLECTING HEAT IN EITHER DIRECTION.

THE DAMPER AND STEEL "T" SHOULD NOT BE BUILT IN SOLID AT THE ENDS, BUT ALLOWED TO EXPAND WITH HEAT.

PLAN

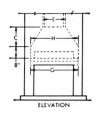

ELEVATION

SECTION

FIREPLACE OPEN ON ALL SIDES

Hearth Size A	B	Maximum Opening Height For Standard Flue Tile (C) 13x18	18x18	20x24	24x24
34	34	20	28	32	—
41	41	—	—	28	32
38	24	22	30	—	—
42	28	20	28	32	—
46	28	—	26	31	—
48	28	—	24	30	35
58	32	—	21	27	32

A	B	C	Non-Modular Flue D	Non-Modular Flue E	Modular Flue Size D	Modular Flue Size E	G	H
32"	29"	21"	13"	18"	16"	16"	42"	40"
36"	29"	21"	13"	18"	16"	20"	42"	44"
40"	29"	27"	18"	18"	16"	20"	48"	48"
48"	32"	32"	18"	18"	20"	20"	54"	56"

WARM AIR CIRCULATING FIREPLACES

BECAUSE OF THE SCARCITY of skilled masons who know how to build an all-masonry fireplace, and because fireplaces constructed with liners have proved to be more efficient heating units, many builders are constructing the all-masonry type only in cases where unusual shapes may prevent the use of the standard fireplace liner.

Cost difference between the all-masonry and liner type units is nominal; because of this the builders can put more sales appeal into their houses by installing the type of fireplace which will give more heat per fuel consumed.

These circulator liners for fireplaces are constructed of sheet metal shells; with a duct system where circulating air, taken into the air heating chamber, is warmed by coming in contact with the hot sides of the fire box and the fins and baffles placed inside of the chamber, and is discharged back into the room or rooms through ductwork and grilles.

The advantages of the circulating fireplaces are easily recognized. The all-masonry units can provide no amount of circulation through the fire box opening, or mouth, all of the heat delivered to the room must be delivered by radiation.

Construction of the fireplace is greatly simplified by using the liner since it provides a form for the mason to work to, hence journeyman experience is not required. All-masonry units, because of the intricacies of corbelling for the smoke chamber, mounting the damper, building the smoke shelf, laying the firebrick, etc., require men of experience in fireplace construction to do the job, in order to produce a fireplace which will perform properly.

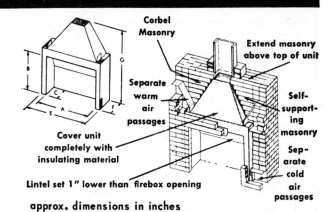

Corbel Masonry

Extend masonry above top of unit

Separate warm air passages

Self-supporting masonry

Separate cold air passages

Cover unit completely with insulating material

Lintel set 1" lower than firebox opening

approx. dimensions in inches

A	B	C	D	E	G	Flue Opening	Size of Flue Liner
33	27½	16	39½	19½	53	10 x 10	12 x 12 or 8½ x 13
37	27½	16	43½	19½	53	10 x 10	12 x 12 or 8½ x 13
41	30	18	47½	23½	58½	10 x 13¾	12 x 16 or 13 x 13
49	30	18	55½	23½	61	10 x 13¾	12 x 16 or 13 x 13

KITCHENS · APPLIANCES · ELECTRICAL

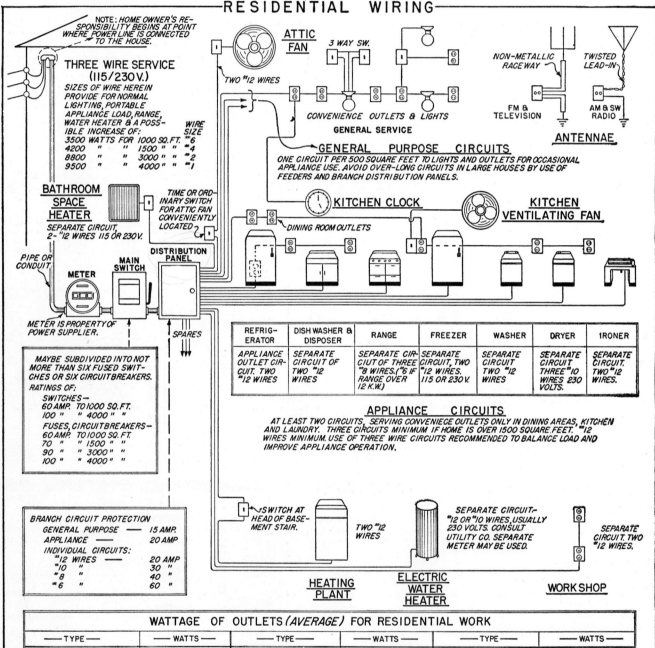

RESIDENTIAL WIRING

NOTE: HOME OWNER'S RESPONSIBILITY BEGINS AT POINT WHERE POWER LINE IS CONNECTED TO THE HOUSE.

THREE WIRE SERVICE (115/230 V.)

SIZES OF WIRE HEREIN PROVIDE FOR NORMAL LIGHTING, PORTABLE APPLIANCE LOAD, RANGE, WATER HEATER & A POSSIBLE INCREASE OF:

		WIRE SIZE
3500 WATTS FOR 1000 SQ.FT.		#6
4200 " " 1500 " "		#4
8800 " " 3000 " "		#2
9500 " " 4000 " "		#1

BATHROOM SPACE HEATER

SEPARATE CIRCUIT, 2-#12 WIRES 115 OR 230 V.

PIPE OR CONDUIT

METER

METER IS PROPERTY OF POWER SUPPLIER.

MAIN SWITCH

DISTRIBUTION PANEL

SPARES

MAYBE SUBDIVIDED INTO NOT MORE THAN SIX FUSED SWITCHES OR SIX CIRCUIT BREAKERS. RATINGS OF:

SWITCHES—
60 AMP. TO 1000 SQ. FT.
100 " " 4000 " "

FUSES, CIRCUIT BREAKERS—
60 AMP. TO 1000 SQ. FT.
70 " " 1500 " "
90 " " 3000 " "
100 " " 4000 " "

BRANCH CIRCUIT PROTECTION

GENERAL PURPOSE — 15 AMP.
APPLIANCE — 20 AMP.
INDIVIDUAL CIRCUITS:
#12 WIRES — 20 AMP
#10 " 30 "
#8 " 40 "
#6 " 60 "

ATTIC FAN

3 WAY SW.

TWO #12 WIRES

CONVENIENCE OUTLETS & LIGHTS
GENERAL SERVICE

NON-METALLIC RACEWAY

TWISTED LEAD-IN

FM & TELEVISION

AM & SW RADIO

ANTENNAE

GENERAL PURPOSE CIRCUITS

ONE CIRCUIT PER 500 SQUARE FEET TO LIGHTS AND OUTLETS FOR OCCASIONAL APPLIANCE USE. AVOID OVER-LONG CIRCUITS IN LARGE HOUSES BY USE OF FEEDERS AND BRANCH DISTRIBUTION PANELS.

TIME OR ORDINARY SWITCH FOR ATTIC FAN CONVENIENTLY LOCATED

KITCHEN CLOCK

KITCHEN VENTILATING FAN

DINING ROOM OUTLETS

REFRIG-ERATOR	DISH WASHER & DISPOSER	RANGE	FREEZER	WASHER	DRYER	IRONER
APPLIANCE OUTLET CIRCUIT. TWO #12 WIRES	SEPARATE CIRCUIT OF TWO #12 WIRES	SEPARATE CIRCIUT OF THREE #8 WIRES.(#6 IF RANGE OVER 12 K.W.)	SEPARATE CIRCUIT, TWO #12 WIRES. 115 OR 230 V.	SEPARATE CIRCUIT TWO #12 WIRES	SEPARATE CIRCUIT THREE #10 WIRES 230 VOLTS.	SEPARATE CIRCUIT. TWO #12 WIRES.

APPLIANCE CIRCUITS

AT LEAST TWO CIRCUITS, SERVING CONVENIECE OUTLETS ONLY IN DINING AREAS, KITCHEN AND LAUNDRY. THREE CIRCUITS MINIMUM IF HOME IS OVER 1500 SQUARE FEET. #12 WIRES MINIMUM. USE OF THREE WIRE CIRCUITS RECOMMENDED TO BALANCE LOAD AND IMPROVE APPLIANCE OPERATION.

SWITCH AT HEAD OF BASEMENT STAIR.

TWO #12 WIRES

SEPARATE CIRCUIT—#12 OR #10 WIRES, USUALLY 230 VOLTS. CONSULT UTILITY CO. SEPARATE METER MAY BE USED.

SEPARATE CIRCUIT. TWO #12 WIRES.

HEATING PLANT

ELECTRIC WATER HEATER

WORK SHOP

WATTAGE OF OUTLETS (AVERAGE) FOR RESIDENTIAL WORK

— TYPE —	— WATTS —	— TYPE —	— WATTS —	— TYPE —	— WATTS —
AIR CONDITIONER	700 –1200 –3100	HOME FREEZER	300–350	REFRIGERATOR	200–300
ATTIC FAN	500 — 1500	HOT PLATE	600 –1000	ROASTER	1150 –1350
TABLE COOKER	660	INFRA-RED LAMP	500	STOKER	400 –1250
CLOTHES DRYER	UP TO 4500	IRON (HAND)	660 –1000	SUNLAMP	250
DISHWASHER	200 — 500	IRONER (HOME)	1275 —1620	TELEVISION	200 –400
DISPOSER	250 — 500	JUICE EXTRACTOR	60 – 100	TOASTER	600 –1350
EGG COOKER	660	MIXER	125 – 150	TOWEL DRYER	100 – 500
ELECTRIC FAN	50 – 300	MOTOR, 1/4 H.P.	530	VACUUM CLEANER	300
FURNACE BLOWER	300	OIL BURNER	300 –550	WAFFLE IRON	660 – 1000
GRILL	1000	COFFEE MAKER	400 –600	WASHING MACHINES:	
HAIR DRYER	350	RADIO	50 — 200	AUTOMATIC	350 –1600
HEATER	1000 – 1320	RANGE	7000 – 16000	WRINGER TYPE	375 – 450
HEATING PAD	65	RAZOR SHARPENER	50	WATER HEATER	750 – 4000

THE ABOVE DATA WAS CHECKED & FOUND TO BE IN AGREEMENT WITH THE NATIONAL ADEQUATE WIRING BUREAU STANDARDS

Graphic symbols shown on this page have been extracted from American Standard Y32.9–1943, with the permission of the publisher, The American Institute of Electrical Engineers. These symbols have been made as simple as possible and are not intended to depict the structure of the electrical devices shown. The symbols should be drawn to a size commensurate with the particular drawing being made. Additional symbols, or those not yet commonly accepted, should be included in a legend.

ELECTRICAL SYMBOLS FOR ARCHITECTURAL PLANS
Prepared by American Standards Association and published by Industry Committee on Interior Wiring Design

Description	Ceiling	Wall	Description	Symbol	Description	Symbol
GENERAL OUTLETS			**SWITCHES**		**PANELS, CIRCUITS, MISC.**	
Outlet	○	–○	Single Pole Switch	S	Generator	Ⓖ
Blanket Outlet	Ⓑ	–Ⓑ	Double Pole Switch	S_2	Motor	Ⓜ
Clock Outlet	Ⓒ	–Ⓒ	Three Way Switch	S_3	Instrument	Ⓘ
Drop Cord	Ⓓ		Four Way Switch	S_4	Transformer	Ⓣ
Electrical Outlet: *use when plain circle may be confused with column or other symbols*	Ⓔ	–Ⓔ	Automatic Door Switch	S_D	Controller	⊠
			Electrolier Switch	S_E	Isolating Switch	
Fan Outlet	Ⓕ	–Ⓕ	Key Operated Switch	S_K	**AUXILIARY or Low Voltage SYSTEMS**	
Junction Box	Ⓙ	–Ⓙ	Switch and Pilot Lamp	S_P	Push Button	▣
Lamp Holder	Ⓛ	–Ⓛ	Circuit Breaker	S_{CB}	Buzzer	◱
Lamp Holder with Pull Switch	Ⓛ$_{PS}$	–Ⓛ$_{PS}$	Weatherproof Circuit Breaker	S_{WCB}	Bell	▭○
Pull Switch	Ⓢ	–Ⓢ	Momentary Contact Switch	S_{MC}	Annunciator	◇
			Remote Control Switch	S_{RC}	Telephone	◀
Outlet for Vapor Discharge Lamp	Ⓥ	–Ⓥ	Weatherproof Switch	S_{WP}	Interconnecting Telephone	◁
			SPECIAL OUTLETS		Telephone Switchboard	◁|
Exit Light Outlet	Ⓧ	–Ⓧ			Electric Door Opener	Ⓓ
CONVENIENCE OUTLETS			Any standard symbol, with a lower case subscript added, may be used for special indications. When so used, a legend on each drawing and description in specifications are strongly recommended	○$_{a,b,c \, etc.}$ ⊖$_{a,b,c \, etc.}$ S$_{a,b,c \, etc.}$	Fire Alarm Bell	ꜰ○
					Fire Alarm Station	ꜰ
Duplex Convenience Outlet	⊖				City Fire Alarm Station	⊠
Convenience Outlet other than Duplex 1 = Single, 3 = Triplex, etc.	⊖$_{1,3}$		**PANELS, CIRCUITS, MISC.**		Fire Alarm Central Station	ꜰᴀ
			Lighting Panel	▬	Automatic Fire Alarm Device	ꜰꜱ
Weatherproof Conv. Outlet	⊖$_{WP}$		Power Panel	▨	Watchman's Station	ᴡ
Range Outlet	⊖$_R$		*Branch Circuit — Ceiling or Wall	——	Watchman's Central Station	[ᴡ]
Switch and Convenience Outlet	⊖–S		*Branch Circuit — Floor	----	Horn	ʜ
Radio and Convenience Outlet	⊖ Ⓡ		*without other designation indicates 2-wire circuit. For 3 wires, use For 4 wires	⫲⫲	Nurse's Signal Plug	ɴ
					Maid's Signal Plug	ᴹ
Special Purpose Outlet (desc. in Spec.)	▲		Feeders: *use heavy lines and designate by number for quick reference*	▬▬	Radio Outlet	ʀ
					Signal Central Station	ꜱᴄ
Floor Outlet	◉		Underfloor Duct & Junction Box - Triple System: *for double or single systems use two lines or one. Symbol also adaptable to Auxiliary or Low Voltage systems*	≡▭≡	Interconnection Box	▭
					Battery	‖‖‖‖‖
					Auxiliary System Circuits: *without other designation indicates 2-wire circuit. For others, use numbers, as: — - - —12 - #18 W - ¾"C. or designate by number for quick reference*	------
					Special Auxiliary Outlets: *subscripts refer to notes in plans, schedules or specifications*	▢$_{a,b,c}$

Computing Wattage

The following table is designed to compute the wattage required to light a certain room to a given level of illumination. Because of the great number of variables involved in lighting problems, the information presented here represents only average conditions for a few selected situations. When used with the formula shown, this data will yield approximate answers which will serve as useful guides.

A-18 Lighting Requirements

Area of activity	Footcandles on task
Benchwork	50–100
Drafting	200
Entrance hall	10
Reading and writing	
Large type	30
Small type	70
Sales area	50
Sewing	
Dark cloth	200
Light cloth	50
Shaving	50
Show windows, general	200
Show windows, feature	1,000
Storage	10
Toilet room	30

The formula for finding the number of lumens required to produce a given general illumination level expressed as footcandles is

$$LL = \frac{FC \times A}{CU \times MF}$$

where LL = lamp lumens

FC = footcandles in service

A = room area, sq ft

CU = coefficient of utilization—depends upon room proportions, absorption of light by the fixtures, and absorption of light by the room surfaces. For the purposes of this discussion, an average factor of .35 will be used.

MF = maintenance factor—depends upon the type, accessibility, and maintenance of the fixture. An average factor of .6 should be used here.

Only two light sources will be considered, namely, incandescent and the ordinary, widely used cool-white fluorescent. Most incandescent lamps produce about 15 lumens per watt; a 48-in. fluorescent produces 2,650 lumens; a 24-in. fluorescent produces 1,450 lumens.

The procedure in sizing the lamps to produce the required general light level in a room follows:

1. Select the light level from A-18.
2. Compute the floor area of the room.
3. Substitute these values in the equation. Use the values given for CU and MF.
4. Divide this value in lumens by the number of lumens produced by the light sources you choose.

A-19 Recommended Spacing of Convenience Outlets

Any habitable room	1 per 12' of wall plus 1 in each 4' wall segment—at least 3.
Kitchens	1 each side of sink plus 1 for each fixed appliance.
Hall	At least 1.
Office space	1 per 12' of wall plus 1 for each desk.
Garage	At least 2.
Bathroom	At least 1 near sink.
Outside of residence	At least 2 near points of greatest use. Must be weatherproof.

A-20 Recommended Indoor Design Temperatures (°F)

Type of occupancy	Winter	Summer
Residences	72°	75°
Stores	68°	80°
Offices	72°	75°
Hotels	70°	75°
School classrooms	72°	80°

A-21 Outside Design Temperatures for Winter (from "Engineering Databook.")

DRY AND WET BULB DESIGN TEMPERATURES FOR SUMMER

The table which follows is intended as a guide in determining outside air temperatures for air conditioning design work. It is not recommended for direct use excepting where the designer lacks more complete data; experience data from local installations are of great help in determining the exact figure to use.

The table is based on a detailed study of noon temperatures in summer for 55 cities covering the years 1932 to 1937, inclusive. The wet bulb temperature given is that temperature which occurred at least once each year during the six-year period covered. Since the wet bulb temperature was available only for three times a day — morning, noon and late afternoon, the noon figures had to suffice. However, other evidence indicated that the noon wet bulb was very close, in most cases, to the highest for the day. Therefore, the wet bulb data are reasonably close to representing what can be expected to occur at least once each summer.

On the other hand, noon dry bulb temperatures are not, in most cases, the high temperature for the day. However, the absolute maximum for a six year period is known to occur too infrequently to be of use for design. By comparison of these two sets of data with design temperatures known to be satisfactory for a smaller number of cities, it was found that the mean between the maximum and the maximum occurring annually was in almost perfect agreement with the experience data. Consequently, this mean was used in the column for dry bulb temperatures.

The data have been extended in two ways: (1) by mapping from the original 55 cities to include adjacent cities; (2) by using for some cities figures recommended by the 1936 code of the Air Conditioning and Refrigerating Machinery Association. The data are believed to represent good practice in all cases.

Summer Design Temperature Data

State	City	Dry Bulb Temperature F	Wet Bulb Temperature F	State	City	Dry Bulb Temperature F	Wet Bulb Temperature F
Alabama	Birmingham	97	78	Georgia	Atlanta	95	76
	Mobile	91	80		Augusta	95	78
	Montgomery	95	70		Macon	95	75
					Savannah	95	79
Arizona	Flagstaff	100	70				
	Phoenix	108	75	Idaho	Boise	100	66
	Yuma	105	73		Lewiston	95	65
					Pocatello	95	65
Arkansas	Fort Smith	100	78				
	Little Rock	100	78	Illinois	Cairo	100	78
					Chicago	97	76
California	Fresno	105	70		Moline	95	76
	Los Angeles	91	68		Peoria	102	78
	Needles	103	70				
	Oakland	82	64	Indiana	Evansville	94	78
	Red Bluff	100	68		Fort Wayne	97	74
	Sacramento	103	72		Indianapolis	97	76
	San Francisco	89	64				
	San Diego	79	66	Iowa	Des Moines	100	76
					Dubuque	95	75
Colorado	Denver	96	63				
	Grand Junction	96	64	Kansas	Concordia	103	78
	Pueblo	95	65		Dodge City	103	78
					Wichita	104	74
Connecticut	Hartford	93	76		Topeka	100	78
	New Haven	95	75				
				Kentucky	Louisville	96	78
Delaware	Wilmington	95	78				
				Louisiana	New Orleans	94	79
District of Columbia	Washington	95	78		Shreveport	97	80
				Maine	Eastport	90	70
Florida	Jacksonville	95	78		Portland	90	73
	Key West	93	80				
	Miami	91	79	Maryland	Baltimore	98	77
	Tampa	93	78	Massachusetts	Boston	93	76

Summer Design Temperature Data — Continued

State	City	Dry Bulb Temperature F	Wet Bulb Temperature F	State	City	Dry Bulb Temperature F	Wet Bulb Temperature F
Michigan.....	Detroit	97	75	Oklahoma.....	Oklahoma City	104	76
	Duluth	93	72		Tulsa	102	76
	Houghton	93	73				
	Grand Rapids	99	76	Oregon.......	Baker	90	70
	Sault Ste. Marie	93	73		Portland	88	66
Minnesota.....	Duluth	93	73	Pennsylvania..	Erie	95	73
	Minneapolis	94	74		Harrisburg	95	75
					Philadelphia	96	77
Mississippi....	Meridian	95	79		Pittsburgh	94	75
	Jackson	96	80		Scranton	95	75
	Vicksburg	95	80				
				Rhode Island..	Providence	93	75
Missouri......	Columbia	99	78				
	Kansas City	101	77	South Carolina.	Charleston	92	80
	St. Louis	101	77		Columbia	96	78
	Springfield	93	75				
				South Dakota .	Huron	98	71
Montana......	Billings	95	65		Pierre	98	75
	Havre	95	70		Rapid City	96	68
	Helena	90	62				
	Kalispell	95	65	Tennessee.....	Chattanooga	97	76
	Miles City	95	70		Knoxville	92	75
					Memphis	96	79
Nebraska.....	Lincoln	104	76		Nashville	98	79
	North Platte	98	71				
	Omaha	102	76	Texas........	Abilene	102	98
	Valentine	99	76		Amarillo	98	70
					Brownsville	92	79
Nevada......	Reno	97	62		Corpus Christi	100	80
	Elkins	95	60		Dallas	100	77
					El Paso	97	69
New Hampshire	Concord	90	75		Ft. Worth	103	77
					Galveston	98	80
New Jersey....	Atlantic City	96	77		Houston	96	78
	Camden	91	76		Palestine	101	78
	Newark	91	75		San Antonio	97	78
New Mexico...	Albuquerque	94	66				
	Santa Fe	98	70	Utah........	Modena	92	64
					Salt Lake City	96	66
New York.....	Albany	92	72				
	Buffalo	88	72	Vermont......	Burlington	90	73
	New York	92	76				
	Syracuse	92	75	Virginia.......	Lynchburg	95	78
					Norfolk	93	78
North Carolina	Asheville	95	75		Richmond	96	78
	Charlotte	94	77				
	Raleigh	93	78	Washington...	Seattle	84	63
	Wilmington	90	78		Spokane	96	65
North Dakota.	Bismarck	102	73	West Virginia..	Elkins	95	75
	Devils Lake	95	73		Parkersburg	96	75
	Fargo	95	73				
	Grand Forks	95	73	Wisconsin.....	Green Bay	88	72
	Williston	95	73		La Crosse	92	76
					Milwaukee	97	74
Ohio.........	Cincinnati	97	77				
	Cleveland	92	74	Wyoming.....	Cheyenne	95	65
	Columbus	97	76		Lander	95	65
	Toledo	96	76				

RESIDENTIAL HEATING SURVEY

Name _James Smith Residence_   Date _____

Contractor _Alta Constructors._   Estimator _____

Address _1343 Parnel_   Salesman _____

City _Bakersfield, Calif._

INSIDE DESIGN TEMPERATURE   _75_ °F.

OUTSIDE DESIGN TEMPERATURE   _25_ °F.

DESIGN TEMPERATURE DIFFERENCE _50_ °F.

HOUSE   ☑ NEW   ☐ EXISTING

TYPE PAYNE FURNACE _Upflow_   SIZE _____ MODEL _____

BLOWER: ☐ DIRECT DRIVE   ☑ BELT DRIVE _____ H.P. MOTOR _____ SPEE

GAS: ☑ NATURAL;   ☐ L.P.G.;   ☐ _____ ;   SERVICE PRESSURE _____ " W.C. _1100_ BTU/CU. FT

UNIT LOCATION: ☑ CLOSET   ☐ BASEMENT   ☐ ATTIC   ☐ _____

ELECTRIC: _120/240_ VOLTS _1ø_ PHASE _60_ CYCLE

WALLS: ☑ FRAME

    ☐ HEAVY MASONRY

    ☐ LIGHT MASONRY

    Insulated

    ☑ YES   ☐ 1"   ☐ 2"   (4")

    ☐ NO

ROOF OR CEILING: ☐ PITCHED   ☑ FLAT

    Insulated

    ☑ YES   ☐ 1"   ☐ 2"   ☑ 3½"

    ☐ NO

FLOOR: ☐ WOOD

    ☑ SLAB ON GRADE

    ☐ OVER CRAWL SPACE

    ☐ OVER BASEMENT

    ☐ OPEN

    ☐ INSULATED

WINDOWS: ☐ DOUBLE HUNG

    ☐ CASEMENT

    ☐ DOUBLE GLAZED

    ☑ WEATHERSTRIPPED

    ☐ STORM SASH

    ☑ SLIDING DOOR

(continued on pages 201–211)

RESIDENTIAL HEATING ESTIMATE

ROOM	EXPOSED WALL & WINDOW					CEILING (3+" INSUL.) & FLOOR			ROOM HEAT LOSS		ROOM C.F.M.	SUPPLY REGISTER AND PIPE SIZE	RETURN GRILLE AND PIPE SIZE
	SASH AND DOORS		WALLS		BTU/HR (1000)	LENGTH	WIDTH	BTU/HR (1000)	CALCUL. (70° T.D.)	CORRECTED HEAT LOSS			
	Type	Sq. Ft.	Constr. L.F.	Lin. Ft.									
Entry	F.G / Door	14 / 24		5	.8	10	5	.3	1000	790 / 210 / 1,000	12		
Living	F.&S.	144		30	9.5	20	12	1.7	11,000	8,700 / 1,300 / 10,000	124		
Family	S.	42		20	5.7	18	14	1.8	7,500	5,900 / 900	87		
Kitchen	S. / Door	35 / 20		18	6.5	18	9	1.3	8,000	6,800 / 6,300 / 800 / 7,100	87		
Hall						12	3	.3	500	400	6		
Bath #1	S.	9		8	1.7	6	6	.3	2,000	400 / 1,600 / 200	25		
Bath #2	S.	9		5	1.4	7	5	.3	1,500	1,800 / 1,200 / 200	18		
B.R. #1	F.G.	56		24	7.0	16	12	1.4	8,500	1,400 / 6,700 / 1,100	96		
B.R. #2	F.G	56		25	7.1	13	11	1.1	8,000	7,800 / 6,300 / 1,000 / 7,300	90		
B.R. #3	F.G	56		23	6.9	11	11	1.6	8,000	6,300 / 1,000 / 7,300	90		

SUM OF ROOM HEAT LOSSES (OUTPUT OF FURNACE) . . . 50,900 BTU/HR

SUM OF ROOM C.F.M. . . . 635 C.F.M.

CHECK FIGURES

BTU/SQ. FT. = 3.63

EQUIPMENT SELECTION

TYPE PAYNE FURNACE 80 FAU-14-AC   MODEL

SIZE _____ INPUT 80,000 OUTPUT 64,000

INPUT _____ OUTPUT _____

Less Correction for Altitude (4% per 1000' above Sea Level)

RESIDENTIAL HEATING LOAD ESTIMATE

INSTRUCTIONS

1. **SURVEY:** Complete survey by checking items and filling blanks pertaining to the house to be estimated.

2. **WINDOWS:** List type of windows, i.e. Weatherstripped, Double Hung (Plain), Metal Casement, Storm Sash, etc. List square feet of glass under "Sq. Ft." columns for each room opposite the type you indicated.

3. **WALLS:** List type of construction, i.e. Light Masonry, Frame, Heavy Masonry, 1" insulated or 2" insulated Frame. List linear ft. of exposed walls under "Lin. Ft." columns for each room opposite the type you indicated. See TABLE 1 and select the combined heat loss for the amount of glass and wall you indicated for each room and list in "Btu/Hr" columns for each room.

4. **CEILING & FLOORS:** List the amount of insulation. List room dimensions under "Length & Width" columns for each room. Be sure to include dimensions of closets and halls adjacent to proper rooms. From TABLE 2, select the heat loss for ceilings and floors and list in "Btu/Hr" columns for each room, opposite the amount of insulation you listed. Slab floors should be listed separately from ceiling.

5. **ROOM HEAT LOSS (70° F. difference):** Total the heat losses for each room and list in this space for each room.

6. **ROOM HEAT LOSS (for Design difference):** See SURVEY for *your* DESIGN TEMPERATURE DIFFERENCE (Room Temperature — Outside Temperature). From TABLE 3 correct each ROOM HEAT LOSS based on *your* DESIGN TEMPERATURE DIFFERENCE.

7. **20% RESERVE FOR SPECIAL ROOMS:** For Baths, Sun Porches, Basement Rooms, Rooms over Garages and Isolated Rooms; increase Heat Loss 20%.
Total the final losses and enter for each room.

8. **ROOM C.F.M.:** See TABLE 4. Select the desired REGISTER TEMPERATURE for *your* installation. 135° REGISTER TEMPERATURE is usually considered the optimum. Others are listed here for your convenience or customer's specifications. Notes under TABLE 4 explain its use. Record ROOM C.F.M. under each ROOM to be conditioned. Space is provided to list NUMBER AND SIZE of SUPPLY REGISTERS AND RETURN GRILLES.

9. **SUM OF ROOM HEAT LOSSES:** Add the TOTAL ROOM HEAT LOSSES and enter here.

   Note: If outside air is to be used the above HEAT LOSS must be adjusted.

   Example: a. Calculated Load before outside air = 76,000 (Includes duct loss).
   b. C.F.M. for 135° Register Temperature = 940 C.F.M.
   c. Room Temperature 70° F.
   d. Outside Temperature 20° F.
   e. 20% outside air desired.

   Find: a. New TOTAL HEAT LOSS.

   Solution: a. C.F.M. Outside Air = .20 x 940 = 188 C.F.M.
   b. Outside Air HEAT LOSS = 188 x 1.08 (70° - 20°) = 10,200 Btu/Hr.
   c. Outside Air HEAT LOSS = 76,000 + 10,200 = 86,200 Btu/Hr.

10. **SUM OF ROOM C.F.M.:** Add the ROOM CFM and enter here.

11. **EQUIPMENT SELECTION:** Space is provided to list (1) Type of Furnace; (2) Model Number; (3) Btu/Hr. Input and Output; and correction for altitude, if any. Make sure the furnace you select fills the requirements you have calculated.

12. See APPLICATION SECTION under LOAD CALCULATION for more information.

TABLE 1
COMBINED HEAT LOSSES IN 1000 BTU/HOUR THROUGH WALLS, WINDOWS AND INFILTRATION

SQ. FT. SASH AREA	TYPE	Linear Ft. Exposed Wall 5				10				15				20				25				30				35				40			
		Light Masonry	Frame or Hev. Mas.	1" Ins. Frame	2" Ins. Frame	Light Masonry	Frame or Hev. Mas.	1" Ins. Frame	2" Ins. Frame	Light Masonry	Frame or Hev. Mas.	1" Ins. Frame	2" Ins. Frame	Light Masonry	Frame or Hev. Mas.	1" Ins. Frame	2" Ins. Frame	Light Masonry	Frame or Hev. Mas.	1" Ins. Frame	2" Ins. Frame	Light Masonry	Frame or Hev. Mas.	1" Ins. Frame	2" Ins. Frame	Light Masonry	Frame or Hev. Mas.	1" Ins. Frame	2" Ins. Frame	Light Masonry	Frame or Hev. Mas.	1" Ins. Frame	2" Ins. Frame
0		1.5	.9	.5	.3	3.0	1.7	.9	.6	4.4	2.6	1.4	.9	5.9	3.5	1.8	1.2	7.4	4.3	2.3	1.6	8.9	5.2	2.7	1.9	10.4	6.1	3.2	2.2	11.8	7.0	3.6	2.5
5	Weatherst'pd	1.9	1.4	1.0	.8	3.4	2.2	1.5	1.1	4.9	3.1	1.9	1.5	6.4	4.0	2.4	1.8	7.9	4.8	2.8	2.1	9.3	5.7	3.3	2.4	10.8	6.6	3.7	2.7	12.3	7.4	4.2	3.0
5	Double Hung	2.0	1.4	1.1	.9	3.5	2.3	1.5	1.3	5.0	3.2	2.0	1.6	6.5	4.0	2.4	2.0	7.9	4.8	2.9	2.2	9.4	5.8	3.3	2.5	10.9	6.6	3.8	2.8	12.4	7.5	4.2	3.1
5	Casement	2.1	1.5	1.2	1.0	3.6	2.4	1.6	1.4	5.1	3.3	2.1	1.7	6.6	4.1	2.5	2.0	8.0	5.0	3.0	2.3	9.5	5.9	3.4	2.6	11.0	6.8	3.9	2.9	12.5	7.6	4.3	3.2
10	Weatherst'pd	2.4	1.8	1.6	1.4	3.9	2.7	2.0	1.7	5.4	3.6	2.5	2.1	6.8	4.4	2.9	2.4	8.3	5.3	3.4	2.7	9.8	6.2	3.8	3.0	11.3	7.0	4.3	3.3	12.8	7.9	4.7	3.6
10	Double Hung	2.6	2.0	1.7	1.6	4.0	2.9	2.2	1.9	5.5	3.7	2.6	2.3	7.0	4.6	3.1	2.6	8.5	5.5	3.5	2.8	10.0	6.3	4.0	3.1	11.4	7.2	4.4	3.4	12.9	8.1	4.9	3.8
10	Casement	2.8	2.2	1.9	1.8	4.3	3.1	2.4	2.1	5.7	3.9	2.8	2.5	7.2	4.8	3.3	2.8	8.7	5.7	3.7	3.0	10.2	6.5	4.2	3.3	11.7	7.4	4.6	3.6	13.1	8.3	5.1	4.0
15	Weatherst'pd	2.8	2.3	2.1	2.0	4.3	3.2	2.6	2.3	5.8	4.1	3.0	2.7	7.3	4.9	3.5	3.0	8.8	5.8	3.9	3.2	10.2	6.7	4.4	3.5	11.7	7.5	4.8	3.8	13.2	8.4	5.3	4.2
15	Double Hung	3.1	2.5	2.3	2.2	4.6	3.4	2.8	2.5	6.0	4.3	3.2	3.0	7.5	5.1	3.7	3.2	9.0	6.0	4.1	3.4	10.5	6.9	4.6	3.8	12.0	7.8	5.0	4.1	13.5	8.6	5.5	4.4
15	Casement	3.4	2.9	2.7	2.5	4.9	3.7	3.1	2.8	6.4	4.6	3.6	3.4	7.9	5.5	4.0	3.5	9.3	6.3	4.5	3.8	10.8	7.2	4.9	4.1	12.3	8.1	5.4	4.4	13.8	9.0	5.8	4.7
20	Weatherst'pd	3.3	2.8	2.7	2.5	4.8	3.7	3.1	2.8	6.3	4.5	3.6	3.4	7.7	5.4	4.0	3.5	9.2	6.3	4.5	3.8	10.7	7.1	4.9	4.1	12.2	8.0	5.4	4.4	13.8	8.9	5.8	4.7
20	Double Hung	3.6	3.1	3.0	2.8	5.1	4.0	3.4	3.1	6.6	4.8	3.9	3.7	8.1	5.7	4.3	3.8	9.5	6.6	4.8	4.1	11.0	7.4	5.2	4.4	12.5	8.3	5.7	4.7	14.0	9.2	6.1	5.0
20	Casement	4.1	3.5	3.4	3.3	5.5	4.4	3.8	3.6	7.0	5.3	4.3	4.2	8.5	6.1	4.7	4.2	10.0	7.0	5.2	4.5	11.5	7.9	5.7	4.8	13.0	8.8	6.1	5.1	14.4	9.6	6.6	5.4
25	Weatherst'pd	3.8	3.3	3.2	3.1	5.2	4.2	3.7	3.4	6.7	5.0	4.1	4.0	8.2	5.9	4.6	4.0	9.7	6.8	5.0	4.3	11.2	7.6	5.5	4.6	12.6	8.5	5.9	4.9	14.1	9.4	6.4	5.3
25	Double Hung	4.2	3.7	3.6	3.4	5.6	4.5	4.0	3.8	7.1	5.4	4.5	4.1	8.6	6.3	5.0	4.4	10.1	7.1	5.4	4.7	11.6	8.0	5.8	5.0	13.1	8.9	6.3	5.3	14.5	9.7	6.7	5.6
25	Casement	4.7	4.2	4.1	4.0	6.2	5.1	4.6	4.3	7.7	6.0	5.0	5.0	9.1	6.8	5.5	5.0	10.6	7.7	5.9	5.2	12.1	8.5	6.4	5.6	13.6	9.4	6.8	5.9	15.1	10.3	7.3	6.2
30	Weatherst'pd	4.2	3.8	3.8	3.6	5.7	4.6	4.2	3.9	7.2	5.5	4.7	4.7	8.7	6.4	5.1	4.6	10.1	7.2	5.6	4.9	11.6	8.1	6.0	5.2	13.1	9.0	6.5	5.4	14.6	9.9	6.9	5.8
30	Double Hung	4.7	4.2	4.2	4.0	6.2	5.1	4.7	4.4	7.7	6.0	5.1	4.7	9.1	6.8	5.6	5.1	10.6	7.7	6.0	5.3	12.1	8.6	6.5	5.6	13.6	9.4	6.9	5.9	15.1	10.3	7.4	6.3
30	Casement	5.3	4.9	4.9	4.7	6.8	5.7	5.3	5.0	8.3	6.6	5.8	5.6	9.8	7.5	6.2	5.7	11.3	8.3	6.7	6.0	12.8	9.2	7.1	6.3	14.2	10.1	7.6	6.6	15.7	10.9	8.0	6.9
35	Weatherst'pd	4.7	4.3	4.3	4.2	6.1	5.1	4.8	4.5	7.6	6.0	5.2	5.2	9.1	6.9	5.7	5.2	10.6	7.7	6.1	5.4	12.1	8.6	6.6	5.7	13.5	9.5	7.0	6.0	15.0	10.3	7.5	6.4
35	Double Hung	5.2	4.8	4.8	4.7	6.7	5.6	5.3	4.8	8.2	6.5	5.7	5.6	9.7	7.4	6.2	5.6	11.1	8.2	6.6	5.8	12.6	9.1	7.1	6.3	14.1	10.0	7.5	6.6	15.6	10.9	8.0	6.9
35	Casement	6.0	5.5	5.5	5.5	7.5	6.4	6.1	5.8	9.0	7.3	6.5	6.4	10.4	8.1	7.0	6.4	11.9	9.0	7.4	6.6	13.4	9.9	7.9	7.1	14.9	10.8	8.3	7.6	16.4	11.6	8.8	7.6
40	Weatherst'pd					6.6	5.6	5.3	5.3	8.1	6.5	5.8	5.8	9.6	7.3	6.3	5.8	11.5	8.2	6.8	6.2	13.0	9.6	7.7	6.8	14.5	9.9	8.1	6.8	15.5	10.8	8.0	7.5
40	Double Hung					7.2	6.2	5.9	5.6	8.7	7.1	6.4	6.3	10.2	7.9	6.8	6.6	12.2	8.8	7.3	6.9	13.7	10.2	8.3	7.5	15.2	10.5	8.7	7.5	16.1	11.4	8.6	8.1
40	Casement					8.1	7.1	6.8	6.5	9.6	7.9	7.2	7.2	11.1	8.8	7.9	7.6	12.6	9.7	8.1	7.4	14.0	11.1	9.3	8.4	15.5	11.4	9.0	8.2	17.0	12.3	9.5	8.4
45	Weatherst'pd					7.1	6.1	5.9	5.9	8.5	6.9	6.3	6.3	10.0	7.3	6.8	6.2	11.5	8.7	7.2	6.5	13.0	9.6	8.2	7.4	14.5	10.4	8.1	7.5	15.9	11.3	8.6	7.8
45	Double Hung					7.8	6.8	6.5	6.3	9.3	7.6	7.2	7.2	10.7	7.9	7.4	6.9	12.2	9.4	7.9	7.2	13.7	10.2	9.0	7.9	15.2	11.1	8.8	7.9	16.7	12.0	9.2	8.1
45	Casement					8.8	7.7	7.5	7.2	10.2	8.6	8.0	8.0	11.7	9.5	8.4	8.2	13.2	10.3	8.9	8.2	14.7	11.2	9.3	8.4	16.2	12.1	9.8	8.8	17.6	13.0	10.2	9.1
50	Weatherst'pd					7.5	6.6	6.4	6.1	9.0	7.4	6.9	6.8	10.5	8.3	7.3	7.1	11.9	9.2	7.8	7.4	13.4	10.0	8.2	7.8	14.9	10.9	8.7	8.1	16.4	11.8	9.1	8.0
50	Double Hung					8.3	7.3	7.2	6.9	9.8	8.2	7.6	7.6	11.3	9.1	8.1	7.8	12.8	9.9	8.5	8.1	14.2	10.8	9.0	8.2	15.7	11.7	9.4	8.5	17.2	12.5	9.9	8.8
50	Casement					9.4	8.4	8.3	8.0	10.9	9.3	8.7	8.3	12.4	10.1	9.2	8.7	13.8	11.0	9.6	8.9	15.3	11.9	10.1	9.2	16.8	12.8	10.5	9.5	18.3	13.6	10.2	9.9
6 Ft. High Picture Window Wall		3.5	3.4	3.3	3.3	7.1	6.8	6.6	6.5	10.6	10.2	9.9	9.8	14.2	13.6	13.2	13.0	17.7	17.0	16.4	16.3	21.3	20.4	19.7	19.5	24.8	23.8	23.0	22.8	28.4	27.2	26.3	26.0

NOTES

1. Light Masonry .... U = .46
   Frame or Heavy Masonry .... U = .27
   Insulated Frame (1" Ins.) .... U = .14
   Insulated Frame (2" Ins.) .... U = .097

2. Based on 8 ft. wall height and 70° temperature difference between inside and out.

3. For partitions adjoining unheated space, figure ½ linear feet of length.

4. Consider wall adjoining garage as outside wall.

5. Consider wall adjoining attic spaces as ceiling.

6. For basement walls under ground, use 25% of value for heavy masonry wall.

7. Consider outside doors as double hung plain glass.

8. For storm sash or door; or double panel glass, use ½ actual glass area.

9. Table includes 15% for duct heat loss.

EXAMPLE

Room has 33 linear ft. of exposed frame wall and 13 sq. ft. of weatherstripped glass. Find the HEAT LOSS for 70°F. temperature difference.

1. Round glass area and linear ft. of wall off to nearest 5.
   i.e., 13 sq. ft. glass = 15 sq. ft. glass
   i.e., 33 linear ft. wall = 35 linear ft. wall

2. Reading in TABLE 1 opposite 15 sq. ft. of frame wall—glass and below 35 linear ft. of frame wall—
   Heat Loss = 7.5 × 1000 = 7,500 Btu/Hr for 70°F. temperature difference.

TABLE 2

HEAT LOSSES IN 1000 BTU/HOUR THROUGH FLOORS AND CEILINGS

Length or Width of Room			LENGTH OR WIDTH OF ROOM 3	4	5	6	7	8	9	10	11	12	13	14	15	16	17	18	19	20	21	22	23	24	25	26	27	28	29	30
4	Floor	No Insulation	0.3	0.4	0.5	0.6	0.7	0.8	0.9	1.0	1.1	1.2	1.3	1.4	1.5	1.6	1.7	1.8	1.9	2.0	2.1	2.2	2.3	2.4	2.5	2.6	2.7	2.8	2.9	3.0
	Ceiling	No Insulation	0.3	0.4	0.5	0.6	0.7	0.8	0.9	1.0	1.1	1.2	1.3	1.4	1.5	1.6	1.8	1.9	2.0	2.1	2.2	2.3	2.4	2.5	2.6	2.7	2.8	2.9	3.0	3.1
		2" Insulation	0.1	0.2	0.2	0.2	0.3	0.3	0.3	0.4	0.4	0.5	0.5	0.5	0.6	0.6	0.7	0.7	0.7	0.8	0.8	0.9	0.9	0.9	1.0	1.0	1.0	1.1	1.1	1.2
		3⅝" Insulation	0.1	0.1	0.1	0.2	0.2	0.2	0.3	0.3	0.3	0.3	0.4	0.4	0.4	0.5	0.5	0.5	0.6	0.6	0.6	0.6	0.7	0.7	0.7	0.8	0.8	0.8	0.8	0.9
6	Floor	No Insulation	0.4	0.6	0.8	0.9	1.1	1.2	1.4	1.5	1.7	1.8	2.0	2.1	2.3	2.4	2.6	2.7	2.9	3.0	3.2	3.3	3.5	3.6	3.8	3.9	4.1	4.3	4.4	4.6
	Ceiling	No Insulation	0.5	0.6	0.8	0.9	1.1	1.2	1.4	1.5	1.7	1.9	2.0	2.2	2.3	2.5	2.6	2.8	2.9	3.1	3.2	3.4	3.6	3.7	3.9	4.0	4.2	4.3	4.5	4.6
		2" Insulation	0.2	0.2	0.3	0.3	0.4	0.5	0.5	0.6	0.6	0.7	0.8	0.8	0.9	0.9	1.0	1.0	1.1	1.2	1.2	1.3	1.3	1.4	1.4	1.5	1.6	1.6	1.7	1.7
		3⅝" Insulation	0.1	0.2	0.2	0.3	0.3	0.3	0.4	0.4	0.5	0.5	0.6	0.6	0.7	0.7	0.7	0.8	0.8	0.9	0.9	1.0	1.0	1.0	1.1	1.1	1.2	1.2	1.3	1.3
8	Floor	No Insulation	0.6	0.8	1.0	1.2	1.4	1.6	1.8	2.0	2.2	2.4	2.6	2.8	3.0	3.2	3.4	3.6	3.8	4.0	4.3	4.5	4.7	4.9	5.1	5.3	5.5	5.7	5.9	6.1
	Ceiling	No Insulation	0.6	0.8	1.0	1.2	1.4	1.6	1.9	2.1	2.3	2.5	2.7	2.9	3.1	3.3	3.5	3.7	3.9	4.1	4.3	4.5	4.7	5.0	5.2	5.4	5.6	5.8	6.0	6.2
		2" Insulation	0.2	0.3	0.4	0.5	0.5	0.6	0.7	0.8	0.9	0.9	1.0	1.1	1.2	1.2	1.3	1.4	1.5	1.5	1.6	1.7	1.8	1.9	1.9	2.0	2.1	2.2	2.2	2.3
		3⅝" Insulation	0.2	0.2	0.3	0.3	0.4	0.5	0.5	0.6	0.6	0.7	0.8	0.8	0.9	0.9	1.0	1.0	1.1	1.2	1.2	1.3	1.3	1.4	1.5	1.5	1.6	1.6	1.7	1.7
10	Floor	No Insulation	0.8	1.0	1.3	1.5	1.8	2.0	2.3	2.5	2.8	3.0	3.3	3.5	3.8	4.0	4.3	4.6	4.8	5.1	5.3	5.6	5.8	6.1	6.3	6.6	6.8	7.1	7.3	7.6
	Ceiling	No Insulation	0.8	1.0	1.3	1.5	1.8	2.1	2.3	2.6	2.8	3.1	3.3	3.6	3.9	4.1	4.4	4.6	4.9	5.2	5.4	5.7	5.9	6.2	6.4	6.7	7.0	7.2	7.5	7.7
		2" Insulation	0.3	0.4	0.5	0.6	0.7	0.8	0.9	1.0	1.1	1.2	1.3	1.4	1.4	1.5	1.6	1.7	1.8	1.9	2.0	2.1	2.2	2.3	2.4	2.5	2.6	2.7	2.8	2.9
		3⅝" Insulation	0.2	0.3	0.4	0.4	0.5	0.6	0.7	0.7	0.8	0.9	0.9	1.0	1.1	1.2	1.2	1.3	1.4	1.5	1.5	1.6	1.7	1.7	1.8	1.9	2.0	2.0	2.1	2.2
12	Floor	No Insulation	0.9	1.2	1.5	1.8	2.1	2.4	2.7	3.0	3.3	3.6	3.9	4.3	4.6	4.9	5.2	5.5	5.8	6.1	6.4	6.7	7.0	7.3	7.6	7.9	8.2	8.5	8.8	9.1
	Ceiling	No Insulation	0.9	1.2	1.5	1.9	2.2	2.5	2.8	3.0	3.4	3.7	4.0	4.3	4.6	5.0	5.3	5.6	5.9	6.2	6.5	6.8	7.1	7.4	7.7	8.0	8.3	8.7	9.0	9.3
		2" Insulation	0.3	0.5	0.6	0.7	0.8	0.9	1.0	1.2	1.3	1.4	1.5	1.6	1.7	1.9	2.0	2.1	2.2	2.3	2.4	2.6	2.7	2.8	2.9	3.0	3.1	3.2	3.4	3.5
		3⅝" Insulation	0.3	0.3	0.4	0.5	0.6	0.7	0.8	0.9	1.0	1.0	1.1	1.2	1.3	1.4	1.5	1.6	1.7	1.7	1.8	1.9	2.0	2.1	2.2	2.3	2.3	2.4	2.5	2.6
14	Floor	No Insulation	1.1	1.4	1.8	2.1	2.5	2.8	3.2	3.5	3.9	4.3	4.6	5.0	5.3	5.7	6.0	6.4	6.7	7.1	7.4	7.8	8.1	8.5	8.9	9.2	9.6	9.9	10.3	10.6
	Ceiling	No Insulation	1.1	1.4	1.8	2.2	2.5	2.9	3.2	3.6	4.0	4.3	4.7	5.0	5.4	5.8	6.1	6.5	6.9	7.2	7.6	7.9	8.3	8.7	9.0	9.4	9.7	10.1	10.5	10.8
		2" Insulation	0.4	0.5	0.7	0.8	0.9	1.1	1.2	1.4	1.5	1.6	1.8	1.9	2.0	2.2	2.3	2.4	2.6	2.7	2.8	3.0	3.1	3.2	3.4	3.5	3.7	3.8	3.9	4.1
		3⅝" Insulation	0.3	0.4	0.5	0.6	0.7	0.8	0.9	1.0	1.1	1.2	1.3	1.4	1.5	1.6	1.7	1.8	1.9	2.0	2.1	2.2	2.3	2.4	2.5	2.6	2.7	2.8	2.9	3.0
16	Floor	No Insulation	1.2	1.6	2.0	2.4	2.8	3.2	3.6	4.0	4.5	4.9	5.3	5.7	6.1	6.5	6.9	7.3	7.7	8.1	8.5	8.9	9.3	9.7	10.1	10.5	10.9	11.3	11.7	12.1
	Ceiling	No Insulation	1.2	1.6	2.1	2.5	2.9	3.3	3.7	4.1	4.5	5.0	5.4	5.8	6.2	6.6	7.0	7.4	7.8	8.2	8.7	9.1	9.5	9.9	10.3	10.7	11.1	11.5	12.0	12.4
		2" Insulation	0.4	0.6	0.8	0.9	1.1	1.2	1.4	1.5	1.7	1.9	2.0	2.2	2.3	2.5	2.6	2.8	2.9	3.1	3.2	3.4	3.6	3.7	3.9	4.0	4.2	4.3	4.5	4.6
		3⅝" Insulation	0.3	0.5	0.6	0.7	0.8	0.9	1.0	1.2	1.3	1.4	1.5	1.6	1.7	1.9	2.0	2.1	2.2	2.3	2.4	2.6	2.7	2.8	2.9	3.0	3.1	3.2	3.4	3.5
18	Floor	No Insulation	1.4	1.8	2.3	2.7	3.2	3.6	4.1	4.6	5.0	5.5	5.9	6.4	6.8	7.3	7.7	8.2	8.7	9.1	9.6	10.0	10.5	10.9	11.4	11.8	12.3	12.8	13.2	13.7
	Ceiling	No Insulation	1.4	1.9	2.3	2.8	3.2	3.7	4.2	4.6	5.1	5.6	6.0	6.5	7.0	7.4	7.9	8.3	8.8	9.3	9.7	10.2	10.7	11.1	11:6	12.1	12.5	13.0	13.4	13.9
		2" Insulation	0.5	0.7	0.9	1.0	1.2	1.4	1.6	1.7	1.9	2.1	2.3	2.4	2.6	2.8	3.0	3.1	3.3	3.5	3.7	3.8	4.0	4.2	4.3	4.5	4.7	4.9	5.0	5.2
		3⅝" Insulation	0.4	0.5	0.7	0.8	0.9	1.0	1.2	1.3	1.4	1.6	1.7	1.8	2.0	2.1	2.2	2.3	2.5	2.6	2.7	2.9	3.0	3.1	3.3	3.4	3.5	3.7	3.8	3.9
20	Floor	No Insulation	1.5	2.0	2.5	3.0	3.5	4.0	4.6	5.1	5.6	6.1	6.6	7.1	7.6	8.1	8.6	9.1	9.6	10.1	10.6	11.1	11.6	12.1	12.7	13.2	13.7	14.2	14.7	15.2
	Ceiling	No Insulation	1.5	2.1	2.6	3.1	3.6	4.1	4.6	5.2	5.7	6.2	6.7	7.2	7.7	8.2	8.8	9.3	9.8	10.3	10.8	11.3	11.9	12.4	12.9	13.4	13.9	14.4	14.9	15.5
		2" Insulation	0.6	0.8	1.0	1.2	1.4	1.5	1.7	1.9	2.1	2.3	2.5	2.7	2.9	3.1	3.3	3.5	3.7	3.9	4.1	4.3	4.4	4.6	4.8	5.0	5.2	5.4	5.6	5.8
		3⅝" Insulation	0.4	0.6	0.7	0.9	1.0	1.2	1.3	1.5	1.6	1.7	1.9	2.0	2.2	2.3	2.5	2.6	2.8	2.9	3.0	3.2	3.3	3.5	3.6	3.8	3.9	4.1	4.2	4.4
22	Floor	No Insulation	1.7	2.2	2.8	3.3	3.9	4.5	5.0	5.6	6.1	6.7	7.2	7.8	8.3	8.9	9.5	10.0	10.6	11.1	11.7	12.2	12.8	13.4	13.9	14.5	15.0	15.6	16.1	16.7
	Ceiling	No Insulation	1.7	2.3	2.8	3.4	4.0	4.5	5.1	5.7	6.2	6.8	7.4	7.9	8.5	9.1	9.6	10.2	10.8	11.3	11.9	12.5	13.0	13.6	14.2	14.7	15.3	15.9	16.4	17.0
		2" Insulation	0.6	0.9	1.1	1.3	1.5	1.7	1.9	2.1	2.3	2.6	2.8	3.0	3.2	3.4	3.6	3.8	4.0	4.3	4.5	4.7	4.9	5.1	5.3	5.5	5.7	6.0	6.2	6.4
		3⅝" Insulation	0.5	0.6	0.8	1.0	1.1	1.3	1.4	1.6	1.8	1.9	2.1	2.2	2.4	2.6	2.7	2.9	3.0	3.2	3.4	3.5	3.7	3.8	4.0	4.1	4.3	4.5	4.6	4.8
24	Floor	No Insulation	1.8	2.4	3.0	3.6	4.3	4.9	5.5	6.1	6.7	7.3	7.9	8.5	9.1	9.7	10.3	10.9	11.5	12.1	12.8	13.4	14.0	14.6	15.2	15.8	16.4	17.0	17.6	18.2
	Ceiling	No Insulation	1.9	2.5	3.1	3.7	4.3	5.0	5.6	6.2	6.8	7.4	8.0	8.7	9.3	9.9	10.5	11.1	11.7	12.4	13.0	13.6	14.2	14.8	15.5	16.1	16.7	17.3	17.9	18.5
		2" Insulation	0.7	0.9	1.2	1.4	1.6	1.9	2.1	2.3	2.6	2.8	3.0	3.2	3.5	3.7	3.9	4.2	4.4	4.6	4.9	5.1	5.3	5.6	5.8	6.0	6.3	6.5	6.7	7.0
		3⅝" Insulation	0.5	0.7	0.9	1.0	1.2	1.4	1.6	1.7	1.9	2.1	2.3	2.4	2.6	2.8	3.0	3.1	3.3	3.5	3.7	3.8	4.0	4.2	4.4	4.5	4.7	4.9	5.0	5.2
26	Floor	No Insulation	2.0	2.6	3.3	3.9	4.6	5.3	5.9	6.6	7.2	7.9	8.6	9.2	9.9	10.5	11.2	11.8	12.5	13.2	13.8	14.5	15.1	15.8	16.4	17.1	17.8	18.4	19.1	19.7
	Ceiling	No Insulation	2.0	2.7	3.4	4.0	4.7	5.4	6.0	6.7	7.4	8.0	8.7	9.4	10.0	10.7	11.4	12.1	12.7	13.4	14.1	14.7	15.4	16.1	16.7	17.4	18.1	18.8	19.4	20.1
		2" Insulation	0.8	1.0	1.3	1.5	1.8	2.0	2.3	2.5	2.8	3.0	3.3	3.5	3.8	4.0	4.3	4.5	4.8	5.0	5.3	5.5	5.8	6.0	6.3	6.5	6.8	7.0	7.3	7.5
		3⅝" Insulation	0.6	0.8	0.9	1.1	1.3	1.5	1.7	1.9	2.1	2.3	2.5	2.6	2.8	3.0	3.2	3.4	3.6	3.8	4.0	4.1	4.3	4.5	4.7	4.9	5.1	5.3	5.5	5.7
28	Floor	No Insulation	2.1	2.8	3.5	4.3	5.0	5.7	6.4	7.1	7.8	8.5	9.0	9.9	10.6	11.3	12.0	12.8	13.5	14.2	14.9	15.6	16.3	17.0	17.7	18.4	19.1	19.8	20.5	21.3
	Ceiling	No Insulation	2.2	2.9	3.6	4.3	5.0	5.8	6.5	7.2	7.9	8.7	9.4	10.1	10.8	11.5	12.3	13.0	13.7	14.4	15.1	15.9	16.6	17.3	18.0	18.8	19.5	20.2	20.9	21.6
		2" Insulation	0.8	1.1	1.4	1.6	1.9	2.2	2.4	2.7	3.0	3.2	3.5	3.8	4.1	4.3	4.6	4.9	5.1	5.4	5.7	6.0	6.2	6.5	6.8	7.0	7.3	7.6	7.8	8.1
		3⅝" Insulation	0.6	0.8	1.0	1.2	1.4	1.6	1.8	2.0	2.2	2.4	2.6	2.8	3.0	3.2	3.4	3.7	3.9	4.1	4.3	4.5	4.7	4.9	5.1	5.3	5.5	5.7	5.9	6.1
30	Floor	No Insulation	2.3	3.0	3.8	4.6	5.3	6.1	6.8	7.6	8.3	9.1	9.9	10.6	11.4	12.1	12.9	13.7	14.4	15.2	15.9	16.7	17.5	18.2	19.0	19.7	20.5	21.3	22.0	22.8
	Ceiling	No Insulation	2.3	3.1	3.9	4.6	5.4	6.2	7.0	7.7	8.5	9.3	10.0	10.8	11.6	12.4	13.1	13.9	14.7	15.5	16.2	17.0	17.8	18.5	19.3	20.1	20.9	21.6	22.4	23.2
		2" Insulation	0.9	1.2	1.4	1.7	2.0	2.3	2.6	2.9	3.2	3.5	3.8	4.1	4.3	4.6	4.9	5.2	5.5	5.8	6.1	6.4	6.7	7.0	7.2	7.5	7.8	8.1	8.4	8.7
		3⅝" Insulation	0.7	0.9	1.1	1.3	1.5	1.7	2.0	2.2	2.4	2.6	2.8	3.0	3.3	3.5	3.7	3.9	4.1	4.4	4.6	4.8	5.0	5.2	5.4	5.7	5.9	6.1	6.3	6.5

NOTES

1. Floor (No Insulation)........................U = .34
   Ceiling (No Insulation)........................U = .32
   Ceiling (2" Insulation)........................U = .10
   Ceiling (3⅝" Insulation)........................U = .0726
2. Based on 70° F. temperature difference between outside and inside.
3. [illegible]

perimeter x 58 Btu/Hr.

4. No heat loss is to be figured through floor over heated basement or ceiling of first floor of two story house when second floor is heated.
5. For wood floors over unheated spaces that are enclosed, multiply floor loss By 0.46.
6. [illegible]

EXAMPLE

Room has dimensions of 18 ft. x 27 ft. Ceiling has 2" insulation and floor has no insulation. Find the HEAT LOSS for ceiling and floor for 70° F. temperature difference.
Opposite 18 ft. ceiling with 2" insulation and below 27 ft.
HEAT LOSS = 4.7 x 1000 = 4,700 Btu/Hr. for 70°F. temperature difference.
Opposite 18 ft. floor and below 27 ft.
HEAT LOSS = 12.3 x 1000 = 12,300 Btu/Hr. for 70°F.

TABLE 3
CORRECTION TABLE FOR ADJUSTING CALCULATED HEAT LOSSES TO DESIGN TEMPERATURE DIFFERENCE

TEMPERATURE DIFFERENCE	HEAT LOSSES AT 70° TEMPERATURE DIFFERENCE										
	500	1000	2000	3000	4000	5000	6000	7000	8000	9000	10,000
30	210	430	860	1290	1720	2150	2570	3000	3430	3860	4290
35	250	500	1000	1500	2000	2500	3000	3500	4000	4500	5000
40	290	570	1140	1710	2280	2860	3430	4000	4570	5140	5710
45	320	640	1290	1930	2570	3220	3860	4500	5140	5790	6430
50	360	710	1430	2140	2860	3570	4280	5000	5710	6430	7140
55	390	790	1570	2360	3140	3930	4720	5500	6290	7070	7860
60	430	860	1710	2570	3430	4290	5140	6000	6860	7710	8570
65	460	930	1860	2790	3720	4650	5570	6500	7430	8360	9290
70	500	1000	2000	3000	4000	5000	6000	7000	8000	9000	10,000
75	540	1070	2140	3210	4280	5350	6420	7500	8560	9630	10,700
80	570	1140	2290	3430	4570	5720	6860	8000	9140	10,290	11,430
85	610	1210	2430	3640	4860	6070	7280	8500	9710	10,930	12,140
90	640	1290	2570	3860	5140	6430	7720	9000	10,290	11,570	12,860
95	680	1360	2710	4070	5430	6790	8140	9500	10,860	12,210	13,570
100	720	1430	2860	4290	5720	7150	8570	10,000	11,430	12,860	14,290
105	750	1500	3000	4500	6000	7500	9000	10,500	12,000	13,500	15,000
110	790	1570	3140	4710	6280	7860	9430	11,000	12,570	14,140	15,710

NOTES

1. Round HEAT LOSS off to nearest 500 Btu/Hr, i.e. 27,650 = 27,500 or 27,670 = 28,000 Btu/Hr.

2. *Example:* ROOM HEAT LOSS from Heating Estimate = 27,350 Btu/Hr. DESIGN TEMPERATURE DIFFERENCE from SURVEY is 55.

So
$$10,000 = 7,860$$
$$10,000 = 7,860$$
$$7,000 = 5,500$$
$$350 \text{ say } 500 = 390$$
$$\overline{}$$
$$\text{Corrected} = 21,610 \text{ Btu/Hr}$$

TABLE 4
ROOM CFM FOR VARYING BTU/HOUR HEAT LOSSES AND REGISTER TEMPERATURES

BTU/HR. HEAT ‡ LOSS	REGISTER TEMPERATURE °F. *					
	130°	135°	140°	145°	150°	155°
500	7	6	6	5	5	5
1,000	14	12	12	11	10	10
2,000	27	25	23	21	20	19
3,000	41	37	35	32	30	29
4,000	54	50	46	43	40	38
5,000	68	62	58	54	51	48
6,000	81	74	69	64	61	57
7,000	95	87	81	75	71	67
8,000	108	99	92	86	80	76
9,000	122	112	104	96	90	86
10,000	135	124	115	107	101	95

ROOM CFM FOR VARYING BTU/HOUR HEAT LOSSES AND REGISTER TEMPERATURES

1. Round ROOM HEAT LOSS off to nearest 500 Btu/Hr.

Example: TOTAL ROOM HEAT LOSS = 21,610 Btu/Hr, ROOM TEMPERATURE desired is 70° and 135° REGISTER TEMPERATURE is selected.

$$10,000 \text{ Btu/Hr} = 124 \text{ C.F.M.}$$
$$10,000 = 124$$
$$1,000 = 12$$
$$610 \text{ Say } 500 = 6$$
$$\overline{}$$
So C.F.M. for 21,600 Btu/Hr = 266 C.F.M.

* Room temperature 70° F.
‡ 15% duct loss included.
CFM in table is based on air at standard conditions.

RESIDENTIAL 24-HOUR COOLING LOAD SURVEY

Name __James Smith Residence__   Date _____

Contractor __Alta Constructors__   Estimator _____

Address __1343 Pornel__   Salesman _____

City __Bakersfield, Calif.__

OUTSIDE DESIGN TEMPERATURE __105__ °F.   DAILY TEMPERATURE RANGE __25__ °F

HOUSE ☑ NEW   ☐ EXISTING

HOUSE FACES   ☐ N   ☐ NE   ☐ E   ☐ SE   ☑ S   ☐ SW   ☐ W   ☐ NW

UNIT LOCATION: ☑ CLOSET   ☐ BASEMENT   ☐ ATTIC   — OTHER _____

TYPE EVAPORATOR COIL: ☑ UP FLOW   ☐ DOWN FLOW   ☐ HORIZONTAL FLOW   ☐ FAN COIL

CONDENSER OR TOWER LOCATION: __North side__

ELECTRICAL VOLTS __240v__   PHASE __1 ø__   CYCLE __60__

FURNACE: TYPE __Up-flow__   SIZE _____   MODEL __80 FAU 14-AC__

BLOWER: ☐ DIRECT DRIVE   ☑ BELT DRIVE _____ H.P. MOTOR _____ SPEED

GAS: ☑ NATURAL; ☐ L.P.G. ☐ _____; SERVICE PRESSURE _____ " W.C. __1,100__ BTU/CU. FT

UNIT LOCATION: ☐ CLOSET   ☐ BASEMENT   ☐ ATTIC   ☐ _____

ELECTRIC: __120/240__ VOLTS __1 ø__   PHASE __60__ CYCLE

WALLS: ☑ FRAME
    ☐ HEAVY MASONRY
    ☐ LIGHT MASONRY

Insulated
☐ YES   ☐ 1"   ☐ 2"   (4")
☐ NO

Color
☐ DARK   ☑ LIGHT
__40__ INCH ROOF OVERHANG

FLOOR: ☐ WOOD
    ☑ SLAB ON GRADE
    ☐ OVER CRAWL SPACE
    ☐ OVER BASEMENT
    ☐ OPEN
    ☐ INSULATED

ROOF OR CEILING: ☐ PITCHED
    ☑ FLAT

Insulated
☐ YES   ☐ 1"   ☐ 2"   ☑ 3⅝"
☐ NO

Color
☐ DARK   ☑ LIGHT

WINDOWS: ☑ SLIDING DOOR
    ☐ DOUBLE HUNG
    ☐ CASEMENT
    ☐ DOUBLE GLAZED
    ☐ VENETIAN BLINDS
    ☐ KOOLSHADE
    ☐ AWNINGS
    __40__ INCH ROOF OVERHANG

RESIDENTIAL 24-HOUR COOLING LOAD ESTIMATE

Factors (top of sheet): 1.3 · Shaded Wall (U = .97) 1.4 · Sunlit Walls (U = .91) 1.4 · 1.3 Roof (4" Insul.) .0726 · Floor 1.4 (.097)

Room	Windows Overhang	Exposure	Sq. Ft.	Btu/Hr	Sunlit Walls Overhang	Length	Btu/Hr	Shaded Wall Length	Btu/Hr	Roof Length	Width	Btu/Hr	Floor Area	Btu/Hr	People Cooking	Total	C.F.M.	Register	Return
Entry	36	S	35	1,200						10	5		56		0	1416	5% 60	10x4	10x4
Living	36 / 24	N / S	84 / 49	2,680 / 3,500 (6,180)	24	6	155 (155)	8	120	20	12	210 / 1000	240		800	9,135	27% 320	16x6 (2)	16x6
Family	36	N	42	300 (1,300)	36	18	320 (1,300)	18	320	18	14	1656	250		800	4,150	15% 180	20x6	
Kitchen	36	S	40	350 (1,350)	36	10	240 (240)			18	9		160		1840	5,030	15% 180	12x6	
Hall										12	3	60	40	60	920	160	2% 20	6" Ø	
Bath #1	36	S	9	310 (310)	36	6	140 (140)			6	6	60	40	60		610	4% 40	10x4	
Bath #2	36	N	9	290				5	85	5	7	180	35			470	4% 40	10x4	
B.R. #1	36 / 24	S	56	1,850 / 1,850 (1,850)	36 / 24	4 / 12	100 / 320 (420)			16	12	800	190			3,070	12% 140	16x6	
B.R. #2	36 / 24	S / E	56	1,850 / 1,850 (1,850)	36 / 24	4 / 12	320 (420)			13	11	650	140			2,920	10% 120	14x6	
B.R. #3	36 / 24	N	56	1,800 (1,800)	24	11	300 (300)	4	70	11	11	550	130			2,650	10% 100	14x6	

CHECK FIGURES

Over-all Size 25' × 56' = 1400 Total Sq. Ft.

Sq. Ft. floor area per ton 560

% Glass area per Wall Area = Sq. Ft. Glass / Sq. Ft. Wall = ____ %

EQUIPMENT SELECTION

MODEL NO. COND. UNIT 360-AR-1

MODEL NO. EVAP. COIL 36VC-2-1200 CFM

H.T.H. = 30   TOTAL CFM = 1000

MINIMUM C.F.M. = ____   HOUSE VOLUME CU. FT. = 880

SUMMARY

29,615

HOUSE TOTAL HEAT GAIN = ... Btu/Hr

For ducts in Slab, closed crawl space or basement; or in attic with 2" mineral wool insulation, multiply HOUSE TOTAL HEAT GAIN by 0.96

15

RESIDENTIAL 24-HOUR COOLING LOAD ESTIMATE

INSTRUCTIONS

1. **SURVEY:** Complete survey by checking items and filling blanks pertaining to the house to be estimated.

2. **WINDOWS:** Under "Overhang" column, indicate for each window facing the amount of roof overhang. Under "Exposure", indicate each window facing. Under "Sq. Ft." columns for each room, indicate the sq. ft. of glass area. From Table 1, find the proper Btu/Hr from appropriate roof overhang and window facing. Under Table 1, find the correction factor for YOUR "Outside Design Temperature" and "Daily Temperature Range" and see Table 4 for adjusting "Window Sub-Total" for each room.

3. **WALLS:** Under "Overhang" column, indicate for each wall facing the amount of roof overhang. Under "Length" columns for each room, indicate the linear ft. of exposed wall opposite its overhang. From Table 2, find the proper Btu/Hr from appropriate roof overhang and construction. When all wall Btu/Hr have been found, add each room. Under Table 2, find the correction factor for YOUR "Outside Design Temperature" and "Daily Temperature Range" and see Table 4 for adjusting totals for each room. If exterior walls are *light colored*, apply the 0.75 color correction factor.

4. **ROOF:** Enter room dimensions under "Length & Width" column for each room. Be sure to include closets and hall adjacent to proper rooms. From Table 3, find the proper Btu/Hr from appropriate construction. Under Table 3, find the correction factor for YOUR "Outside Design Temperature" and "Daily Temperature Range" and see Table 4 for adjusting the roof values for each room. If roof color is *white, light* or *white marble chip,* apply the 0.75 color correction factor.

5. **FLOOR:** If floors are over unconditioned space or with underside exposed to outside, enter area of room under "Area" for each room and multiply times appropriate factor found under Table 3 *Floor* Notes to get the Btu/Hr.

6. **PEOPLE:** The Total Heat Gain from people is estimated at 460 Btu/Hr each. The number of people is generally known. For a speculative house where the number of people is unknown, the recommendation is one per bedroom plus one. Include People load with Living Room load.

7. **COOKING:** The average Total Heat Gain from cooking is estimated at 1840 Btu/Hr and is added to the Kitchen Load.

8. **ROOM TOTAL HEAT:** Total the figures in each Room Btu/Hr column. Add these figures horizontally to get the "ROOM TOTAL HEAT GAIN" and enter the results in the column. House Total Heat Gain is sum of room totals. If duct is to be installed in the slab, closed crawl space or basement, or in attic with 2" mineral wool insulation, multiply "HOUSE TOTAL HEAT GAIN" by 0.96. All ducts except those in slab must be insulated with 1" mineral wool with a vapor barrier covering.

9. **EQUIPMENT SELECTION:** Selection is made on the "HOUSE TOTAL HEAT GAIN." Enter the size of the air conditioning unit in the proper spaces. The "TOTAL C.F.M." is obtained by dividing the "HOUSE TOTAL HEAT GAIN" by 30. The "TOTAL C.F.M." should *always* equal or exceed the "MINIMUM C.F.M." which is obtained by dividing the "HOUSE VOLUME CU. FT." by 15, which is equal to 4 air changes per hour.

10. **ROOM C.F.M.:** Divide ROOM TOTAL HEAT by 30 to arrive at ROOM C.F.M. — Space is provided to record the above C.F.M. as well as number and sizes of supply registers and return grilles.

11. See APPLICATION SECTION under LOAD CALCULATION for information, concerning register and grille sizing, and duct-work sizing.

© The Payne Company

TABLE I
SOLAR AND TRANSMISSION HEAT GAIN THROUGH WINDOWS OR GLASS DOORS
(GRAND TOTAL HEAT — BTU/HR PER SQ. FT. SASH AREA)

0" OVERHANG

WINDOW FACING	SQ. FT. SASH AREA	1	2	3	4	5	6	7	8	9	10	20	30	40	50	60	70	80	90	100
	N	30	50	80	100	130	160	180	210	230	260	520	780	1040	1300	1560	1820	2080	2350	2610
	NE - NW	40	90	130	180	220	270	310	360	400	440	890	1330	1780	2220	2670	3110	3560	4000	4450
	E - W	60	120	180	240	300	360	420	480	540	600	1200	1790	2390	2990	3590	4190	4780	5380	5980
	SE - SW	50	110	160	210	270	320	380	430	480	540	1070	1610	2150	2680	3220	3760	4290	4830	5370
	S	40	70	110	140	180	210	250	280	320	350	710	1060	1410	1760	2120	2470	2820	3170	3530

12" OVERHANG

WINDOW FACING	SQ. FT. SASH AREA	1	2	3	4	5	6	7	8	9	10	20	30	40	50	60	70	80	90	100
	N	30	50	80	100	130	160	180	210	230	260	520	780	1040	1300	1560	1820	2080	2350	2610
	NE - NW	40	90	130	170	210	260	300	340	390	430	860	1290	1720	2150	2580	3000	3430	3870	4290
	E - W	60	120	170	230	290	350	410	470	520	580	1170	1750	2330	2910	3500	4080	4660	5240	5830
	SE - SW	50	100	150	200	250	300	350	400	460	510	1010	1520	2020	2530	3040	3540	4050	4550	5060
	S	30	60	90	120	150	180	210	250	280	310	610	920	1230	1530	1840	2150	2450	2760	3070

24" OVERHANG

WINDOW FACING	SQ. FT. SASH AREA	1	2	3	4	5	6	7	8	9	10	20	30	40	50	60	70	80	90	100
	N	20	50	70	100	120	150	170	200	220	250	490	740	980	1230	1470	1720	1960	2210	2450
	NE - NW	40	80	120	160	200	240	280	320	360	400	800	1200	1600	2000	2390	2790	3190	3590	3990
	E - W	50	110	160	210	270	320	380	430	480	540	1070	1610	2150	2680	3220	3760	4290	4830	5370
	SE - SW	40	90	130	170	210	260	300	340	390	430	860	1290	1720	2150	2580	3000	3430	3870	4290
	S	30	50	80	100	130	160	180	210	230	260	520	780	1040	1300	1560	1820	2080	2350	2610

36" OVERHANG

WINDOW FACING	SQ. FT. SASH AREA	1	2	3	4	5	6	7	8	9	10	20	30	40	50	60	70	80	90	100
	N	20	50	70	100	120	150	170	200	220	250	490	740	980	1230	1470	1720	1960	2210	2450
	NE - NW	40	70	110	150	180	220	260	290	330	370	740	1100	1470	1840	2210	2580	2940	3310	3680
	E - W	50	100	150	200	250	290	340	390	440	490	980	1470	1960	2450	2940	3430	3920	4420	4910
	SE - SW	40	80	110	150	190	230	270	310	340	380	770	1150	1530	1910	2300	2700	3060	3450	3830
	S	30	50	80	100	130	160	180	210	230	260	520	780	1040	1300	1560	1820	2080	2350	2610

48" OVERHANG

WINDOW FACING	SQ. FT. SASH AREA	1	2	3	4	5	6	7	8	9	10	20	30	40	50	60	70	80	90	100
	N	20	50	70	100	120	150	170	200	220	250	490	740	980	1230	1470	1720	1960	2210	2450
	NE - NW	40	70	110	140	180	210	250	280	320	350	710	1060	1410	1760	2120	2470	2820	3170	3530
	E - W	40	90	130	180	220	270	310	360	400	440	890	1330	1780	2220	2670	3110	3560	4000	4450
	SE - SW	30	70	100	130	170	200	240	270	300	340	670	1010	1350	1690	2020	2360	2700	3030	3370
	S	30	50	80	100	130	160	180	210	230	260	520	780	1040	1300	1560	1820	2080	2350	2610

CORRECTION FACTORS

	90°	95°	100°	105°
15° D.R.	.90	1.10	1.30	1.50
20°	.80	1.00	1.20	1.40
25°	.70	.90	1.10	1.30

NOTES

a. Based on drapes, venetian blinds or roll shades full drawn.
b. For omission of above—increase values 17%.
c. For awnings use values under 48" overhang.
d. For double glazing use 0.80 Table values.
e. Overhangs greater than 48", use North values.
f. Roof overhang shading applies to single story house or second floor of two story house.
g. Windows with KOOLSHADE, use North values.
h. Windows shaded all day, by trees or buildings, use North values.
i. Outside solid doors considered as outside walls.

EXAMPLE

46 sq. ft. east glass with 24" roof overhang:
40 sq. ft. = 2150
6 sq. ft. = 320
46 sq. ft. = 2470 Btu/Hr

TABLE 2
HEAT GAIN THROUGH SUNLIT AND SHADED WALLS
(GRAND TOTAL HEAT — BTU/HR PER LINEAR FT. OF EXPOSED PERIMETER)

0" ROOF OVERHANG — SUNLIT WALLS

Linear Ft. Exposed Wall	U	1	2	3	4	5	6	7	8	9	10	20	30	40
Light Masonry	.46	110	210	320	430	540	640	750	860	970	1070	2150	3220	4290
Frame or Heavy Masonry	.27	60	130	190	250	310	380	440	500	570	630	1260	1890	2520
Insulated Frame (1" Ins.)	.14	30	60	100	130	160	190	230	260	290	320	640	970	1290
Insulated Frame (2" Ins.)	.097	20	50	70	90	120	140	160	180	210	230	460	690	920

12" ROOF OVERHANG — SUNLIT WALLS

Linear Ft. Exposed Wall	U	1	2	3	4	5	6	7	8	9	10	20	30	40
Light Masonry	.46	100	190	290	390	480	580	680	770	870	970	1930	2900	3860
Frame or Heavy Masonry	.27	60	110	170	230	280	340	400	450	510	570	1130	1700	2260
Insulated Frame (1" Ins.)	.14	30	60	90	120	150	170	200	230	260	290	580	870	1160
Insulated Frame (2" Ins.)	.097	20	40	60	80	100	120	140	170	190	210	410	620	830

24" ROOF OVERHANG — SUNLIT WALLS

Linear Ft. Exposed Wall	U	1	2	3	4	5	6	7	8	9	10	20	30	40
Light Masonry	.46	90	170	260	350	430	520	610	700	780	870	1740	2610	3480
Frame or Heavy Masonry	.27	50	100	150	200	250	310	360	410	460	510	1020	1530	2040
Insulated Frame (1" Ins.)	.14	30	50	80	100	130	160	180	210	230	260	520	780	1040
Insulated Frame (2" Ins.)	.097	20	40	60	70	90	110	130	150	170	190	370	560	740

36" ROOF OVERHANG — SUNLIT WALLS

Linear Ft. Exposed Wall	U	1	2	3	4	5	6	7	8	9	10	20	30	40
Light Masonry	.46	80	150	230	310	390	460	540	620	700	770	1550	2320	3090
Frame or Heavy Masonry	.27	50	90	140	180	230	270	320	360	410	450	910	1360	1810
Insulated Frame (1" Ins.)	.14	20	50	70	90	120	140	160	190	210	230	460	700	930
Insulated Frame (2" Ins.)	.097	20	30	50	70	80	100	120	130	150	170	330	500	660

48" ROOF OVERHANG — SUNLIT WALLS

Linear Ft. Exposed Wall	U	1	2	3	4	5	6	7	8	9	10	20	30	40
Light Masonry	.46	70	150	220	290	370	440	510	580	660	730	1460	2190	2920
Frame or Heavy Masonry	.27	40	90	130	170	210	260	300	340	380	430	850	1280	1710
Insulated Frame (1" Ins.)	.14	20	40	70	90	110	130	150	180	200	220	440	660	880
Insulated Frame (2" Ins.)	.097	20	30	50	60	80	90	110	120	140	160	310	470	620

NORTH OR SHADED WALLS — ALL OVERHANGS

Linear Ft. Exposed Wall	U	1	2	3	4	5	6	7	8	9	10	20	30	40
Light Masonry	.46	50	110	160	210	270	320	380	430	480	540	1070	1610	2150
Frame or Heavy Masonry	.27	30	60	90	130	160	190	220	250	280	310	630	940	1260
Insulated Frame (1" Ins.)	.14	20	30	50	60	80	100	110	130	140	160	320	480	640
Insulated Frame (2" Ins.)	.097	10	20	30	50	60	70	80	90	100	110	230	350	460

CORRECTION FACTORS

	90°	95°	100°	105°
15° D.R.	.90	1.2	1.5	1.8
20°	.70	1.0	1.3	1.6
25°	.50	.80	1.1	1.4

NOTES

a. Based on 8 ft. wall height.
b. Wall adjoining unconditioning space—use North values.
c. Wall adjoining attic space—use roof values.
d. Roof overhang shading applies to single story house or second floor of two story house.
e. Listed construction are common to most residences. For others, heat gain values are proportional to U factor.
g. For picture window walls, use glass values only.
h. For light walls, use 0.75 times Table values.
i. Overhangs greater than 48", use North or Shade values.

EXAMPLE

36 linear ft. sunlit frame wall with 24" roof overhang:
30 ft. = 1530
6 ft. = 310
36 ft. = 1840 Btu/Hr

TABLE 3

HEAT GAIN THROUGH SUNLIT PITCHED AND FLAT ROOFS (GRAND TOTAL HEAT — BTU/HR PER SQ. FT.)

Width of Ceiling Ft.	Ceiling Insulation	Length of Ceiling (Ft.) 3	4	5	6	7	8	9	10	11	12	13	14	15	16	17	18	19	20	21	22	23	24	25	26	27	28	29	30	Width of Ceiling Ft.
4	0″	170	230	290	350	400	460	520	580	630	690	750	810	860	920	980	1040	1090	1150	1210	1270	1320	1380	1440	1500	1560	1610	1670	1730	4
	2″	50	70	90	110	130	140	160	180	200	220	230	250	270	290	310	320	340	360	390	400	410	430	450	470	490	500	520	540	
	3⅝″	40	50	60	80	90	100	120	130	140	160	170	180	190	210	220	230	250	260	270	280	300	310	320	340	350	360	370	390	
6	0″	260	350	430	520	600	690	780	860	950	1040	1120	1210	1300	1380	1470	1560	1640	1730	1810	1900	1990	2070	2160	2250	2330	2420	2510	2590	6
	2″	80	110	140	160	190	220	240	270	300	320	350	380	410	430	460	490	510	540	570	590	620	650	680	700	730	760	780	810	
	3⅝″	60	80	100	120	140	160	170	190	210	230	250	270	290	310	330	350	370	390	410	430	450	460	480	500	520	540	560	580	
8	0″	350	460	580	690	810	920	1040	1150	1270	1380	1500	1610	1730	1840	1960	2070	2190	2300	2420	2530	2650	2760	2880	3000	3110	3230	3340	3460	8
	2″	110	140	180	220	250	290	320	360	400	430	470	500	540	580	610	650	680	720	760	790	830	860	900	940	970	1010	1040	1080	
	3⅝″	80	100	130	160	180	210	230	260	280	310	340	360	390	410	440	470	490	520	540	570	590	620	650	670	700	720	750	780	
10	0″	430	580	720	860	1010	1150	1300	1440	1580	1730	1870	2020	2160	2300	2450	2590	2740	2880	3020	3170	3310	3460	3600	3740	3890	4030	4180	4320	10
	2″	140	180	190	270	320	360	410	450	500	540	590	630	680	720	770	810	860	900	950	990	1040	1080	1130	1170	1220	1260	1310	1350	
	3⅝″	100	130	160	190	230	260	290	320	360	390	420	450	480	520	550	580	610	650	680	710	740	780	810	840	870	900	940	970	
12	0″	520	690	860	1040	1210	1380	1560	1730	1900	2070	2250	2420	2590	2760	2940	3110	3280	3460	3630	3800	3970	4150	4320	4490	4670	4840	5010	5180	12
	2″	160	220	270	320	380	430	490	540	590	650	700	760	810	860	920	970	1030	1080	1130	1190	1240	1300	1350	1400	1460	1510	1570	1620	
	3⅝″	120	160	190	230	270	310	350	390	430	460	500	540	580	620	660	700	740	780	810	850	890	930	970	1010	1050	1090	1120	1160	
14	0″	600	810	1010	1210	1410	1610	1810	2020	2220	2420	2620	2820	3020	3230	3430	3630	3830	4030	4230	4440	4640	4840	5040	5240	5440	5640	5850	6050	14
	2″	190	250	320	380	440	500	570	630	690	760	820	880	950	1010	1070	1130	1200	1260	1320	1390	1450	1510	1580	1640	1700	1760	1830	1890	
	3⅝″	140	180	230	270	320	360	410	450	500	540	590	630	680	720	770	810	860	900	950	990	1040	1090	1130	1180	1220	1270	1310	1360	
16	0″	690	920	1150	1380	1610	1840	2070	2300	2530	2760	3000	3230	3460	3690	3920	4150	4380	4610	4840	5070	5300	5530	5760	5990	6220	6450	6680	6910	16
	2″	220	290	360	430	500	580	650	720	790	860	940	1010	1080	1150	1220	1300	1370	1440	1510	1580	1660	1730	1800	1870	1940	2020	2090	2160	
	3⅝″	160	210	260	310	360	410	470	520	570	620	670	720	780	830	880	930	980	1030	1090	1140	1190	1240	1290	1340	1400	1450	1500	1550	
18	0″	780	1040	1300	1560	1810	2070	2330	2590	2850	3110	3370	3630	3890	4150	4410	4670	4920	5180	5440	5700	5960	6220	6480	6740	7000	7260	7520	7780	18
	2″	240	320	410	490	570	650	730	810	890	970	1050	1130	1220	1300	1380	1460	1540	1620	1700	1780	1860	1940	2030	2110	2190	2270	2350	2430	
	3″⅝	170	230	290	350	410	470	520	580	640	700	760	810	870	930	990	1050	1100	1160	1220	1280	1340	1400	1450	1510	1570	1630	1690	1740	
20	0″	860	1150	1440	1730	2020	2300	2590	2880	3170	3460	3740	4030	4320	4610	4900	5180	5470	5760	6050	6340	6620	6910	7200	7490	7780	8060	8350	8640	20
	2″	270	360	450	540	630	720	810	900	990	1080	1170	1260	1350	1440	1530	1620	1710	1800	1890	1980	2070	2160	2250	2340	2430	2520	2610	2700	
	3⅝″	190	260	320	390	450	520	580	650	710	780	840	900	970	1030	1100	1160	1230	1290	1360	1420	1490	1550	1620	1680	1740	1810	1870	1940	
22	0″	950	1270	1580	1900	2220	2530	2850	3170	3480	3800	4120	4440	4750	5070	5390	5700	6020	6340	6650	6970	7290	7600	7920	8240	8550	8870	9190	9500	22
	2″	300	400	500	590	690	790	890	990	1090	1190	1290	1390	1490	1580	1680	1780	1880	1980	2080	2180	2280	2380	2480	2570	2670	2770	2870	2970	
	3⅝″	210	280	360	430	500	570	640	710	780	850	920	990	1070	1140	1210	1280	1350	1420	1490	1560	1630	1710	1780	1850	1920	1990	2060	2130	
24	0″	1040	1380	1730	2070	2420	2760	3110	3460	3800	4150	4490	4840	5180	5530	5880	6220	6570	6910	7260	7600	7950	8290	8640	8990	9330	9680	10020	10370	24
	2″	320	430	540	650	760	860	970	1080	1190	1300	1400	1510	1620	1730	1840	1940	2050	2160	2270	2380	2480	2590	2700	2810	2920	3020	3130	3240	
	3⅝″	230	310	390	460	540	620	700	780	850	930	1010	1090	1160	1240	1320	1400	1470	1550	1630	1710	1780	1860	1940	2020	2090	2170	2250	2330	
26	0″	1120	1500	1870	2250	2620	3000	3370	3740	4120	4490	4870	5240	5620	5990	6360	6740	7110	7490	7860	8240	8610	8990	9360	9730	10110	10480	10860	11230	26
	2″	350	470	590	700	820	940	1050	1170	1290	1400	1520	1640	1760	1870	1990	2110	2220	2340	2460	2570	2690	2810	2930	3040	3160	3280	3390	3510	
	3⅝″	250	340	420	500	590	670	760	840	920	1010	1090	1180	1260	1340	1430	1510	1600	1680	1760	1850	1930	2020	2100	2180	2270	2350	2440	2520	
28	0″	1210	1610	2020	2420	2820	3230	3630	4030	4440	4840	5240	5640	6050	6450	6850	7260	7660	8060	8470	8870	9270	9680	10080	10480	10890	11290	11690	12100	28
	2″	380	500	630	760	880	1010	1130	1260	1390	1510	1640	1760	1890	2020	2140	2270	2390	2520	2650	2770	2990	3020	3150	3280	3400	3530	3650	3780	
	3⅝″	270	360	450	540	630	720	810	900	990	1090	1180	1270	1360	1450	1540	1630	1720	1810	1900	1990	2080	2170	2260	2350	2440	2530	2620	2710	
30	0″	1300	1730	2160	2590	3020	3460	3890	4320	4750	5180	5620	6050	6480	6910	7340	7780	8210	8640	9070	9500	9940	10370	10800	11230	11660	12100	12380	12820	30
	2″	410	540	680	810	950	1080	1220	1350	1490	1620	1760	1890	2030	2160	2300	2430	2570	2700	2840	2970	3110	3240	3380	3510	3650	3780	3920	4050	
	3⅝″	290	390	480	580	680	780	870	970	1070	1160	1260	1360	1450	1550	1650	1740	1840	1940	2030	2130	2230	2330	2420	2520	2620	2710	2810	2910	
		3	4	5	6	7	8	9	10	11	12	13	14	15	16	17	18	19	20	21	22	23	24	25	26	27	28	29	30	

0″ Insulation $U = .32$
2″ Insulation $U = .10$
3⅝″ Insulation $U = .0726$

ROOF CORRECTION FACTORS

	90°	95°	100°	105°
15° D.R.	.90	1.1	1.3	1.5
20°	.80	1.0	1.2	1.4
25°	.70	.90	1.1	1.3

NOTES:
a. Use floor area for roof area.
b. No positive ventilation in attic. (With positive attic ventilation and ceiling insulation, use 0.75 Table values.)
c. For white marble chip, white or aluminum color roofs, use 0.75 Table values.
d. Listed construction are common to most residences. For others, heat gain values are proportional to U factor.

EXAMPLE

Room has dimensions of 18 ft. x 27 ft. Ceiling has 2″ insulation. Opposite 18 ft. with 2″ insulation and below 27 ft. ROOF HEAT GAIN = 2190 BTU/HR.

FLOOR

a. No floor heat gain for floors over cool basements, crawl space or concrete slab on ground.
b. For floor over unconditioned space such as apartment over non-conditioned store, floor heat gain equals 3 Btu/Hr. per sq. ft.
c. For floor with underside exposed to outside air such as car port, floor heat gain equals 6 Btu/Hr. per sq. ft.

TABLE 4

CORRECTION FACTOR TABLE
(BTU/HR BEFORE CORRECTION)

Correction Factor	BTU/HR BEFORE CORRECTION																	
	50	100	200	300	400	500	600	700	800	900	1000	2000	3000	4000	5000	6000	7000	8000
0.50	25	50	100	150	200	250	300	350	400	450	500	1000	1500	2000	2500	3000	3500	4000
0.70	40	70	140	210	280	350	420	490	560	630	700	1400	2100	2800	3500	4200	4900	5600
0.75	40	80	150	230	300	380	450	530	600	680	750	1500	2250	3000	3750	4500	5250	6000
0.80	40	80	160	240	320	400	480	560	640	720	800	1600	2400	3200	4000	4800	5600	6400
0.90	45	90	180	270	360	450	540	630	720	810	900	1800	2700	3600	4500	5400	6300	7200
0.96	50	100	190	290	380	480	580	670	770	860	960	1920	2880	3840	4800	5760	6720	7680
1.10	60	110	220	330	440	550	660	770	880	990	1100	2200	3300	4400	5500	6600	7700	8800
1.17	60	120	230	350	470	590	700	820	940	1050	1170	2340	3510	4680	5850	7020	8190	9360
1.20	60	120	240	360	480	600	720	840	960	1080	1200	2400	3600	4800	6000	7200	8400	9600
1.30	70	130	260	390	520	650	780	910	1040	1170	1300	2600	3900	5200	6500	7800	9100	10,400
1.40	70	140	280	420	560	700	840	980	1120	1260	1400	2800	4200	5600	7000	8400	9800	11,200
1.50	80	150	300	450	600	750	900	1050	1200	1350	1500	3000	4500	6000	7500	9000	10,500	12,000
1.60	80	160	320	480	640	800	960	1120	1280	1440	1600	3200	4800	6400	8000	9600	11,200	12,800
1.80	90	180	360	540	720	900	1080	1260	1440	1620	1800	3600	5400	7200	9000	10,800	12,600	14,400

NOTES

a. This Table has been prepared to eliminate correction factor multiplications.

EXAMPLE

A room has a "Window Sub-Total" heat of 9,640 Btu/Hr. The house is located in an area of 100° "Outside Design Temperature" and 25° Daily Range Temperature." Under Table 1 we find a correction factor of 1.10. Reading across Table 4 opposite the 1.10 correction factor line we find that the correction for

$$
\begin{array}{rcl}
8000 \text{ Btu/Hr} &=& 8,800 \text{ Btu/Hr} \\
1000 &=& 1,100 \\
600 &=& 660 \\
40 \text{ (Use 50)} &=& 60 \\
\hline
\text{Corrected figure} &=& 10,620
\end{array}
$$

HIGH SIDE WALL REGISTERS FOR RESIDENTIAL

CFM	SINGLE DEFLECTION MULTI-SHUTTER VOLUME DAMPER		DOUBLE DEFLECTION OPPOSED BLADE VOLUME DAMPER	
	Size	Throw-Feet	Size	Throw-Feet
60	10x4	10	8x4	5-10
80	10x6	12	8x4	7-12
100	14x6	14	12x4	7-12
120	14x6	16	12x4	8-14
140	16x6	16	10x6	8-16
160	16x6	18	10x6	10-17
180	20x6	14	14x6	10-17
200	20x6	16	14x6	10-19
220	20x6	18	14x6	11-20
240	20x6	20	20x6	11-19
260	24x6	20	20x6	11-20
280	30x6	18	20x6	12-22
300	30x6	20	20x6	13-23

NOTES:

1. Sizes are based on the recommended velocities for residential applications.
2. The sizes shown for the single deflection, multi-shutter volume damper are minimum sizes.
3. Double-deflection, opposed blade volume damper sizes are on registers set to the maximum (55°) deflections. For a straight flow, select the next smaller size and the throw will be doubled.
4. The throw should equal ¾ of the distance to the wall opposite the register.
5. For further information, reference should be made to the manufacturer's catalogs.

PERIMETER OUTLETS

CFM	LOW SIDE WALL		FLOOR		CONTINUOUS BASEBOARD	
	Size	Spread	Size	Spread	Length	Spread
60	10x6	10 ft.	2¼x10	7 ft.	4 ft.	12 ft.
80	10x6	11 ft.	2¼x12	11 ft.	4 ft.	14 ft.
100	10x6	13 ft.	2¼x14	11 ft.	6 ft.	16.5 ft.
120	12x6	13 ft.	4x10	11 ft.	6 ft.	18 ft.
140	14x6	13 ft.	4x10	13 ft.	8 ft.	19.5 ft.
160	14x6	14 ft.	4x12	13 ft.	10 ft.	22 ft.

NOTE: The "spread" figure represents the horizontal length that will be effectively blanketed with air.

CEILING OUTLETS

CFM	SIZE
100	6″
120	8″
140	8″
160	8″
180	8″
200	10″
220	10″
240	10″

NOTES:

1. Diffusers should be located in the center of the ceiling of each room.
2. In cases where the room is rectangular and the long side is more than one and one-half times the length of the shorter side, two diffusers should be used.

RETURN AIR GRILLES FOR RESIDENTIAL

CFM	SQ. IN. FREE AREA	SIDE WALL RETURN GRILLES	FLOOR GRILLES		
60- 140	40	10x 6	4x14		
140- 170	48	12x 6	4x18	6x10	
170- 190	55	10x 8	4x18	6x12	
190- 235	67	12x 8		6x14	
235- 260	74	18x 6		6x16	8x14
260- 370	106	12x12			8x20
370- 560	162	18x12			8x30
560- 760	218	24x12	10x30	12x24	
760- 870	252	18x18		12x30	
870- 960	276	30x12		12x30	
960-1,170	340	24x18			14x30
1,170-1,470	423	30x18	18x30		
1,470-1,580	455	24x24		20x30	
1,580-1,770	510	36x18			22x30
1,770-1,990	572	30x24	24x30		
1,990-2,400	690	36x24	24x36		
2,400-3,020	870	36x30		30x36	

MINIMUM SUPPLY AND RETURN DUCT SIZES FOR RESIDENTIAL APPLICATION

	Supply Ducts				Return Ducts			
CFM	Round	Rectangular		Riser	Round	Rectangular		Riser
50	5″	8x 6		10x3¼	6″	8x 6		10x3¼
75	6″	8x 6		10x3¼	7″	8x 6		12x3¼
100	6″	8x 6		10x3¼	8″	8x 6		14x3¼
125	7″	8x 6		12x3¼	8″		8x 8	
150	7″	8x 6		14x3¼	9″		8x 8	
175	8″	8x 6			9″		10x 8	
200	8″		8x 8		10″	8x10	10x 8	
250	9″		8x 8		12″	10x10	12x 8	
300	10″	8x10	10x 8		12″	10x10	14x 8	
350	10″	8x10	10x 8		12″	12x10	16x 8	
400	10″	10x10	12x 8		12″	14x10	16x 8	
500	12″	10x10	14x 8		14″	16x10	20x 8	
600	12″	12x10	14x 8		16″	18x10	24x 8	
700	12″	14x10	16x 8		16″	20x10	26x 8	
800	14″	16x10	20x 8		16″	22x10	30x 8	
900	14″	16x10	22x 8		18″	24x10	32x 8	
1,000	16″	18x10	24x 8		18″	26x10	22x12	
1,200	16″	22x10	28x 8		20″	30x10	24x12	
1,400	18″	26x10	22x12		20″	36x10	28x12	
1,600	18″	28x10	24x12		22″	40x10	32x12	
1,800	20″	32x10	24x12		22″	28x14	36x12	
2,000	20″	34x10	26x12		24″	32x14	38x12	
2,500	22″	40x10	32x12		26″	38x14	46x12	
3,000	24″	32x14	38x12		26″	44x14	38x16	
3,500	24″	36x14	44x12		28″	50x14	42x16	
4,000	26″	40x14	48x12		30″	56x14	48x16	

MINIMUM AIR DISTRIBUTION SIZES FOR COMMERCIAL APPLICATION

| CFM | Supply or Return Sizes | | | | High Side Wall Registers | | Ceiling Diffuser | Return Grille |
	Round	Rectangular			Size	Throw Feet	Inches	
50	5″	8x 6			8x 4	5- 8	6″	10x 6
75	5″	8x 6			8x 4	6-12	6″	10x 6
100	6″	8x 6			8x 4	9-16	6″	10x 6
125	6″	8x 6			10x 6	8-14	6″	10x 6
150	7″	8x 6			10x 6	9-16	6″	10x 6
175	7″	8x 6			10x 6	11-20	8″	10x 6
200	7″	8x 6			10x 6	12-22	8″	10x 6
250	8″	6x10	8x 8	6x12	14x 6	13-23	8″	10x 8
300	9″	6x10	8x 8	6x12	14x 6	15-28	10″	12x 8
350	9″	8x10	8x 8	6x12	14x 6	18-32	10″	18x 6
400	9″	8x10	10x 8	6x12	20x 6	17-30	10″	12x12
500	10″	10x10	12x 8	8x12	20x 6	21-38	12″	12x12
600	12″	10x10	12x 8	8x12	20x 8	22-40	12″	18x12
700	12″	12x10	14x 8	10x12	20x 8	26-45	15″	18x12
800	12″	12x10	16x 8	10x12	30x 8	24-43	15″	24x12
900	14″	14x10	18x 8	12x12	30x 8	27-47	15″	24x12
1,000	14″	14x10	18x 8	12x12	30x 8	30-52	15″	24x12
1,200	14″	16x10	22x 8	14x12				18x18
1,400	16″	18x10	24x 8	16x12				24x18
1,600	16″	20x10	28x 8	18x12				24x18
1,800	16″	24x10	30x 8	20x12				30x18
2,000	18″	26x10	32x 8	20x12				30x18
2,500	18″	30x10	20x14	24x12				30x24
3,000	20″	36x10	24x14	28x12				36x24
3,500	22″	40x10	28x14	32x12				36x30
4,000	24″	26x16	32x14	38x12				36x30

NOTES:

1. Shorter throws indicated for the high sidewall registers refer to 55° deflection settings, while the longer throws indicated are for straight deflection.

2. The figures for high sidewall registers refer to those of the double deflectional type.

Graphic symbols shown on this and the following four pages have been extracted from American Standards Z32.2.3–1949 (reaffirmed 1953), Z32.2.4–1949 (reaffirmed 1953), and Y32.4–1955, with the permission of the publisher, The American Society of Mechanical Engineers. Designations of the relevant publications are also given at the bottom of each page.

AIR CONDITIONING

Brine Return

Brine Supply

Circulating Chilled or
Hot-Water Flow

Circulating Chilled or
Hot-Water Return

Condenser Water Flow

Condenser Water Return

Drain

Humidification Line

Make-Up Water

Refrigerant Discharge

Refrigerant Liquid

Refrigerant Suction

HEATING

Air-Relief Line

Boiler Blow Off

Compressed Air

Condensate or Vacuum
Pump Discharge

Feedwater Pump Discharge

Fuel-Oil Flow

Fuel-Oil Return

Fuel-Oil Tank Vent

High-Pressure Return

High-Pressure Steam

Hot-Water Heating Return

Hot-Water Heating Supply

Low-Pressure Return

Low-Pressure Steam

Make-Up Water

Medium-Pressure Return

Medium-Pressure Steam

PLUMBING

Acid Waste

Cold Water

Compressed Air

Drinking-Water Flow

Drinking-Water Return

Fire Line

Gas

Hot Water

Hot-Water Return

Soil, Waste or Leader
(Above Grade)

Soil, Waste or Leader
(Below Grade)

Vacuum Cleaning

Vent

PNEUMATIC TUBES

Tube Runs

SPRINKLERS

Branch and Head

Drain

Main Supplies

(continued on pages 216–218)

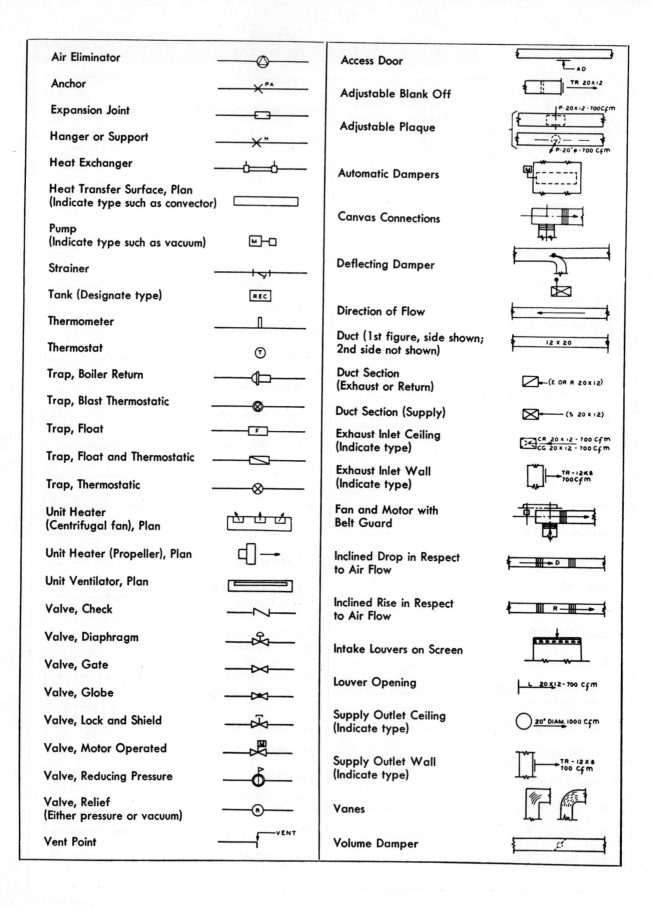

Air Eliminator		Access Door	
Anchor		Adjustable Blank Off	
Expansion Joint		Adjustable Plaque	
Hanger or Support			
Heat Exchanger		Automatic Dampers	
Heat Transfer Surface, Plan (Indicate type such as convector)		Canvas Connections	
Pump (Indicate type such as vacuum)		Deflecting Damper	
Strainer			
Tank (Designate type)		Direction of Flow	
Thermometer		Duct (1st figure, side shown; 2nd side not shown)	
Thermostat			
Trap, Boiler Return		Duct Section (Exhaust or Return)	
Trap, Blast Thermostatic		Duct Section (Supply)	
Trap, Float		Exhaust Inlet Ceiling (Indicate type)	
Trap, Float and Thermostatic		Exhaust Inlet Wall (Indicate type)	
Trap, Thermostatic			
Unit Heater (Centrifugal fan), Plan		Fan and Motor with Belt Guard	
Unit Heater (Propeller), Plan		Inclined Drop in Respect to Air Flow	
Unit Ventilator, Plan		Inclined Rise in Respect to Air Flow	
Valve, Check		Intake Louvers on Screen	
Valve, Diaphragm			
Valve, Gate		Louver Opening	
Valve, Globe		Supply Outlet Ceiling (Indicate type)	
Valve, Lock and Shield			
Valve, Motor Operated		Supply Outlet Wall (Indicate type)	
Valve, Reducing Pressure			
Valve, Relief (Either pressure or vacuum)		Vanes	
Vent Point		Volume Damper	

Capillary Tube	
Compressor	
Compressor, Enclosed, Crankcase, Rotary, Belted	
Compressor, Open Crankcase, Reciprocating, Belted	
Compressor, Open Crankcase, Reciprocating, Direct Drive	
Condenser, Air Cooled, Finned, Forced Air	
Condenser, Air Cooled, Finned, Static	
Condenser, Water Cooled, Concentric Tube in a Tube	
Condenser, Water Cooled, Shell and Coil	
Condenser, Water Cooled, Shell and Tube	
Condensing Unit, Air Cooled	
Condensing Unit, Water Cooled	
Cooling Tower	
Dryer	
Evaporative Condenser	
Evaporator, Circular, Ceiling Type, Finned	
Evaporator, Manifolded, Bare Tube, Gravity Air	
Evaporator, Manifolded, Finned, Forced Air	
Evaporator, Manifolded, Finned, Gravity Air	
Evaporator, Plate Coils, Headered or Manifold	
Filter, Line	
Filter & Strainer, Line	
Finned Type Cooling Unit, Natural Convection	
Forced Convection Cooling Unit	
Gauge	
High Side Float	
Immersion Cooling Unit	
Low Side Float	
Motor-Compressor, Enclosed Crankcase, Reciprocating, Direct Connected	

Motor-Compressor, Enclosed Crankcase, Rotary, Direct Connected	
Motor-Compressor, Sealed Crankcase, Reciprocating	
Motor-Compressor, Sealed Crankcase, Rotary	
Pressurestat	
Pressure Switch	
Pressure Switch With High Pressure Cut-Out	
Receiver, Horizontal	
Receiver, Vertical	
Scale Trap	
Spray Pond	
Thermal Bulb	
Thermostat (Remote bulb)	
Valve, Automatic Expansion	
Valve, Compressor Suction Pressure Limiting, Throttling Type (Compressor Side)	
Valve, Constant Pressure, Suction	
Valve, Evaporator Pressure Regulating, Snap Action	
Valve, Evaporator Pressure Regulating, Thermostatic Throttling Type	
Valve, Evaporator Pressure Regulating, Throttling Type (Evaporator side)	
Valve, Hand Expansion	
Valve, Magnetic Stop	
Valve, Snap Action	
Valve, Suction Vapor Regulating	
Valve, Thermo Suction	
Valve, Thermostatic Expansion	
Valve, Water	
Vibration Absorber, Line	

HEADING SYMBOLS

Unless otherwise noted, these are A.S.A. Standards (Z 14.2, 1935), as recommended by A.S.H.V.E... Symbols starred (*) are assembled from other sources. When possibility of misinterpretation exists, incorporate symbols in a key or legend. See also T-S.S. A I.3.1

PIPING

General
Air - *Pressure Flow*
*Air - *Return*
Gas
Oil
Refrigerant
Steam - *Supply*
Steam - *Return (Condensate)*
Vacuum
Water - *Cold*
Water - *Hot, Flow*
*Water - *Hot, Return*

PIPE FITTINGS

Screwed type shown; for other types & fittings see T-S.S. A I.3.1

Bushing
Expansion Joint, *Flanged*
*Sleeve
Stop Cock
Trap - *Radiator (Elev.)*
Trap - *Radiator (Plan)*
Union
Valves (*see also "Controls"*)
Check
Float Operated
Gate
Globe
Lock and Shield
Quick Opening
Safety

RADIATION

Indirect Radiator - *Plan*
Indirect Radiator - *Elev.*
Pipe Coil - *Plan*
Pipe Coil - *Elev.*
Tube Radiator - *Plan*
Tube Radiator - *Elev.*
Wall Radiator - *Plan*
Wall Radiator - *Elev.*

AIR DUCTS and FITTINGS

Ducts
Supply - *Section*
*Supply - *Plan*
Exhaust - *Section*
*Exhaust - *Plan*

Dampers
Butterfly - *Plan*
Butterfly - *Elev.*
Deflecting
Vanes
Supply Outlet
Exhaust Inlet

CONTROLS

*Aquastat
*Damper Motor - *General*
*Damper Motor - *Modulating*
*Damper Motor - 2 *Position*
*Diaphragm Damper Motor
*Ductstat - *Extended Tube*
*Ductstat - *Rigid Tube*
*Humidistat - *Room Type*
*Relay
*Stop and Waste Cock
*Switch
Thermostat - *Room Type*

Valves
*Air Reducing
Diaphragm
Gate - *Motor Operated*
*Globe - *Motor Operated*
Reducing - *Steam*
*Self-contained Thermostatic

INSULATION SYMBOLS

Symbols shown here have been proposed to the Research Committee on Insulation, A.S.H.V.E., for use on working drawings to assist in calculating heating and cooling loads. In scale details, show type, location and amount of insulation by any clear graphic indication.

Any insulation type not determined

Any fill type batt or loose

Rigid board as sheathing

Rigid board on interior

Any flexible blanket or curtain

Reflective curtain 2 sides or multiple

Reflective metal one side only

To show transmittance "u"

$u = .09$

Kind of Fixture	Minimum Trap Size	Units
Bathtubs	1½"	2
Bidets	1½"	2
Dental Units or Cuspidors	1½"	1
Drinking Fountains	1¼"	1
Floor Drains	2"	2
Interceptors for grease, oil, solids, etc.	2"	3
Interceptors for sand, auto wash, etc.	3"	6
Laundry tubs or clotheswashers (residential)	1½"	2
Laundry tubs or clotheswashers (self-service laundry—2 units each)	1½"	2
Receptors (floor sinks) indirect waste receptors for refrigerators, coffee urn, water station, etc.	1½"	1
Receptors, indirect waste receptors for commercial sinks, dishwashers, airwashers, etc.	2"	3
Showers, single stalls	2"	2
Showers, gang, (one unit per head)	2"	
Sinks, bar, residential (1½ min. waste)	1½"	1
Sinks, bar, commercial (2" min. waste)	1½"	2
Sinks, commercial or industrial, schools, etc. including dishwashers, wash up sinks and wash fountains (2" min. waste)	1½"	3
Sinks, flushing rim, clinic	3"	6
Sinks, and/or dishwashers (residential) (2" min. waste)	1½"	2
Sinks, service	2"	3
Trailer park traps (one for each trailer)	3"	6
Urinals, pedestal	3"	6
Urinals, stall	2"	2
Urinals, wall (2" min. waste)	1½"	2
Urinals, wall trough (2" min. waste)	1½"	3
Wash basins (lavatories) single	1½"	1
Wash basins, in sets	1½"	2
Water closets	3"	6

Lists Maximum Unit Loading and Maximum Length of Drainage and Vent Piping

Size of Pipe (Inches)	1¼"	1½"	2"	2½"	3"	4"	5"	6"	8"	10"	12"
Max. Units											
Drainage Piping											
Vertical	0	†2	**16	**32	***48	256	600	1380	3600		
Horizontal	0	1	**8	**14	***27	180	256	600	2200	3900	6912
Max. Length (Feet)											
Drainage Piping											
Vertical	0	65	85	148	212	300	390	510	750		
Horizontal Unlimited											
Vent Piping											
Horizontal and Vertical											
Max. Units	*1	**8	24	48	84	256	600	1380	3600		
Max. Length	*45	60	120	180	212	300	390	510	750		
(See note)											

†Except Sinks and Urinals

*Vertical Only

**Except Six-Unit Traps or Fixtures

***Only two 6-unit traps or fixtures allowed on any horizontal branch or drain and four 6-unit fixtures allowed on any vertical pipe or stack, provided that not more than two 6-unit fixtures are connected to the stack in any one story and that water closets are limited to flush tank type.

NOTE: The diameter of an individual vent shall be not less than one and one quarter (1¼) inches, nor less than one half (½) the diameter of the drain to which it is connected. Not to exceed one third (⅓) of the total permitted length of any vent may be installed in a horizontal position.

Equivalent Fixture Units

(Includes Combined Hot and Cold Water Demand)

Fixture	Number of Fixture Units Private Use	Public Use
Bar sink	1	2
Bathtub (with or without shower over)	2	4
Dental unit or cuspidor	—	1
Drinking fountain (each head)	—	1
Hose bibb or sill cock (standard type)	3	5
House trailer (each)	6	6
Laundry tub or clotheswasher (each pair of faucets)	2	4
Lavatory	1	2
Lavatory (dental)	1	1
Lawn sprinklers (standard type, each head)	1	1
Shower (each head)	2	4
Sink (bar)	1	2
Sink or dishwasher	2	4
Sink (flushing rim, clinic)	—	10
Sink (washup, each set of faucets)	—	2
Sink (washup, circular spray)	—	4
Urinal (pedestal or similar type)	—	10
Urinal (stall)	—	5
Urinal (wall)	—	5
Urinal (flush tank)	—	3
Water closet (flush tank)	3	5
Water closet (flushometer valve)	6	10

Water supply outlets for items not listed above shall be computed at their maximum demand, but in no case less than:

	Private Use	Public Use
⅜ inch	1	2
½ inch	2	4
¾ inch	3	6
1 inch	6	10

FIXTURE UNIT TABLE FOR DETERMINING WATER PIPE AND METER SIZES FOR FLUSH TANK SYSTEMS PRESSURE RANGE—30 to 45 psi

Meter and Street Service	Building Supply & Branches	40	Maximum Allowable Length in Feet 60	80	100	150	200
¾"	½"	6	5	4	4	3	2
¾"	¾"	18	16	14	12	9	6
¾"	1"	29	25	23	21	17	15
1"	1"	36	31	27	25	20	17
1"	1¼"	54	47	42	38	32	28
1½"	1¼"	90	68	57	48	38	32
1½"	1½"	151	124	105	91	70	57
2"	1½"	210	162	132	110	80	64
1½"	2"	220	205	190	176	155	138
2"	2"	372	329	292	265	217	185
2"	2½"	445	418	390	370	330	300

MINIMUM DEMAND OF TYPICAL GAS APPLIANCES IN CUBIC FEET PER HOUR (CFH)

(Based on Natural Gas of 1100 B.T.U. per cubic foot)

Appliance	Demand
Domestic Gas Range	75
Domestic Recessed top burner section	50
Domestic Recessed oven section	25
Storage Water Heater—up to 30 gal. tank	30
Storage Water Heater—40 to 50 gal. tank	45
Domestic Clothes Drier	20
Fireplace Log Lighter	25
Barbecue (Residential)	50
Gas Refrigerator	3
Bunsen Burner	3
House Trailers (each)	*
Gas Engines (per horsepower)	10
Steam Boilers (per horsepower)	50

*Branches and mains serving house trailer sites shall be sized using the following values beginning with the most remote outlet on each branch or main:

For the first outlet on any branch or main .... 125 CFH
For the second outlet on any branch or main ...... 100 CFH
For the third outlet on any branch or main .... 75 CFH

After the third outlet, subsequent main line loadings may be computed using a value of fifty (50) cubic feet per outlet.

Maximum delivery capacity in cubic feet of gas per hour (CFH)
of I.P.S. pipe carrying natural gas of 0.65 specific gravity
LENGTH IN FEET

Pipe Size	10'	20'	30'	40'	50'	60'	70'	80'	90'	100'	125'
½	170	118	95	80	71	64	60	55	52	49	44
¾	360	245	198	169	150	135	123	115	108	102	92
1	670	430	370	318	282	255	235	220	205	192	172
1¼	1,320	930	740	640	565	510	470	440	410	390	345
1½	1,990	1,370	1,100	950	830	760	700	650	610	570	510
2	3,880	2,680	2,150	1,840	1,610	1,480	1,350	1,250	1,180	1,100	1,000
2½	6,200	4,120	3,420	2,950	2,600	2,360	2,180	2,000	1,900	1,800	1,600
3	10,900	7,500	6,000	5,150	4,600	4,150	3,820	3,550	3,300	3,120	2,810
3½	16,000	11,000	8,900	7,600	6,750	6,200	5,650	5,250	4,950	4,650	4,150
4	22,500	15,500	12,400	10,600	9,300	8,500	7,900	7,300	6,800	6,400	5,700

Pipe Size	150'	200'	250'	300'	350'	400'	450'	500'	550'	600'
½	40	34	30	27	25	23	22	21	20	19
¾	83	71	63	57	52	48	45	43	41	39
1	158	132	118	108	100	92	86	81	77	74
1¼	315	270	238	215	200	185	172	162	155	150
1½	460	400	350	320	295	275	255	240	230	220
2	910	780	690	625	570	535	500	470	450	430
2½	1,450	1,230	1,100	1,000	920	850	800	760	720	690
3	2,550	2,180	1,930	1,750	1,600	1,500	1,400	1,320	1,250	1,200
3½	3,800	3,200	2,860	2,600	2,400	2,200	2,100	2,000	1,900	1,800
4	5,200	4,400	3,950	3,600	3,250	3,050	2,850	2,700	2,570	2,450

A-33 Pipe Sizes Based on Gas Demand (from Uniform Plumbing Code)

Minimum Horizontal Distance In Clear Required From:	Building Sewer	Septic Tank	Disposal Field	Seepage pit or Cesspool
Buildings or Structures*	2 feet	5 feet	8 feet	8 feet
Property line adjoining private property	Clear	5 feet	5 feet	8 feet
Water supply wells	50 feet	50 feet	50 feet	100 feet
Streams	50 feet	50 feet	50 feet	100 feet
Large trees	—	10 feet	10 feet	10 feet
Seepage pits or cesspools	—	5 feet	5 feet	12 feet
Disposal field	—	5 feet	4 feet**	5 feet
Domestic water line	1 foot	5 feet	5 feet	5 feet
Distribution box	—	—	5 feet	5 feet

A-34 Location of Sewage-disposal System (from Uniform Plumbing Code)

NOTE:

When disposal fields and/or seepage pits are installed in sloping ground the minimum horizontal distance between any part of the leaching system and ground surface shall be fifteen (15) feet.

All non-metallic drainage piping shall clear domestic water supply wells by at least fifty (50') feet. This distance may be reduced to not less than twenty-five (25) feet when approved type metallic piping is installed.

Where special hazards are involved the distance required shall be increased, as may be directed by the Health Officer or the Administrative Authority.

All non-metallic drainage piping shall clear domestic water supply wells by at least fifty (50)
*Including porches and steps whether covered or uncovered, breezeways, roofed porte-cocheres, roofed patios, car ports, covered walks, covered doorways and similar structures or appurtenances.

**Two (2) times width of trench for trenches wider than two (2) feet (See also Section 1116).

TYPE OF BUILDING	DAILY PER CAPITA	BASIC FACTOR
Grammar School	15 gallons	
Grammar School with Cafeteria	20 gallons	35 students per class room
High School with Cafeteria and shower baths	25 gallons	
Factories	20 gallons (without showers)	Each 8-hour shift
	25 gallons (with showers)	Each 8-hour shift
Restaurants	50 gallons	Per seat
Trailer Parks—Community Baths	50 gallons	3 persons per trailer
Trailer Parks—Private Baths or independent trailers	60 gallons	3 persons per trailer
Motels—Baths and Toilets	50 gallons	3 persons per unit
Motels—Bath, Toilet & Kitchen	60 gallons	3 persons per unit
Self-Service Laundry	300 gallons per machine per day	
Drive-in Theaters	5 gallons per car per day	

A-35 Fixture Demand for Commercial Usage (from Uniform Plumbing Code)

*NOTE: In order to provide sludge retention capacity, when computing septic tank sizes for occupancies listed in this table, multiply the total daily sewage production by two (2) to obtain the septic tank size.

A-36 Sizes of Septic Tanks Based on Fixture Demand (from Uniform Plumbing Code)

Single family dwellings—number of bedrooms	Multiple dwelling units or apartments— one bedroom each	Other uses; maximum fixture units served	Minimum septic tank capacity in gallons
1 or 2		15	750
3		20	1000
4	2 units	25	1200
5 or 6	3	33	1500
	4	45	2000
	5	55	2250
	6	60	2500
	7	70	2750
	8	80	3000
	9	90	3250
	10	100	3500

Extra bedroom, 150 gallons each
Extra dwelling units over 10, 250 gallons each
Extra fixture units over 100, 25 gallons per fixture unit

NOTE:
Septic tank sizes in this table include sludge storage capacity and the connection of domestic food waste disposal units without further volume increase.

A-37 Required Absorption Areas for Leaching Systems (from Uniform Plumbing Code)

Required absorption area in square feet per one hundred (100) gallons of septic tank liquid capacity for five (5) types of soil.

Type of Soil	Square feet per 100 gallons
(1) Coarse sand or gravel	20
(2) Fine sand	25
(3) Sandy loam or sandy clay	40
(4) Clay with considerable sand or gravel	60
(5) Clay with small amount of sand or gravel	90

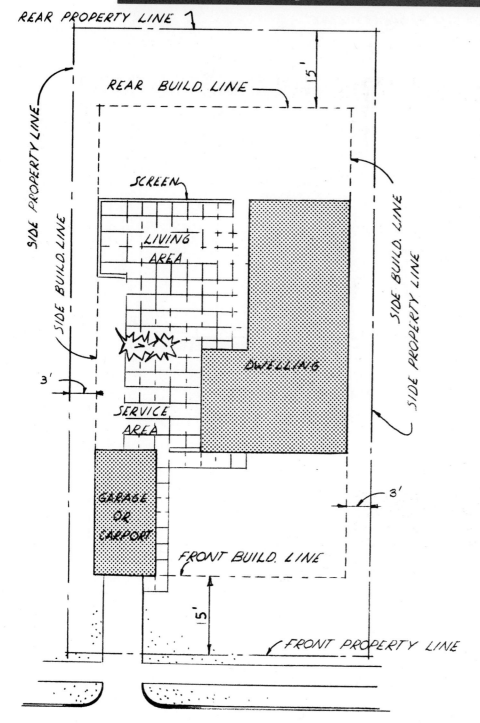

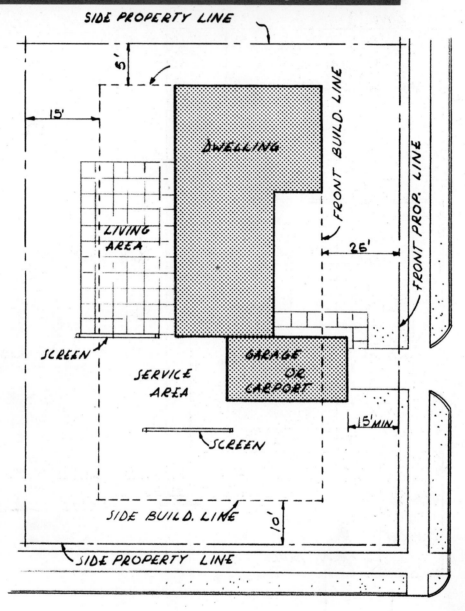

SIDE PROPERTY LINE

5'

15'

DWELLING

FRONT BUILD. LINE

FRONT PROP. LINE

LIVING AREA

25'

SCREEN

SERVICE AREA

GARAGE OR CARPORT

SCREEN

15' MIN

SIDE BUILD. LINE

10'

SIDE PROPERTY LINE

NOTE: ON A CORNER LOT, EITHER YARD FACING STREET MAY BE CONSIDERED *FRONT*. YARD OPPOSITE SELECTED FRONT IS REAR YARD.

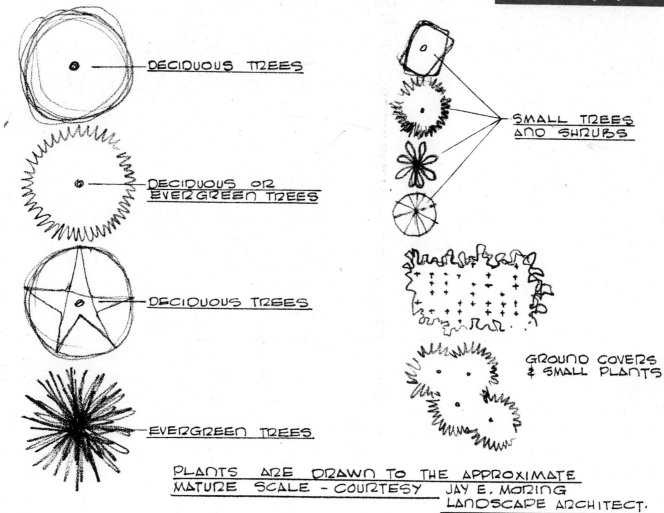

DECIDUOUS TREES

DECIDUOUS OR EVERGREEN TREES

DECIDUOUS TREES

EVERGREEN TREES

SMALL TREES AND SHRUBS

GROUND COVERS & SMALL PLANTS

PLANTS ARE DRAWN TO THE APPROXIMATE MATURE SCALE - COURTESY JAY E. MORING LANDSCAPE ARCHITECT.

225

Bibliography

BOOKS

AEC Architectural Catalog File, Times Mirror Press, 1115 S. Boyle, Los Angeles 23, Calif. Published annually.

Architectural Catalog File, Sweets Catalog Service, McGraw-Hill Book Company, New York. Published annually.

Aronin, Jeffrey E.: "Climate and Architecture," Reinhold Publishing Corporation, New York, 1953.

Atkin, W. W., and others: "Pencil Techniques in Modern Design," Reinhold Publishing Corporation, New York, 1963.

Callender, J. H. (ed.): "Time-Saver Standards," 4th ed., McGraw-Hill Book Company, New York, 1964.

Choate, C.: "Architectural Presentation in Opaque Water Colors," Reinhold Publishing Corporation, New York, 1962.

"Concrete Masonry Design Manual," Concrete Masonry Association, 3250 W. 6th St., Los Angeles 5, Calif., 1955.

"Concrete Masonry Handbook," Portland Cement Association, 33 W. Grand Avenue, Chicago 10, Ill., 1951.

Cowgill, Clinton H., and Ben John Small: "Architectural Practice," Reinhold Publishing Corporation, New York, 1959.

Eckbo, Garret: "The Art of Home Landscaping," McGraw-Hill Book Company, New York, 1956.

French, Thomas E., and Charles J. Vierck: "Fundamentals of Engineering Drawing," McGraw-Hill Book Company, New York, 1960.

Halse, Albert O.: "Architectural Rendering," McGraw-Hill Book Company, New York, 1960.

"Handbook of Residential Wiring Design," Industry Committee on Interior Wiring Design, Room 2650, 420 Lexington Avenue, New York.

Harris, Norman C.: "Modern Air Conditioning Practice," McGraw-Hill Book Company, New York, 1959.

Kautzky, Theodore: "Pencil Broadsides," Reinhold Publishing Corporation, New York.

Kennedy, Robert Woods: "The House and the Art of Its Design," Progressive Architecture Library, Reinhold Publishing Corporation, New York, 1953.

"Manual of Millwork," Woodwork Institute of Calif., 1833 Broadway, Fresno, Calif., 1957.

McPartland, J. F.: "Electrical Systems Design," McGraw-Hill Book Company, New York, 1960.

Merritt, Frederick S. (ed.): "Building Construction Handbook," McGraw-Hill Book Company, New York, 1958.

"National Electric Code," National Fire Protection Association, 60 Batterymarch St., Boston 10, Mass., 1959.

Olgyay, Aladar: "Solar Control and Shading Devices," Princeton University Press, Princeton, N.J., 1957.

Parker, Harry E.: "Simplified Engineering for Architects and Builders," 3d ed., John Wiley & Sons, Inc., New York, 1961.

"Practical Builder Data and Specification Files," Industrial Publications Inc., 55 Wabash Ave., Chicago 3, Ill., 1955.

Ramsey, Charles G., and Harold R. Sleeper: "Architectural Graphic Standards," 5th ed., John Wiley & Sons, Inc., New York, 1956.

Schroeder, Francis D.: "Anatomy for Interior Designers," Whitney Publications, New York, 1948.

Simonds, John O.: "Landscape Architecture," McGraw-Hill Book Company, New York, 1961.

Strock, Clifford: "Heating and Ventilating's Engineering Databook," 1948, The Industrial Press, 148 Lafayette Street, New York, 1948.

Sunset Magazine, "How to Plan and Build Your Fireplace," Lane Publishing Co., San Francisco, Calif., 1951.

"Uniform Building Code, Vol. I," International Conference of Building Officials, 610 S. Broadway, New York, 1961.

"Uniform Plumbing Code," Western Plumbing Officials Association, P.O. Box 752711, Los Angeles 5, Calif., 1958.

MAGAZINES

Architectural Forum, Time Inc., Rockefeller Center, New York.

Architectural Record, F. W. Dodge Company, a Division of McGraw-Hill, Inc., New York.

Arts and Architecture, 3305 Wilshire Blvd., Los Angeles.

House and Home, McGraw-Hill, Inc., New York.

Progressive Architecture, Reinhold Publishing Corporation, 430 Park Ave., New York.

Answers to Review Questions

Some of the questions in the text are intended as subjects for discussion and research, and the answers will vary with the locality. Other questions have exact answers that can be derived from the tables and forms in the Appendix; these answers are listed below.

CHAPTER 14

9. *a.* 9 in.
   b. 4½ in.
   c. 12 in.
10. *a.* 5,600 lb
    b. 1,680 lb
    c. 1,440 lb
    d. 7,680 lb
    e. 6,000 lb
    f. 1,728 lb
    g. 10,800 lb
    h. 5,400 lb
11. *a.* 8,960 lb
    b. 14,400 lb
    c. 2,000 psi
12. 6½ in.
13. 2¾ in.
14. 12 in.
15. Yes, 5
16. 2 × 10, 12 o.c.
17. 2 × 12, 12 o.c.
18. 1,390 lb
19. 10 ft 6 in.
20. 13 ft 7 in.
21. 25 ft 6 in.
22. 4 × 10
23. *a.* 2 × 6, *b.* 2 × 8, *c.* 23 ft 6 in.
24. 16 ft 8 in.

CHAPTER 19

7. *a.* No. 4
   b. 100 amp
   c. 70 amp
   d. 3
   e. No. 8
   f. No. 10
   g. 2
   h. No. 8
   i. 530 watts
8. 200
9. $LL = \dfrac{FC \times A}{CU \times MF}$
10. 15
11. 6.4 or 7 lamps
12. 3.6 or 4 lamps

CHAPTER 20

3. *a.* 15,600 Btu/hr
   b. 2,200 Btu/hr
   c. 4,060 Btu/hr
   d. 4,570 Btu/hr
   e. 140 cfm
4. *a.* 1,932 Btu/hr
   b. 4,186 Btu/hr
   c. 403 Btu/hr
   d. 1,944 Btu/hr
   e. 4,680 Btu/hr
5. *a.* 16 ft
   b. 11 ft
   c. 10 in.
   d. 30 × 12 in.
   e. 40 × 10 in. or 32 × 12 in.
   f. 30 × 10 in., 20 × 14 in., 24 × 12 in.
6. 80°

CHAPTER 21

6. *a.* 1½ in.
   b. 6
   c. 20
7. *a.* 600
   b. 256
   c. 300 ft
   d. 84
8. *a.* 5
   b. 3
9. *a.* 42
   b. 2 in.
10. *a.* 75 cfh
    b. 45 + 20 + 50 = 115 cfh
11. *a.* ¾ in.
    b. No, 1¼ in.
12. *a.* 100 ft
    b. 6 ft
13. *a.* 300 gal
    b. 1,500 gal
14. *a.* 1,200 gal

b. 2,500 gal
c. 3,250 gal
d. 9
15. 300 sq ft

CHAPTER 22

1. 37½°
2. *a.* 13°17′25″
   b. 166°42′35″
   c. 180°00′00″
3. No answers
4. No answers
5. *a.* 15 ft
   b. 3 ft
   c. 15 ft
6. *a.* 25 ft
   b. 15 ft
   c. 10 ft
   d. 5 ft
   e. 15 ft

Index

Air-conditioning design, ducts, 213
   indoor temperatures, 196
   outside temperatures, 198
   registers, 212
   survey, 206
All-purpose room, 17

Basement, 17
Bedroom, 17

Checklist, 180
   use of, 14
Client, 14
Contour lines, 151
Cooling design, indoor temperatures, 196
   outdoor temperatures, 198
   survey, 206

Decking, wood, 189
Den, 17
Design, local conditions, 46
Details, cabinet work, 170
   door, definition of, 164
     drafting of, 164
   foundation, 123
   miscellaneous, 17
   window, definition of, 164
     drafting of, 164
Dining room, 17
Drains and gutters, 96

Drawings, agreement among, 63
   arrangement of, 55
   changes in, 63
   preliminary study, 23
   presentation, format, 51
     media, 51
   working, 52
     procedure, 55

Easements, 154
Eave line, procedure in determining, 38
Electrical line voltage, 133
Electrical plan, definition of, 128
   drafting of, 133
Electrical service, 128
Electrical symbols, 195
Electrical wiring design, 194
Elevations, development of, 29
   exterior, definition of, 109
     drafting of, 109
   interior, definition of, 159
     drafting of, 159
Entry, 15

Family room, 17
Fastenings, 96
Final data sheet, 182
   use of, 33
Fireplace, design, 192
   details, 99
   drafting of, 101
   warm air circulating, 193

Floor plan, definition of, 66
   development of, 24
   drafting of, 66
   multistory, 74
Floor systems, concrete, slab above grade, 87
   slab on grade, 87
   steel joist, 89
   wood joist, 87
     plank and beam, 89
Footings, 83
   design of, 187
   size, arbitrary, one-story frame, 188
     two-story frame, 188
Format, presentation drawing, 51
   sheet, 185
   working drawing, 54
Foundation, details, 123
   plan, definition of, 115
     drafting of, 118
   types of, 115
   wall, 83

Gas lines, design of, 220
Girders, wood, 191
Ground line, 8

Hall, 17
Heater room, 17
Heating, design, ducts, 213
   indoor temperatures, 196
   outdoor temperatures, 197
   registers, 212

Heating, design, survey, 200
   plan, drafting of, 137
Horizon line, 8

Joists, wood, ceiling, 190
   floor, 189, 191

Kitchen, 17

Landscaping, ground covers, 43
   plan, 151, 157
   relationship to orientation, 43
   symbols, 225
   trees, 43
   values of, 43
Leaching lines, design of, 222
Lettering, 11
   guides, 11
Lighting, design, 196
Linework, standards, 54
Lintel, concrete, 190
   wood, 190
Living room, 15
Loads, dead, 187
   live, 187
Lot lines, 151
Low-voltage switching, 133

Materials, construction, 22
   drafting, 52
   sketching, 1
Media, presentation drawings, 51

Orientation, commercial buildings,
   21
   definition of, 35
   local requirements, 38
   relationship to landscaping, 43
Outlets, electrical, 129
Overhangs, design of roof, 38

Pencils, sketching, 1
Perspective, approximate, 3
   eyeball, 3
   grid forms, 8
   mechanical, 3
   procedure, 8
   rubber-band, 8
   shortcuts, 8
   terms, 8
   two-point, 5
Planning, commercial building, 19
   residential, 14
Plot plan, 151
   drafting of, 154
Plumbing, piping, design, 219
   plan, definition of, 142
      drafting of, 143
Preliminaries, 23

Rafters, wood, 190
Roof, framing plan, drafting of, 124
   shapes, 93
   structures, 92
   types, 31
Roofing materials, 93
Rumpus room, 17

Scale, human, 15
Schedules, door, 75
   electrical fixture, 131
   mechanical equipment, 139
   pictorial door and window, 75
   plumbing fixture, 147
   room finish, 75
Sections, structural, definition of, 83
   drafting of, 97
Septic tank, 147
   design of, 221
Setbacks, 154, 223
Site, 14
Sketching, 1
Soil, bearing values, 187
Soil and waste lines, 143

Specifications, 177
Stair, details, 99
   drafting of, 99
Storage, commercial, 19
Storage room, 17
Structural shapes, 31
Summer design temperatures, 198
Sun, angles, 35
   tables, 184
Symbols, air conditioning, 215
   electrical, 195
   elevation, 186
   landscape, 225
   plan, 186
   plumbing, 215
   section, 225

Templates, drafting, 54
Texture, 114
Tracings, reversed, 55
Traffic flow, commercial, 21
   residential, 15
Treillage, 35

Utility room, 17

Vanishing lines, 8
Vanishing point, 8
Vertical measure line, 8

Wall openings, 92
Wall structures, masonry, 91
   metal stud, 91
   wood frame, 90
Water lines, design of, 220
   drafting of, 144
Weights, building materials, 187
Winter design temperatures, 197

Zoning, commercial, 21